THE DAY BEFORE
YESTERDAY

THE DAY BEFORE YESTERDAY

COLIN TUDGE

JONATHAN CAPE
LONDON

First published 1995

1 3 5 7 9 10 8 6 4 2

Figures II.1–II.6 are taken from *Quarternary Environments* (Edward Arnold, 1993)
and are reproduced by kind permission of M. A. J. Williams

First published in the United Kingdom in 1995 by
Jonathan Cape
Random House, 20 Vauxhall Bridge Road, London SW1V 2SA

Random House Australia (Pty) Limited
20 Alfred Street, Milsons Point, Sydney,
New South Wales 2061, Australia

Random House New Zealand Limited
18 Poland Road, Glenfield,
Auckland 10, New Zealand

Random House South Africa (Pty) Limited
PO Box 337, Bergvlei, 2012 South Africa

Random House UK Limited Reg. No. 954009

A CIP catalogue record for this book
is available from the British Library

Papers used by Random House UK Limted are natural,
recyclable products made from wood grown in sustainable forests.
The manufacturing processes conform to the environmental
regulations of the country of origin.

ISBN 0–224–03772–2

Printed and bound in Great Britain by
Mackays of Chatham PLC

To my children: Mandy, Amy and Robin

CONTENTS

Acknowledgments

The ideas in this book have largely been inspired by long conversations I have enjoyed with biologists and other scientists over many years. They are too numerous to mention; my thanks to all of them. But for this book I am particularly aware of my debt to the following: Professor Bernard Wood and Dr Alan Turner of Liverpool University; Dr Georgina Mace of the Institute of Zoology, London; Dr Elisabeth Vrba and Dr Andrew Hill of Yale University; Dr Michael Archer of the University of New South Wales; Professor Bob Brain, formerly director of the Transvaal Museum, Pretoria; Dr Chris Stringer of the Natural History Museum, London; Professor Bill Ruddiman of the University of Virginia; Dr Tim Partridge of the Transvaal Museum, Pretoria; and Dr David Webb for his continuing advice and encouragement; Neil Belton of Jonathan Cape who is among the most patient and supportive of editors; Liz Smith of Cape who rescued the text from endless lapses of concentration; and Gillian Casey Sowell of Simon & Schuster. But of course, none of the above can be held responsible for any errors or other eccentricities of this book.

Prologue: A Proper History of Humankind

How odd it is to suggest, as historians conventionally do, that the Assyrians, the Egyptians, the Greeks, the Romans were 'ancient'. They had advanced technologies – building, engineering, agriculture; they made war, paid taxes, studied the stars, developed the arts and miscellaneous philosophies, and allowed themselves to be organised by priests, generals, and bureaucrats. If any of us were whisked into their midst we would be struck at first by their quaintness and their foreignness and by the alarming proximity of death, but we would soon feel more or less at home. At least, we would soon be irked by the same day-to-day necessities of house-keeping and social intercourse that beset us now – and stunned, when we found the leisure to look around, by the brilliance of the technologies and the excellence of the arts and crafts.

The truth is, of course, that those people were not 'ancient' at all. The epithet was applied by eighteenth-century historians who thought that the world itself was new and that the people they called 'ancient' had lived near its beginning. But the Assyrians, Egyptians and the rest had inherited several thousand years of civilisation, exactly as we have done – several thousand years of cities and of organised agriculture. Yet those cities, and the paraphernalia of farming, did not grow out of nothing. They in turn were preceded by tens of thousands of years of recognisable culture and invention. For all that time there had been trade of a kind, formal social hierarchies, arts that included extraordinary draughtsmanship as seen in the caves of southern Europe and elsewhere, and a steadily increasing armoury of tools and techniques from the toggle and the needle to the spear and the adze – all of which are still in use, and taken for granted, but each of which was initially a revelation that tightened the human grip on the environment as decisively as any present-day development in electronics. Tiny technical advances, hardly more than 'tricks', have a huge impact on biological success, as can be seen in any group of animals – and the particular trick of human beings is not to forget but to *accumulate*, over time, all the tricks of other people and of previous generations.

But then, before the pre-agricultural cave-painters, potters, tailors, and traders of Europe and Africa there were several million years in which the human stage was set; in which, increment by increment, our ancestors crossed the divide between apedom and humanity. We have a huge amount in common with our fellow creatures. Charles Darwin emphasised that the differences between 'us' and 'them' should be seen as matters of degree. Yet we have tricks – biological tricks – that make us different, and put us qualitatively into a new league, one of which is our supreme manual dexterity, and another the ability to pool our thoughts, ultimately through the medium of speech. These tricks do not make us morally superior to other creatures, I believe, but they do give us enormous power over them and over our environment at large. In short, the people who preceded those whom the historians called 'ancient' had themselves inherited an ancient culture. Conventional history starts almost at the end.

The vauntingly presumptuous purpose of this book is to put that right. I want to tell the history of human beings beginning at the beginning, which in truth was around 5 million years ago. I also want to put that history into perspective, by showing what went before it and why our own history began in the first place. The past 2,000 years of conventional history are effectively the present. The past 40,000 years, when our own species truly got into its stride in recognisably modern form, is only yesterday. The 5 million years that are the main focus of this book are ... 'the day before yesterday'.

I want to look at our whole history – our 5-million-year history – and the time that led up to it, for two reasons. The first is because it is fun, a cracking good yarn – or, to put the matter more portentously, because a knowledge of our own history is a significant part of culture and at present that knowledge is absurdly curtailed.

But the second reason I want to look at our history in its entirety is because it is important. The Spanish-American philosopher George Santayana commented that 'those who do not learn from history are obliged to repeat its mistakes', and that surely is the case. How can we understand what is happening to us now without reference to the past? How could we even begin to guess how any human enterprise might turn out – making war, building dams, farming land that once was forest – except by seeing what happened before? But the 2,000 years or so that we traditionally treat as 'history' simply does not tell us enough. It deals only with the *faits accomplis* – the activities of a peculiar creature that had already taken over the world. It does not begin to show us just *how* peculiar we really are – how we broke away from other animals, and what an enormous effect we had upon them even before conventional history began. Still less can a study of the past 2,000 years reveal the biggest lesson of all: that the planet itself is labile; that we cannot take its benignity for granted; that it can be a very hostile place indeed; and – most strikingly – that we ourselves, feeble though we may seem, have the power to influence its course, to switch the entire Earth from one state to another.

THE FIRST PURPOSE: SCIENCE FOR AESTHETICS

This book deals mainly with ideas of modern science and some may find it odd that science should be pressed to the service of aesthetics. Some even feel that science is an anti-aesthetic and even a blasphemous pursuit – echoing William Wordsworth's somewhat chilling averral that 'we murder to dissect'. His comment was obviously not intended simply to be literal – although it is literally the case that the particular science of biology has progressed in large part by cutting up creatures that were once alive and seeing what is inside. It is generally taken to imply that through our efforts to reveal mechanisms we snuff out the spirit or perhaps simply the mystery of the object under investigation. By finding out, the implication is, we lose our respect.

But to me, the idea that knowledge reduces admiration for the thing in hand seems positively perverse. After all, no one doubts – do they? – that when, say, Alfred Brendel listens to the music of Schubert he hears more than the rest of us do, or doubts that his 'aesthetic' response is of a finer texture than the rest of us. Of course Brendel is a special individual, perhaps endowed with a

more subtle armament of emotions. But the thing that most
obviously distinguishes the professional musician from the rest of
us is *knowledge*. Most of us may hear a faint sadness creep into the
music, or a lift of mood. Musicians could, if they chose, describe
precisely what lies behind each effect – describe and admire: the
shift of key, the half-allusion to some earlier melody. Of course
the knowledge generally remains subliminal. Musicians do not, in
the normal course of listening, list each modulation as it passes.
But because they *know*, they can hear with precision while the
rest of us are merely vaguely aware, and because of that extra acu-
ity they catch an infinity of nuances that pass the rest of us by. But
no one says of musicians that their deep-set knowledge 'murders'
what they listen to. No one seriously doubts that the enhanced
perception is a bonus; that the rest of us are deaf by comparison
because our ears are not informed.

To me the parallel is precise. Living things are thrilling. If I did
not feel this excitement then I would never have elected to study
biology. Virtually all biologists that I know feel the same.
Knowledge of the subject is a way of getting closer to the thing
you love; of maintaining contact; and in the end of refining the
emotional, which means the aesthetic, response. When you know
just a little of how the Universe works (and even the greatest scientists know only a little) then you can *feel* much more of what
is going on.

Specifically, this book is about change – about the rise and fall
of landscapes and the evolution of living lineages. I suggest that
once you become aware of the idea of evolution, once you begin
to feel that things do change, then your perception of everything
around you is enhanced. A fourth dimension has been added to
your view of the world: that of time. You begin to perceive that
an animal or a plant, and the lineage to which each belongs,
and the planet itself, are like a flame – not so much a thing as a
performance, always becoming something else – and that each
of us and our species as a whole are part of the overall unfolding.

This point, strange though some may feel it to be, is plain to
see within the history of art. There can be no doubt, for example, that the Romantic painting of the late eighteenth through the
nineteenth centuries was strongly influenced by the emerging science of the time. The perception of entire generations of
landscape painters was transformed by their knowledge of the

new geology. Look, for example, at James Ward's fabulous painting of 'Gordale Scar' in London's Tate Gallery. 'Scar' is Yorkshire-ese for a face of rock, and Gordale is a gorge – battered cliffs of Carboniferous limestone, almost 300 million years old (see Figure 1.1). Ward has painted them from low down, stretching hugely upwards to a thunderous sky. At the foot of the scar is a rough white bull of some archaic breed and it feels – and the observer also feels through its tension and its rolling eye – the menace of the place. But why is this landscape so menacing? Because Ward has patined a wall of rock that is ancient but far from permanent: a cliff that is poised to crash. The gorge has been carved by a waterfall that one day will level it to the ground. The notion that landscape is transient was emerging from the revolutionary thinkers of the day who first perceived that the tops of mountains were once at the bottom of the sea and that, in the fulness of time, the greatest mountains are beaten to dust. Ward is not an Impressionist who sees with Claude Monet's 'innocent eye'. His eyes are *informed*. He sees the history behind the rocks, and feels the threatening future.

I now spend much of my time in Yorkshire, not far from Gordale Scar. Like Ward, who was here almost two centuries ago, I find that as my knowledge grows so my appreciation deepens. There is a cave in the limestone hills close by that collapsed just a few months before I am writing – perhaps for the hundredth time, perhaps for the thousandth. That same cave has yielded the remains of lions, hyaenas, rhinoceroses and reindeer. Like all of northern Europe these hills have experienced at least ten glaciations in the past million years and those creatures passed through here to escape the encroaching ice, or followed in its wake as it retreated – as it did for the last, or at least most recent, time only about 8,000 years ago. The bleak hills are beautiful; but their excitement is enhanced when you see them in your mind's eye beneath the mile-high mountain of ice that carved them in their present form; or see the Arctic creatures that were never far from the glacier's edge; or the animals now only to be found in tropical Africa that flourished here in the intervals of warmth; or the forest that was here for a few thousand years and was wiped away by the first farmers. And what applies here applies everywhere on Earth. It is thrilling, this thought: that anywhere you stand might at different times have been at the bottom of the sea,

Figure I.1 The Geological Timescale

Eon	Time*	Era	Period	Epoch	
P h a n e r o z o i c		C e n o z o i c	Q u a t e r n a r y	Holocene (recent)	⎫
	— 0.01				⎬ The Age of Hominids
				Pleistocene	⎭
	— 1.6			Pliocene	
	— 5				
			T e r t i a r y	Miocene	⎫
	— 26				
				Oligocene	⎬ The Age of Mammals
	— 38				
				Eocene	
	— 54				
				Palaeocene	⎭
	— 65				◄ The 'K/T' Boundary: Extinction of the Dinosaurs
		M e s o z o i c	Cretaceous		⎫
	— 140				⎬ The Age of Reptiles
			Jurassic		
	— 210				
	— 245		Triassic		⎭
			Permian		
	— 290				
		P a l a e o z o i c	Carboniferous		
	— 365				
			Devonian		
	— 413				
	— 441		Silurian		
			Ordovician		
	— 504				
			Cambrian		
	— 570				◄ The Start of 'Modern' Animals
		'Precambrian'			
	— 4,500				◄ The Beginning of the Earth

*Note: numbers refer to millions of years since the beginning of each period.

or the top of a mountain; might have been desert or tropical forest or buried three miles under ice; might, like my own native region of London, have been the home of sea-lilies or straight-tusked elephants and sabretooths, and our own beleaguered and mystic-minded ancestors. It's a thrilling thought, too, that many of the landscapes and ecosystems of the past were like nothing that exists today. After all, there have at times been tropical forests at high latitudes – hot, vapourous, but with short winter days and long winter nights, or the permanent sunshine of near-polar summer – and these have no parallel in the modern world. Because it is thrilling, it is a pity to be unaware and to miss what is there to be felt if not directly to be seen. The science of palaeontology feeds the aesthetic experience.

To the notion that science is blasphemy – that it is demeaning to God to probe the mechanisms of the Universe – I can only suggest that the opposite applies. The point was made by Isaac Newton, widely acknowledged as the founder of modern science. Like most of his seventeenth-century scientific contemporaries he was deeply religious. He felt that to study the works of God was to gain insight into the mind of God, and he felt it to be an obligation to use his own God-given intellect to probe his Creator's mind more deeply. For Newton, indeed, the pursuit of science was itself an act of reverence.

We live in a more secular age. The fashion of the past few decades (though not, in fact, when I first started studying science at school in Britain in the 1950s) is that science provides the means to produce 'high' technologies which in turn generate wealth. To me, and to most of the best scientists that I know, such material benefits are almost incidental. I suggest, rather – a secularised restatement of Newton – that the true purpose of science is not to change the Universe but to appreciate it. To revert to the language of religion, it is not blasphemous to describe how the Universe works. Rather it is blasphemous to suggest that the Universe is in any way diminished by our feeble essays in description. God is not a conjuror, whose tricks seem tawdry when exposed. Most true scientists agree that the more subtle their descriptions become, the more mysterious and wonderful the Universe appears.

So that is the first purpose of this book: to add the dimension of time to everyday perception and hence, I hope, to enhance the sense of wonder.

THE SECOND PURPOSE: THE LESSONS OF HISTORY

The common lack of true historical perspective has some bizarre consequences, although it demonstrates what an ill wind it must be that blows nobody any good. Thus in 1968 Erich Von Daniken published his extraordinary *Chariots of the Gods?*, which became a bestseller in several countries (I have the fourth reprint in English paperback, dated 1993). Von Daniken claims, among other things, that the pyramids must have been built by aliens because the Egyptians could not possibly have managed the technology themselves. Yet, to revert to my opening statement, the Egyptians were modern people. The pyramids are extraordinary, but we might as well suggest that nineteenth-century Parisians could not have built the Eiffel Tower, or the Americans of the 1920s constructed the Hoover Dam.

Again, to expand upon an earlier point, the pharaonic Egyptians had reached the peak that they did only after several thousands of years of civilisation. This point is made by Plato. In the dialogue *Critias*, the eponymous hero relates a meeting that an acquaintance of his had with an Egyptian sage, who points out that the Greeks have no history and therefore effectively no culture. After all, says the sage, the Greeks are newcomers to southern Europe, while the Egyptians have been *in situ* for millennia, and have correspondingly ancient memories and traditions. His tone is positively disdainful: to him, the Greeks are parvenues. Traditionally, the *Critias* has been thought of simply as a piece of Platonic story-telling but, as Mary Settegast now discusses in her book *Plato Prehistorian* (Lindisfarne Press, New York, 1990), modern archaeology increasingly suggests that the pronouncements of that ancient sage were literally correct. Egyptians in pharaonic times were fully justified both in their sense that they were truly at the forefront of achievement, and in feeling themselves the inheritors of really ancient civilisation. The Greeks, by contrast, were indeed newcomers. The Egyptian sense of history – already embracing, as it did at that time, about 6,000 years – was more realistically developed than ours today.

Intriguingly, the earliest cultural memories of Plato's Egyptian sage would take us back roughly to the end of the last ice age. And this brings me properly to my main historical point, which is that humans are not merely cultural beings, minds on legs, but are a biological species, as prone as any to the deep rhythms of the Earth itself. History and archaeology must become one; archaeology and palaeontology must become one. We can understand ourselves and what is happening to us, and our own impact upon the rest of the world, only when we look at ourselves on the grand scale of time. We count the rhythms of our own lives through the passing of days and seasons. As members of families we note the passing generations. Historians traditionally deal in centuries. But for the most part we remain blissfully unaware of the deep rhythms that lie beneath – rhythms that must be measured in millennia, or in millions of years, or in tens of millions of years. We are like small boats that bob up and down on the surface chop and are oblivious to the deeper and longer surges of the swell and tide. In school we learn of ice ages in one set of books and of 'history' in another and fail to see how the two are connected; fail to perceive, therefore, that beneath the surface tremors of our lives there are much deeper and more powerful forces at work which in the end affect us and all our fellow creatures at least as profoundly as the events of day-to-day.

But why does this matter, this lack of perception – apart from the fact that we miss out on an exciting set of ideas? Because, in fact, the analogy between the human species and the small boat that bobs on the surface and blissfully drifts on the tide is not quite accurate. Small boats do not influence the sea on which they ride. We, tiny creatures though we are when taken individually, have had and are having a huge effect upon our fellow species and, increasingly, upon the fabric of the planet itself. Of course we are vaguely aware of this. Everyone knows, after all, that we are wiping out our fellow creatures – that we might indeed eliminate half of those that are left within the next few decades. Everyone has heard of the greenhouse effect, by which we may heat the planet as profoundly as it was cooled in the ice ages; or of the destruction of the ozone layer which, had it not been spotted and analysed, could (without exaggeration) have wiped out almost all living things of the present day.

But we tend to feel that this present-day destructiveness is just an anomaly. We tend to feel, too, that the world will eventually settle down again into some form that may be slightly different from the present but nonetheless agreeable. The Gaia hypothesis, first mooted by the British physicist James Lovelock in the 1970s,

has tended to reinforce this notion (whether it was intended to or
not): that somehow or other the Earth will revert to some 'normal' state whatever we do to it.

Yet if we look at our own history in its entirety, and briefly at
the 100 million years or so of our prehistory, we see how dangerous this complacency is; the sheer precariousness of our
existence, and of all other creatures. It is not enough just to state
the fact. We need to *feel* that it is so. Only through knowing what
has happened in the past, and therefore what *can* happen, will we
finally see the need to change our ways. Sense in the end derives
from sensibility.

The lessons that come roaring out of our history and our pre-
history, but that are missed if we look only at the past few
centuries, are threefold. First, we can see that apparently small
events can have huge consequences – literally global consequences – which can change the flora and fauna of the whole
world. Now, some people at least are bothered about the pending greenhouse effect. If it occurs as fulsomely as is conceivable
then nothing can ever be the same again. But what is the cause of
it? Just a rise in concentration of a gas in the atmosphere which
in any case is present only in little more than a trace. That is all it
takes to change the climate of the world. When we look at our
own history and prehistory we see this very effect in action, and
the sheer magnitude of what results. Indeed, without such effects
– albeit working in reverse, with a loss in greenhouse gases rather
than a gain – our own species probably would not have come
into existence.

Secondly we can see, when we take the long view, that matters of huge consequence can take many thousands or even
millions of years to unfold. If an influential species is wiped out
then it may take that long for others to adjust fully to its absence;
perhaps to evolve to fill the gap or perhaps not, depending on
how things turn out. If a landscape is flooded or a sea drained, or
if two places are joined that hitherto were separate, or divided
that once were joined, the re-adjustment may take millions of
years. Add this point to the first and we begin to see how
momentous, and long-lasting, it can be to do the kinds of things
that we do now as a matter of course: building highways across
continents, removing forests, diverting rivers.

Thirdly, when we look at the world over time we see that it

can never be the same way twice. The physical environment depends upon the content of the atmosphere, and the heights and positions of mountains, and where the continents happen to be as they migrate around the world, and how the world is situated relative to the Sun – and no combination of circumstance can ever be recaptured. Thus it is that the lessons of history cannot be precise but must be expressed in general terms. But the general lesson is terrifying: that our present-day world, to which we and all other animals and plants are adjusted, does not have to be like this at all. It can be tropical from pole to pole, or iced from the poles almost to the equator. It need not contain oxygen in its atmosphere – or not enough, at least, for any air-loving creature to breathe. It might, if things were ever so slightly different, contain so much greenhouse gas in its atmosphere that it cooks, like Venus. Earth as it stands is a miraculous jewel of a place, an oasis in an astonishingly hostile Universe. But there are other ways for it to be, and at times in the past it has shown how different it can be. The Egyptians, according to Critias's sage, could remember back to the last ice age. Even they – modern people – had some hint of how different the world can be.

Add those thoughts, those memories of how the world can be, to the fact that our own influence is now becoming so obvious and we begin to see what a dangerous game we are playing. More specifically, we begin to see how inadequate it is to think only in short periods of time; to be satisfied with politics and policies of economics that deal only with the here and now. Harry Truman, as president of the United States and hence the most powerful of all world leaders, opined that, 'A week is a long time in politics' – and so it is. Few politicians in democratic societies think beyond the four or five years of their term of office. To economists, thirty years is 'the long term'. As the British economist John Maynard Keynes pointed out, 'The long run is a misleading guide to current affairs. In the long run we are all dead.' Thus do world leaders make a virtue of their immediacy. Thus do they deal only in desperately trivial twinklings of time. But no politician nowadays can hope to succeed for long without at least mentioning the word 'environment'. And as we can see from our own long history – and will see in the course of this book – it is impossible to contemplate the environment unless we think as a matter of course in very long periods of time indeed. In fact I will suggest, as the central message of this book, that *we cannot claim to take the environment seriously until we acknowledge that a million years is a proper unit of political time*. That is the general lesson of history.

But it is difficult to think in very long periods, as our own lives are so brief. Let me then suggest a device: the translation of time into distance.

A SENSE OF TIME

Begin by thinking of one year as one millimetre. A millimetre is not too small to see: it is the size of a perfectly respectable grain of sand, or an insect that is big enough to give you a nasty bite. Ten millimetres – a centimetre – then becomes a decade. A centimetre into the future takes us comfortably into the twenty-first century.

Ten centimetres – what was called three and a half inches when I was a lad, about the length of a man's middle finger – is a century. A finger's length ago Queen Victoria's reign was coming to an end, motor cars were up and running, Orville and Wilbur Wright were preparing to begin the age of air travel, and the world, though far from innocent, had not yet experienced the full horrors of world war. Twenty or so centimetres ago – the length of a man's hand – the French rose up against their aristocracy and the Americans finally told the British that enough was enough. Fifty centimetres ago – finger-tip to elbow – Columbus first landed on islands off the eastern coast of America.

A metre is roughly a yard: another human-sized measure, initially conceived as the distance from the tip of a man's nose to the tip of his fingers when his arm is held outwards at shoulder-height. It corresponds to a thousand years. It was roughly one metre ago that William the Conqueror invaded Britain and transformed its politics and that the Maoris colonised New Zealand and transformed its ecology. A metre and a half, the height of a Jersey cow or indeed of Queen Victoria, takes us back to Mohammed and to the first human colonisation of Madagascar and Hawaii. Two metres, the height of an average basketball player, takes us back to Christ, Herod, John the Baptist, and the Roman invasion of Britain. Thirteen metres, roughly the length of the kind of yacht that competes for the America's Cup, takes us back to the first human invasion of North America: from

Siberia into Alaska, across the land-bridge that now lies deep beneath the Bering Strait.

Go back thirty metres, a standard length for municipal swimming pools, and we find that the Earth is still populated by more than one version of human being. The neanderthals, *Homo neanderthalensis*, still shared a large chunk of Eurasia with modern humans, *Homo sapiens*. *Homo sapiens* began, probably in Africa, a hundred metres back: the length of the straight of an Olympic running track, gloriously bestridden in the time it takes to draw breath by Carl Lewis, Linford Christie and their ilk.

A million years is a kilometre: the length of London's Park Lane. A kilometre ago human begins were of the species known as *Homo erectus*, including types such as 'Peking Man', and they shared the planet with the last of our extinct hominid relatives known as the robust australopithecines, alias paranthropines. *H. erectus* first appeared about 1·8 kilometres ago. Five kilometres or so ago, a pleasant Sunday afternoon stroll, takes us back to the first members of the Hominidae. In fact we are back to the start of the Pliocene.

The length of a marathon – forty kilometres or so – takes us back to the very first appearance of creatures that might reasonably be called apes. The last of the dinosaurs disappeared about 65 kilometres ago. I must ask you to envisage your own version of 65 kilometres – 40 miles. For me, a south Londoner, it is roughly the distance to Canterbury: a Chaucerian pilgrimage, now a quick dash down the M2.

Two hundred kilometres ago takes us back both to the start of the dinosaurs and, roughly, to the start of the mammals – for they both began their glorious reigns at about the same time. Travelling east from London (forgive the continuing chauvinism – you must start where you like) this would take us into Belgium. Five hundred and fifty kilometres – 550 million years – takes us roughly from London to Frankfurt, and to the beginning of the eon known as the Phanerozoic. The first period in the Phanerozoic was the Cambrian, in which almost all of the main groups (phyla) of modern animals first appeared.

Two thousand kilometres and a bit more, London to Istanbul, takes us to the first eukaryotes: that is, the first of the creatures such as animals, plants, and fungi, whose cells had recognisable nuclei (as opposed to the prokaryotes, the bacteria, whose cells have no distinct nucleus). Somewhat more than 3,000 kilometres takes us to Damascus, and to the beginning of life. Four and a half thousand kilometres takes us almost across Iran — and to the beginning of the Earth itself.

This is the first surprise. When I began this exercise, with a year represented as a palpable entity, a unit quite easy to envisage, I thought that the beginning of the Earth would be on the other side of the world. But London to the far side of Iran — that is the kind of distance that St Paul used to take, literally, in his stride.

The Universe itself began, so modern cosmologists suggest, with the Big Bang, about 15 billion years ago (American billion, that is, or thousand million).* That translates into 15,000 kilometres: London to Hong Kong. With the aid of the jumbo jet, some people almost commute from London to Hong Kong. The distance is not so frightening. Thus can we envisage and encompass the vastest reaches of time; in fact, all the time that there has ever been, for before the Universe began the concept of time is meaningless. In practice, however, the time-scales relevant to this book do not extend beyond tens of millions of years: the width of a big city. That does not seem particularly daunting. But the conventional time-scales of historians — dealing at best in centuries, the length of a man's middle finger — really are dangerously small.

But before I finally embark on this 5-million-year extended history, I want briefly to explain the method. I want to tell the story in a way that some people, now, feel is not respectable, not 'scientific'. But I think it is, and would like quickly to say why.

SCIENCE AND MYTH; MYTH AS SCIENCE

In 1979 a young historian of science at Yale, Misia Landau, was researching the history of palaeoanthropology — that is, she was exploring the way in which scientists over the past century or so have described our own evolution. She realised that their descriptions took the form not of cold, 'objective' science, as the scientists themselves liked to believe, but of myth. In their

---

*Or this at least was the conventional view when I started writing this book. Observations made late in 1994 now suggest that the Universe might be only 8 billion years old, although this idea is embarrassing since other calculations suggest that certain stars must be older than this.

descriptions of our ancestry they perceived and projected the genus *Homo* as a hero of the kind who features in the folk-tales of every culture: a hero who begins life humbly, is faced with a series of hurdles, overcomes those hurdles and in doing so is honed and improved until he emerges as *Homo sapiens*. Finally, in many versions of the allegory, *Homo sapiens* commits the sin described by the Greeks as 'hubris' and so is destroyed. Hubris is rather a nice idea, summing up the presumption and conceit of human beings in believing that their destiny is in their own hands or that any success they achieve is gained simply through their own efforts. The Greeks after all believed deep down that the affairs of the world and all the creatures therein were in the hands of the gods, and that if human beings ever succeeded in this world it was only with the gods' approval or as Christians would say 'by God's grace'. Heroes, after their Earthly success, are particularly prone to hubris. But the gods do not tolerate such presumption. Hubris is punished. Death is the usual penalty – either that, or worse.

As Roger Lewin excellently describes in *Bones of Contention*, modern scholars of human history have responded in three main ways to Misia Landau's revelations. Some simply said, 'Nonsense. Science is "objective", and we sift the facts objectively, and tell it like it is'. Others were shocked. They had been brought up to believe that science ought to be objective, but when Landau revealed the literary narrative that runs through so many of their 'scientific' descriptions they realised how deeply they had deceived themselves. Try as they might, scientists find it just as difficult as the rest of us not to impose their own prejudices and stereotypes on what they see. Whether you are a scientist or not, it is all too easy to fit whatever you see into a story that is already inside your own head.

But a third group soon recovered from the shock of Landau and effectively said, 'So be it'; and so do I. For this seems to me to be precisely in line with the modern philosophy of science. For science, try though scientists might, cannot trade in irrefutable, 'objective' truths, as it is traditionally believed to do. It does deal with ideas of a particular kind: ideas that can be tested and in theory refuted. But all of its truths, up to and including Newton's laws of mechanics, must be seen to be provisional. Built in to any idea of science is the realisation that it could be wrong; logically, the possibility must always remain that the theories of the time are flawed, and that the real 'truth' has yet to be envisaged. Science progresses by the proposal of ideas – 'hypotheses' – of the kind that can be tested. More broadly, it also proceeds through grand statements of the kind that can be called 'heuristic'. Heuristic statements (whether in science or any other field) are of the kind that promote understanding, even though they may not literally be true themselves. In practice, a statement may be heuristic and may properly belong in science even though it is not directly testable. This would be the case if the statement, though untestable itself, suggested hypotheses that *were* testable. Such statements provide what the great twentieth-century philosopher Sir Karl Popper has called an 'agenda' for science.

In short, it is perfectly reasonable for palaeoanthropologists (scholars of fossil humans) to be quite unabashed by Landau's thesis – provided they also acknowledge the full significance of what she is saying. They should be unabashed because it is perfectly reasonable to behave precisely as the old style (and new-style!) palaeoanthropologists have done, and describe *Homo* as a hero – because the description of early humans *qua* tragic heroes is (or can be) 'heuristic'. That is, such a description gets the show on the road. It is a coherent idea which pulls the facts together, and gives an overall sense of what went on. Testable hypotheses are generated by, and nest within, this framework, and as they are tested they modify the overall picture. That is the proper dialectic between the real world and our mind-picture of it. In practice, such dialectic provides the only route to progress.

There is one final advantage in telling the history of human beings in the manner of myth. It is that the human brain – unlike a computer – is supremely adapted to grasping narratives. We love stories, with a beginning, a middle, and an end. 'In the beginning was the word,' says St John in the first line of his Gospel; but whatever the theological import of this, as a statement on human psychology it is wrong. In the beginning was the *story*. Stories we remember. There is only one danger, and it really is dangerous, but it is easily avoided once we know what it is. The danger is to imagine that the well-told tale, the myth, which should at best be seen as a working model is, in fact, the truth itself. Many scientists, in other contexts, have made this mistake: erected hypotheses just to get their investigations on the road, and then mistaken them for the truth they were trying to find out. In short, I see no harm in presenting human evolution as myth and human beings as heroes because this is a colourful and memorable way to convey ideas, but I will try to bear in mind, and ask you to as well, that the myth is not intended as the final truth. It merely provides a mental framework on which, in time and with luck, the truth may be hung.

To tell the story properly, however – to get to grips with all the forces and the characters involved – it is necessary to bring several apparently different threads together. It seems worthwhile to provide a guide.

AN INTRODUCTION TO THE REST OF THE BOOK

The first and crucial point is that we, human beings, have in the end been shaped by the world itself. Unless this planet had behaved in particular ways at a particular time in the history of our own lineage, we would not have come into being. Furthermore, the kind of changes that we are now threatening to make – such as greenhouse warming – are the kinds that have been seen in the past. It is necessary, then, to set the stage by describing the *modus operandi* of the Earth itself. That, then, is the subject of the following chapter.

Then we should ask why our lineage – our ancestors – should have responded to Earthly forces the way they did; and why all other animals have responded as they have done. In other words, we should explore the underlying mechanisms of evolution. That is the theme of Chapter 3.

History is not lived in isolation; indeed it is largely the story of relationships. Nations interact with other nations; species with other species. The other creatures that occupied our planet this past 50 million years or so helped to shape our evolution – we evolved in part to cope with them and, in our turn, have influenced them. Again, we cannot understand what we are doing to our fellow creatures now without knowing what has happened to them in the past; without that background knowledge, we cannot see what is different now. So in Chapter 4 I introduce our fellow creatures.

With the scene set and the other characters in place, the rest of the book can focus on our own kind. Chapter 5 shows how the forces discussed in Chapters 2 and 3 acted to produce ourselves. Chapter 6 asks why this was such a big event – for 'What's So Special About Us?'. Then in Chapters 7 and 8 I discuss the effects that we have had upon the world – not in the past few decades, which is obvious enough, but over the past few tens of thousands of years, which is the time in which our influence ceased to be that merely of a large mammal, and we pushed the world into a new ecological phase.

Finally, in Chapter 9 I want to look at how the lessons of history – our proper, extended history – might apply to the future. I consider the next million years: what effect we will have on our fellow creatures during that time; what might happen to us; and indeed what we need to do if our species, or any other creatures, is to last anything like this long.

How the World Works

People the world over congregate each year to give thanks for the harvest – and keep their fingers crossed for the next one. The rituals are largely for appeasement. Every society has cause to know that the beneficence of the Earth cannot be taken for granted. Some of us in temperate islands to the north expect good times and complain when rain delays the tennis but the folklores of at least 500 cultures from the Hopi Indians to Australian aborigines recall horrendous floods: Noah's was only one of many that derive from Mesopotamia, where the Tigris and Euphrates run in parallel into the Persian Gulf. Some people endure five-yearly floods almost as routine. From San Francisco to Azerbaijan people live in the knowledge that one day their cities will succumb to earthquake. Some places are far more vulnerable than others but nowhere is safe. Two-thirds of the city of Lisbon was shaken to pieces one day in 1755.

Volcanoes continue to harry us, too, and always will. In 1980 Mount St Helens in Washington State USA threw out about a cubic kilometre of 'ejecta'. The eruption of Vesuvius in AD 79 was about the same size, and completely obliterated the south Italian city of Pompeii. The eruption of Santorini on the island of Thera north of Crete in 1470 BC produced *ten* cubic kilometres. The ash and acid rain from Santorini wiped out the Cretan civilisation of the Minoans, which had dominated the Mediterranean – after which the way was clear for the mainland Mycaenians and hence the rise of Greece. All that remains of Thera now is a sickle of rock around the 'caldera' – the hole, where once the volcano stood.

Volcanoes affect the climate, too – for the debris they throw into the upper atmosphere can block out the Sun, in the same way that nuclear war might lead to 'nuclear winter'. Ben Franklin first suggested that this might be the case after the eruption of Laki in Iceland in 1783 caused a bluish haze in Europe that spread as far as Siberia and north Africa, and led to the freezing winter in 1783–4, both in Europe and North America. The bluish fog is now known to have been sulphur dioxide, SO_2, dissolved in atmospheric water vapour to form sulphuric acid. It fell in the months after Laki as 100 million tonnes of acid rain, the relics of which can still be clearly seen in cores of ice taken from Greenland. Laki's eruption was about the same size as Santorini's. So too was the one of Krakatoa in Indonesia in 1883, and the climatic changes that resulted from that volcano were the first to be studied by scientists worldwide.

But Santorini, Laki, and Krakatoa were all of them dwarfed by the eruption of Tambora on the island of Sumbawa east of Java. Between April and July of 1815 Tambora produced a series of eruptions which taken all together were ten times bigger than any of them. The worldwide climatic effects of Tambora were not formally studied – but they were obvious enough. The eruptions probably caused the famously awful weather at the Battle of Waterloo. In the following year, 1816, there was effectively no summer: the people of New England in the US spoke of it as 'Eighteen Hundred and Froze to Death'. In Italy, Lord Byron, Clare Claremont, and Percy Bysshe Shelley and his wife Mary made the best of their holiday by making up stories while the cold rain fell – and Mary's efforts resulted in *Frankenstein*. Crops failed across the whole northern hemisphere in 1816. In Europe, still recovering from the Napoleonic wars, the weather may have encouraged the spread of the louse that carries typhus, and have led to the epidemic of 1816–19. The crop failures and the resulting misery in turn inflamed political unrest all over Europe. (In Britain in 1819, troops charged upon a crowd of 60,000 people who had met in Manchester at St Peter's Fields to demand reform. Four hundred people were injured and eleven killed in what became known as the 'Peterloo massacre'.)

Yet no society has ever known or can ever experience the full range of enormity of which the Earth is capable and to which it is subject. To see it all you would have to live an awfully long time. Two and a half billion years ago the composition of the Earth's entire atmosphere changed as profoundly as such change is possible, as free oxygen gas was introduced for the first time from the new organisms that practised photosynthesis. More astonishing yet, throughout the lifetime of the planet the continents which seem so irredeemably solid have *moved*: not a little, but right across the surface of the globe, splitting and rejoining as they went, floating like froth on the hot and slowly swirling rock of the mantle beneath. The earthquakes and the volcanoes that have done us so much harm are simply a side-effect. Of course the earth shudders, of course the turbulent rock beneath bursts through now and again, when entire land masses are on the move.

Five times at least within the past billion years there have been changes of climate so dramatic that the fauna of the entire world has been transformed. The latest such 'mass extinction' was 65 million years ago and wiped out the dinosaurs – and yet it was not the biggest. Since about 50 million years ago the whole Earth has become inexorably cooler – not steadily so but in a series of bursts, with occasional reversals to widespread tropics. Overall the world has now become so cold that the temperature hovers on the point of freezing; and at least ten times in the past million years the balance has flipped, ever so slightly, but enough to take us into ice age. The ice sheets on Antarctica, North America and Eurasia have at times been as big as modest continents and as deep as mountains. So much water was locked within them that the sea level fell worldwide, sufficiently to join continents and countries that previously were apart – Siberia to Alaska via the vast but transient causeway of Beringia, that was as big as Poland; the islands of Indonesia to mainland Asia; New Guinea to Australia – and enough to drain the Mediterranean Sea, and deplete Africa's Lake Victoria, not once but several times. Falling sea-level also combined with drifting continents to create the isthmus of Panama just 3 million years ago, in the Pliocene, and so bring North and South America together for the first time.

Why does this matter? Why is it pertinent to discuss the climate and the movement of continents in a book about the history and the evolution of human beings and of our fellow creatures?

The answer is two-fold. First, climate is not a back-drop, like stage scenery. We realise now it is a crucial force in the evolution of all living things. In general, it seems that the entire evolutionary machine moves towards an uneasy equilibrium unless the system is jolted every now and again. While conditions remain the same, the interacting creatures seem to come to an agreement: in times of stability natural selection tends to encourage them to stay as they are. Conditions can be altered in several ways and for several reasons but the most significant, frequent, and universal causes are those of climate. Indeed, Elisabeth Vrba of Yale

University suggests that global changes of climate every now and again cause ripples of evolutionary change worldwide – a global shift in the fauna. She calls this 'the turnover pulse hypothesis'. Specifically, it seems that our own family, the Hominidae, came into existence after an episode of cooling in the late Miocene, while our own group within that family, the genus *Homo*, evolved as it did in response to another burst of global cooling 2·5 million years ago. Other creatures changed at those times too. Cattle and gazelles, for example, came into existence in the late Pliocene, at about the same time as our own genus.

It is clear, too, that ever since animals and plants appeared on Earth they have changed their location; many indeed seem to have raced around the world several times. How and where they moved affected their own evolution and the ecology of all around them. Whether they chose to move was determined, more often than not, by climate: hostile ice behind, alluring sun and greenery ahead. The opportunity to move or the proscription on movement was provided or imposed by the shifting continents, and the rise and fall of sea-level: whether South America was still joined to Africa, or to North America; whether Africa had yet collided with Eurasia, and whether the Mediterranean was full or dry; whether Madagascar had split from Africa. It *matters*, in short, what the climate and the continents have done. These are the forces of history.

There is a more practical reason, too, why this history matters. For although the underlying forces are so tremendous, although they seem to operate on a scale that is well beyond human compass, *nonetheless it is becoming clear that we can influence the climate*. By changing the climate we influence the ecology and evolution of the whole world effectively for the rest of time. There is nothing, indeed, that is more pertinent to understand than the way that climate behaves, and the extremes of which it is capable, and the ways in which it can be influenced. 'Influence', of course, emphatically does not mean 'control'.

Until just a few decades ago, most of the phenomena that are now known to dominate the Earth's history in general and its climate in particular were not even known to exist. Such ideas as there were – for example the notion that the continents do in fact move – were widely disbelieved or even ridiculed. Now, thanks to an extraordinary coalition of scientists – geophysicists,

astronomers, chemists, palaeontologists and climatologists, all crucially assisted by computers of remarkable power – we seem to be
approaching a grand synthesis. The forces are beginning to be
understood. More than that, we are beginning to understand their
interactions: how the height of the land affects the chemistry of
the atmosphere; how the tilt of the planet relative to the Sun
affects the influx of energy (not how much, but where and when
that energy falls); how the position of the continents affects the
flow of ocean currents, and hence the distribution of energy
around the Earth; and how indeed each combination of factors
may give rise to feedback loops in which the different factors
sometimes suppress and sometimes enhance each other.

This intricate picture has not been easy to put together. It has
required a succession of insights over three centuries, each one
demanding a huge leap of imagination: and Earth scientists,
though little recognised, have been among the most imaginative
of all. But because the insights did require such imagination, each
has met with incredulity. No scientists have been more compre-
hensively scorned than those who have sought to explain how the
world behaves. Yet, time after time, the most extraordinary ideas
have turned out to be right, and the conservative notions have
proved inadequate. So far, however, the Earth has always outstripped its interpreters. Always it has proved more complicated
than anyone expected.

So now we can look, at least in outline, at why the world has
cooled this past 50 million years – and the explanation, I suggest,
represents one of the great scientific insights of the late twentieth
century. We can look too, in general terms, at why the cooling
has not been smooth; why there have been jerks and reversals –
and why there could be jerks and reversals in the future, leaving
little or no time for planning or taking stock. We can begin to see
how it is that small changes – like the apparently trivial rise in
atmospheric carbon dioxide – can have huge sequelae. And finally
we can look at why those sequelae are intrinsically unpredictable
– although we can make guesses, and those guesses are aided by
knowledge of what has happened in the past.

There is no obvious place to begin the description for everything depends upon and interacts with everything else –
landscape, atmosphere, ocean currents, the whole Earth with the
rest of the cosmos. The simplest course is to pick up on the main

themes and then show how they have now been brought together. The full flavour of the ideas is brought out best if we approach them historically.

THE START OF THE MODERN IDEAS

The key ideas of 'classical' geology and palaeontology (the study of fossils) were laid down in the eighteenth and early nineteenth centuries – including the crucial notion that the world has not always been the way it is now.* For example, there are marine fossils at the tops of mountains, showing that those mountain-tops were once at the bottom of the sea. Thus, God did not put all the present-day mountains in position and leave it at that. Mountains have risen, and they have collapsed. Rocks, too, change: mud hardens and debris is crushed into solid rock; rock crumbles to sand and silt. There are rocks that are produced by volcanic action, known as igneous, and those that are deposited from debris over time, called sedimentary. Some of the sedimentary rocks form from river deposits. Others are formed from the skeletons of marine creatures. Skeletons of the planktonic protozoa known as foraminifera are made of carbonates, and sink to the sea-bed to form chalk which may transform into limestone; skeletons of protozoan radiolarians are made of silica, and sink to fossilise into flints. Some rocks are transformed into others by heat and pressure, and thus does limestone become marble. Rocks, however formed, are sculpted by wind and water. Rivers are carvers of caves and gorges that grow deeper by the century.

Underlying these basic ideas was a new sense of time. The nineteenth-century naturalists could see how quickly sediments formed, and could calculate how much sediment would compress to form a particular rock; thus they could guess, roughly, how long it took for a particular sedimentary rock of a particular thickness to form. The result was a general sense that the Earth had been around for a very long time. Underlying the basic ideas, too, was the notion that was consolidated in the seventeenth

---

*For a detailed treatment of who thought what in this key period, see Anthony Hallam's excellent *Great Geological Controversies* (second edition), Oxford University Press, 1990.

century and is epitomised in the physics of Newton: the idea that effects have causes, and that natural things had natural causes. Whether or not the scientists believed in God (and most of the early scientists were extremely devout) it simply was not good enough to say that God had made things as they are. Always the question for science was 'How?'.

Thus in the eighteenth and early nineteenth centuries the traditional commonsensical view of the world – as a landscape created by God according to his mysterious will – was transformed. The Earth came to be seen as a dynamic body, its structure constantly re-formed by volcanoes and sediments, and reshaped by winds and rivers and inundating and retreating seas. The world in short was, and is, an evolving thing; a thing furthermore that took a great deal of time to evolve; but a thing in the end whose transformations could be analysed and understood by applying the still emerging laws of physics and chemistry.

On the crest of these ideas Charles Darwin (1809–82) finally devised his theory of evolution, summarised in *The Origin of Species by Means of Natural Selection* of 1859. To be sure, most of the evidence that Darwin brings to bear to support his ideas is based on the distribution and similarities of existing creatures, such as the famous finches of the Galapagos Islands. But he adduced that evidence in order to demonstrate the specific *mechanism* of evolution: 'by means of natural selection'. Before he began dealing with the mechanism, however, Darwin had needed to satisfy himself that the idea of evolution was necessary in the first place – the idea, that is, that living things had indeed altered over time, and had not been created in exactly the forms in which they appear now. The geology that was emerging when he was young (Charles Lyell published Volume I of *Principles of Geology* in 1830) instilled the general notion that the world as a whole has indeed changed, and has taken a great deal of time to do so. The emerging plethora of fossils did not alone demonstrate that animals and plants had evolved, and still less did the fossils show that animals came to be the way they are by natural selection. But the fossils did demonstrate a crucial fact: that in the deep past there existed hosts of creatures that were sometimes exceedingly different from those of the present, and sometimes intriguingly similar. Thus the emerging geology and palaeontology did not direct Darwin's inquiry but they set its tone. They showed that the Biblical account of the world's past, however powerful and lyrical, was far from complete – and also showed in the broadest way that change, not permanence, was the way of the world.

Yet as these broad ideas unfolded they were held back by the need, or at least the perceived need, to take account of the Bible. The new geologists envisaged seas advancing and retreating not once but many times – but *Genesis* spoke only of a single flood. The new palaeontologists recognised fossils as the remains of animals long gone – but the traditionalists acknowledged only that some creatures had failed to survive the flood (even though Noah was supposed to have collected two of each kind). In practice, the attempt to relate the evidence on the ground directly to the Noachian flood was more or less abandoned after the 1820s. But, as we will see, the general idea that floods accounted for almost everything persisted in some quarters almost until the twentieth century.

The transformations envisaged by the new geologists and palaeontologists required a huge expanse of time to unfold. The great Scottish geologist James Hutton (1726–97), ever ahead of the game, said that the Earth had 'no vestige of a beginning – no prospect of an end'. Yet the idea persisted for a century beyond Hutton that the Earth was comparatively young. Traditionalists continued to look over their shoulders at Archbishop Ussher, who in the seventeenth century calculated from the chronology of the Old Testament that the Earth began in about 4000 BC. More importantly, the physics of the nineteenth century seemed to support the general notion of *Genesis* that the age of the Earth must be measured in hundreds of thousands of years, rather than in thousands of millions as is now accepted to be the case. The assumption then was that when the Earth was formed it contained a fixed amount of heat which, it was believed, must constantly be lost; so if the Earth was older than a few hundred thousand years it would by now be cool right through. Even Darwin was bothered by this idea, late in the nineteenth century, long after he published his ideas on evolution in *Origin of Species*. Not until the end of the nineteenth century did scientists discover the existence of radioactivity. Only in the early twentieth century did they realise that radioactivity is a constant source of heat in the Earth's interior.

Overall, then, the eighteenth and nineteenth centuries were a time of wonderful boldness: of thinkers who envisaged Earth forces of a magnitude and scale that far transcended common experience, but who had to fight the deepest traditions of Church and science that still prevailed. This was not a time for timid thinkers.

By the middle of the nineteenth century, practitioners of the life and earth sciences should have been shock-proof. But even they were astounded by the ideas that are associated with the Swiss geologist Louis Agassiz: the notion that in the past much of the world had been covered by ice, and that much of the landscape had been fashioned not by Noachian floodwaters but by glaciers.

ICE

Louis Agassiz was not actually the first to formulate the notion that parts of the Earth that now are friendly countryside were once deep under ice. The original insight belonged to his naturalist friend Jean de Charpentier, and the term 'ice age' (*Eiszeit*) was coined by another friend of Agassiz's, the botanist Karl Schimper. Indeed, Charpentier had to persuade Agassiz. But once Agassiz grasped the idea he was the one who expanded and promulgated it.

Three kinds of observation led Charpentier, Schimper, and then Agassiz to this idea. First, they were Swiss: in their native Alps they could see glaciers at work, and could see at first hand what they can do. Secondly, they perceived that there is a range of geological phenomena so extraordinary that extraordinary explanations are demanded – and so they provided one. It was perverse of others to object to their ideas on the grounds that they were outlandish, since outlandishness was obviously required. Thirdly (the corollary of the second point), the explanations put forward by the other geologists of the day did not seem convincing.

To be specific, there are, all around northern Europe (and North America, too, but Agassiz knew mainly of Europe), heaps of debris and isolated rocks that just should not be where they are, and rocks and landscapes so damaged and scarred that they must have been subject to awesomely destructive forces. The former include peremptory piles and streaks of mud and stones, known as moraines, and single rocks known as 'erratics', smoothed like pebbles but sometimes big as a hotel, dumped on some hill-top hundreds of kilometres from any bedrock of the same kind. The damage includes great areas scoured of soil, neat round pits gouged in the open ground, valleys smoothed in the shape of a 'U' – not in a 'V' like the cuts of rivers – and pavements and faces of rock scratched deep and long as if by malice, and requiring careless but outrageous power.

The geologists of the nineteenth century were keen to apply science and to explain what they saw by natural law. But they were hampered by theology, and the particular desire to show how the landscape of today had resulted from the phenomena described in *Genesis*. Sometimes, too, their imagination was not quite up to the task. And sometimes (surprisingly often, actually) even good scientists allowed themselves to fudge the physics and to suppose, wishfully, that known phenomena could perform feats which in their bones they must have known were impossible. In short, the standard explanation for the displaced boulders, the smoothed-out valleys and the deep-scored pavements was... flood. Of course, flood can move stones: the pebbles on the beach chirrup with each wave. But it cannot dump a boulder half a kilometre up a mountain, as some erratics have been dumped. It throws rock at rock: but it does not scour rock against rock, pressing the two together for metres at a stretch, in the manner required to produce the etchings seen in nature.

At least, liquid water cannot do this. But frozen water can – and can be seen to do so in the places where glaciers still exist. Here, there is no problem with the physics. Agassiz was the principal proselytiser, and he needed principally to overcome his contemporaries' incredulity. He needed to convince them that the ice-rivers in his native Alps had once spread to the deep south of lowland France and into God's own garden of England's Surrey, and to show them that ice could exist in truly outrageous quantities. The physics was fine. It was just imagination that others were lacking: the ability to see, in their mind's eye, a mountainous sea of ice where now there were green fields and olive trees. Others went to extraordinary lengths to find alternative explanations. One proposed that the erratic boulders had at some time sunk into caverns, compressed the air within, and thence been expelled like a champagne cork – apparently to fly across the valleys and land light as a sparrow on some distant hilltop.

But as the nineteenth century wore on, Agassiz's idea took hold, and scientists of many different kinds have since enlarged upon it. The evidence is difficult to interpret, but overall Agassiz has been vindicated: the landscape of the north and the plants and animals of all the world, including us, have indeed been shaped to a very large extent by the widespread presence of ice in the not so distant past. But the story is also proving to be endlessly involved.

It is now clear, for example, that there was not a single 'ice age'. Over the past million years there have been about ten discrete ice ages, or 'glacial periods', occurring roughly at 100,000-year intervals. The latest began something over 70,000 years ago, reached its height – its 'glacial maximum' – at around 18,000 years ago, and effectively ended around 8,000 years ago (although some argue that it has yet to end). The ice ages were separated by warmer 'interglacials' – which were sometimes warmer than the present day, and allowed a brief re-flowering of tropical animals in northern Europe – and within each ice age there were briefer periods of warming known as 'interstadials'. In many places, the landscape clearly shows the influence of more than one ice age. Sometimes, for example, there are successive waves of moraines, each one dumped by successive waves of glaciers. But such evidence is bound to be limited, because the glaciers and ice mountains of any one ice age are liable to obliterate the geological evidence of the one before.

However, classical geology – the study of landscape and the chemistry of rocks – is now assisted by a battery of techniques that can be astonishingly informative. Conceptually straightforward, though far from simple in practice, is the extraction of cores of rock or mud or ice from the bottoms of ancient lakes, or the sea-bed, or the ice-fields of Antarctica or Greenland. Mud and ice build up over time: the deeper you go, the older the sample. With luck, in some cases, the depth alone tells you the age. In other cases the age of a given sample can be inferred by comparison with samples from other places that seem the same and can be dated. The degree of decay of various radioactive isotopes – potassium or carbon for instance – provides exact dates for at least some of the samples.

The fossils or subfossils of various organisms within the samples show what was going on at the time. Pollen is extremely resilient and extremely informative, because the type of plant can be identified and from the type of plant we can infer the climate. Alder pollen has been trawled from deep in the mud in Indonesia. Yet alder nowadays grows in dank impoverished mud by temperate rivers: clearly, Indonesia has been a very different place in the past. Cores from the sea-bed contain the skeletons of foramenifera ('forams'): from these, as from pollen, the family or even the species can be identified. We know their modern relatives and how they live, and so can infer from the ancient types whether the sea that harboured them was warm or cold.

These relatively simple techniques are now further augmented by extraordinary insights by Nick Shackleton at Cambridge and his colleagues. They base their work on the fact that oxygen exists in two atomic forms or 'isotopes'. The more common isotope is the lighter one, with an atomic weight of 16. The rare one is heavy, with an atomic weight of 18. Water of course contains oxygen, so water molecules in their turn are relatively lighter or heavier depending on which isotope they contain. Most water molecules obviously contain the more common, lighter isotope, but a few contain the heavier one.

Anyway, Shackleton points out that the lighter water molecules, containing oxygen-16, evaporate more readily than the heavier ones. For once, physical theory seems to accord fairly straightforwardly with common sense. In normal times, the water that evaporates from the surface of the sea simply condenses and runs back in again in rain or river water, so nothing changes. But in times of ice age, much of the water that evaporates off the sea is trapped in ice, and does not return. So the proportion of oxygen-18 in the sea increases, since the oxygen-16 that has evaporated away is entrapped on land. The skeletons of forams also contain oxygen, and the proportion of isotopes within them reflects that of the surrounding sea. Hence the isotope ratio of the foram skeletons, revealed in cores from the sea-bed, shows whether or not an ice age was in progress at the time they were formed. Cores from the Pacific now show the coming and going of ice ages throughout the Pleistocene with remarkable precision. In general they support the classical geological data, but they also reveal details which on land have long been obliterated.

The amount of ice that accumulated on Antarctica and on the northern continents during glacial periods was huge. In the latest ice age, the ice in the north was focused in two vast patches: the

Laurentide ice sheet of North America stretched down to what are now the southern states, while the Fennoscandian ice sheet was focused on Finland, Norway, and Sweden but extended south deep into France and southern England. At the height of the last glacial maximum, 18,000 years ago, the ice in the Laurentide sheet lay to a depth of almost four kilometres – the height of the present-day Rockies – while the Fennoscandian ice sheet rose to about three kilometres, the height of the Alps.

Now we see why the sea-level falls during ice ages. Eighteen thousand years ago the ice in the north and at Antarctica at that time contained 5·5 per cent of all the world's water. That results in only a small percentage drop in ocean-level, but since the world's oceans have an average depth of around 3·8 kilometres that small percentage drop translates into 150 metres, or 500 feet. Because the continental shelves are gently sloped that drop in turn translates into a huge land area; so at the last glacial maximum there was 40 per cent more dry land then there is today. The continental shelf of the eastern United States now extends 70–150 kilometres into the Atlantic, but in the fairly recent past it was dry land. Only 1·7 per cent of world's water is now locked up in ice, so presumably we need not fear a further rise of anything like 150 metres if the rest of it were to melt. Nonetheless, some of the world's most populated, productive, and beautiful areas only just have their eaves above the water: Bangladesh, the Florida Everglades, Norfolk, and Holland.

The mass of ice, the cooling, and the locking up of water begin a chain reaction. The weight of the ice causes the continents themselves to sink into the mantle below. But the mantle rock will not be crushed, so sinking in one place must be compensated by a rise elsewhere. As the ice melts, the continents spring back to their natural position. Clearly, the sinking and rise of rock influence the level of the sea relative to the height of the land. Thus the *actual* change in the sea level in any one place is under two main influences: the amount of water left in the oceans (which depends on how much is locked up in ice on land), and whether and by how much the land itself is depressed by the ice upon it.

Because global temperature is low during ice age, and because the area of the sea is reduced, the amount of water evaporating from the ocean surface is reduced. It used to be thought that ice

ages were 'pluvial': cold and wet, like an English winter. Now the
opposite is known to be the case. Ice ages are cold and arid, and
therefore dusty; the dust itself, revealed in sea-bed cores, again
shows whether and when in the past the Earth was cold or warm.
So too does the presence on land of 'loess', a soft rock formed
from dust. China has a huge area of loess that was formed during
the ice ages from Gobi dust.

Taken all in all, palaeoecologists now argue that the drying up
of the world during ice ages – or periods of global cooling in general – is of more importance, biologically, than the ice itself. Of
course the spreading ice drives animals away from the high latitudes and towards the Equator. Because of the fall in sea level,
too, land masses are joined during ice ages that in interglacial
times are separated: Siberia with Alaska; Britain with mainland
Europe; New Guinea with Australia.

But the dryness of ice ages affects the tropics and the tropics is
where most species live. Mainly because of the drying the tropical forests retreat in periods of global cooling. The endless sea of
trees gives way to savanna dotted by islands of forest. Many
species must die; but many others, for various reasons, are
prompted to come into being. Our own species was one of them
– not in an ice age, in fact, but almost certainly at a time of global
cooling that was not far from being an ice age.

When the ice was in place it was far from passive. Continuing
research is showing that the Laurentide sheet, at least, had a 'life'
of its own, apparently producing surges of giant ice floes in the
North Atlantic. Furthermore, these ice floes did not simply break
from the edges of the ice sheet like splinters from an iceberg.
Particles of rock formerly contained within the floes, and now to
be found at the bottom of the ocean, suggest that they emanated
from the *centre* of the Laurentide ice sheet, and crossed half a continent before reaching the sea. How come? Well, the earth itself
is heated by radioactive energy. The huge thickness of ice at the
centre of the ice sheet provided insulation and allowed the earth
beneath it to warm up. So the ice at the earth's surface melted and
the huge mountains of ice found themselves sitting on a surface
that was lubricated. Their weight then rendered them unstable,
and they collapsed and split, sending islands of ice out across the
land and into the ocean, where they floated as giant bergs until
they melted and deposited their accompanying loads of continental

rock on to the sea-bed, where they have now been picked up and tell us what must have happened. As more and more ice was lost, the insulation was reduced and the soil could freeze again, to restore a little stability. Computer models show that a complete cycle, from thaw to thaw or from build-up to build-up, takes around 7,000 years.

These ice floes from the centre of the Laurentide ice sheet are named after Hartmut Heinrich, of the German Hydrographic Institute in Hamburg, who began their discovery in 1988 (see *New Scientist*, 4 September 1993, pp. 36–41). Collectively the Heinrich floes were huge: in the last ice age equivalent to half of all the ice that is now to be found in Greenland. Because of this, they would have affected the ocean currents, and in particular would have interrupted the normal flow of warm water from the tropics to the poles which keeps the poles somewhat warmer than they would otherwise be. Geoff Boulton of the University of Edinburgh has made an intriguing extrapolation from that observation. Thus he points out that if the Earth does indeed begin to warm during the next few decades and centuries because of the greenhouse effect – more of this later – then the Antarctic ice would start to melt. This could cause surges of melting ice, comparable with Heinrich floes of the north. These could interrupt the warm currents flowing south and so make the South Pole even colder. Thus – paradox though it seems – in times of greenhouse the ice of the Antarctic might actually increase.

Indeed the ramifications seem endless. Even the outline of it is salutary, however. That common sense can apparently be defied, when warming the world might conceivably cause more ice to form, shows again how complex the world really is – and how immensely difficult it is to predict what might happen. It shows again how extraordinary the world is: that there is no place for incredulity; that the least plausible explanations so often turn out to be the most likely. It demonstrates the phenomenon known to mathematicians as catastrophe: that an apparently static mountain of ice can *suddenly* break up, and produce radical and global changes in climate perhaps within months. The general point is that the Earth may exist in any one of many different stable states, but the stable states do not form a continuum; so if the Earth is caused to alter then it may fall from one stable state to another in as little time as the physics allows. In the same way, a rock may be at the top of a cliff or at the bottom, but not in the middle. Ice ages seem to end catastrophically. Evidence from Greenland ice cores now suggests that the ice may disappear in as little as twenty years.

This, then, is where the insight of Louis Agassiz has led us. Ice has emerged as a shaper both of landscape and of world climate and a key determinant of sea-level, which in turn may crucially decide whether it is possible to walk from one continent to another.

But there is another force at work, even more momentous, which did not occur to anyone in the nineteenth century – or at best only fleetingly. Indeed it occurred only to a very few people in the twentieth century, and when it did it was resisted vigorously, not to say insultingly, for almost four decades. For in the eighteenth and nineteenth centuries geologists acknowledged, indeed they revelled in the fact, that masses of land may rise and fall. But they never supposed that entire continents moved sideways. Yet this is the notion which, more than any other, explains everything else. It has become the founding-stone of late twentieth-century earth science.

FROM CONTINENTAL DRIFT TO PLATE TECTONICS

We cannot blame the scientists of previous ages for failing to grasp that continents move laterally. On the face of things the idea seems ridiculous. In fact, it did not become fully accepted in the twentieth century until well into the 1960s – post-dating the invention of the laser and the unravelling of the genetic code. It is indeed a pleasant irony that the 'dusty' and gentlemanly science of geology has emerged as the most modern of all: the fundamental idea on which the contemporary discipline is founded is the most recent to be established.

It is a pity, though, that nineteenth-century geologists could not bring themselves to believe that the continents move, for understanding of this would have explained many of the features of the world that bothered them and led them down false paths. For example, although they perceived with wonderful boldness that mountains had once arisen – and were not simply present from the start – they never proposed a convincing mechanism. What, in fact, had pushed them up? At one point it was suggested that the Earth had cooled, and shrunk, and wrinkled like a prune, but few were entirely convinced by this.

There was also the palaeontological puzzle, pointed out not least by the Austrian geologist Edward Suess (1831–1914): that widely separate continents such as Africa and India sometimes contained nearly identical fossils. Yet Charles Darwin had posited in his *Origin of Species* of 1859 that creatures that were similar must have evolved from the same ancestor; they were not simply created separately, as *Genesis* proposed. It followed that different continents with similar fossils must once have been connected, and that the ancestors had flowed from one to the other. Suess accordingly suggested that southern Africa, Madagascar, and peninsular India must once have formed part of a common continent which he called 'Gondwanaland' – better simply called 'Gondwana' since Gondwana *means* 'land'. As we will see, Gondwana – now taken to embrace Australia, South America, and Antarctica, as well as Suess's candidates – plays a big part in modern thinking, albeit not in the way that Suess envisaged.

But in the nineteenth century and well into the twentieth, scientists (including Suess himself) went to the most outrageous lengths to explain the difficulty that Suess had pointed out. They proposed that the now distant continents had once been connected by corridors. They even stretched the myth of Atlantis to embrace a vast hypothetical continent between North America and Europe, which supposedly had disappeared beneath what is now the Atlantic Ocean. The existence of such corridors, flung like aetiolated causeways across entire oceans, would have set a geological precedent for which there is no modern counterpart; the idea is, in fact, absurd. Even more ridiculous – straining the most fundamental laws of physics, and defying almost all the painstaking observations of geology – was the notion of the vast, sinking Atlantic continent. But serious scientists entertained such ideas, showing to what enormous intellectual lengths they would go to resist the idea that continents move.

But then, of course, the idea that continents do move defies common sense. It just happens to be the case, as science continues to demonstrate, that common sense, though indispensable, is not to be trusted.

Credit for the idea belongs to Alfred Wegener (1880–1930), who was recognised primarily as a meteorologist and explorer and *en passant* as a record-breaking balloonist. He aired the notion first in a lecture in 1912, and published it in book form – *Die Entsehung der Kontinente und Ozeane* – in 1915, with several more editions in the 1920s.

Wegener supported his thesis with various lines of argument, some of which now seem stronger than others. His observation that the modern continents can be fitted together in a 'jigsaw' to make one big continent still stands in principle – though modern geologists arrange the 'pieces' differently. More to the point, he argued that the general level of the bottom of the sea, and the general level of the surface of the continents, fall into two distinct bands. It looked as if the continents were indeed discrete blocks that sat on the Earth's surface, towering above the surrounding sea-bed. Traditional theories supposed merely that the surface bumps and depressions were effectively arbitrary. But if that were so, then there would be an entire range of intermediate heights, which in fact there are not.

Wegener also picked up on some nineteenth-century physical notions that have proved valid: notably, the suggestion by an English cleric, the Reverend Osmond Fisher, that the Earth has a relatively fluid interior which swirls by convection like water in a kettle. More of this later, for it is an important idea. In fact, the 'substratum' – better called the 'mantle' – that lies beneath the outer crust is not fluid in the sense of liquid, but in the way that glass is fluid. It *looks* solid, and *feels* solid (or would if it were accessible, and cool enough to 'feel'), but in practice it behaves like an extremely viscous fluid. It does indeed flow – as glass does: the windows in a mediaeval cathedral are discernibly thicker at the bottom than at the top. Lead also seems solid enough, though it 'creeps' along roofs, and old lead pipes are distinctly droopy. But however viscous glass or metals or rock may be, if they flow they are fluid – and the continents, said Wegener, could slide across the fluid mantle like ocean foam.

Wegener also argued, cogently, that rocks on continents on opposite sides of the Atlantic – the east side of South America and the west of Africa – were in line with each other. It was as if, he said, a newspaper had been torn, leaving the newsprint still aligned to show how one piece had once been joined to the other. Similarly, many of the fossils from the Mesozoic (the 'Age of Reptiles') and the preceding Palaeozoic were similar on the southern continents, though these now are widely separated. He was impressed particularly by the Permian aquatic reptile *Mesosaurus* and the seed-fern *Glossopteris*, which are found only in the southern continents and India. Suess had used the same examples as evidence for Gondwana. But Suess, in common with the generality of biologists, assumed that there must have been some land-bridge between the continents that now are separate. Wegener simply pointed out that a land-bridge would have been composed of relatively light continental rock, and could not for reasons of physics have sunk into the denser 'substratum' below. If there had been no land-bridge, said Wegener, then the continents must once have been joined, and had drifted apart.

At first, Wegener's ideas seem to have had a surprisingly easy passage. He certainly received some brickbats – such an astonishing idea was bound to meet incredulity – but he also found excellent support. Notably, the great Milutin Milankovich (one of the boldest thinkers in a bold field) told Wegener after an early meeting, 'I am still totally under the influence of your brilliant lecture.' But he added a cogent philosophical aside: 'You should not be discouraged if you find it more difficult to persuade empiricists [that is, scientists who rely primarily on observation, in the manner of naturalists] than students of the exact sciences [i.e., theoretical physicists]. Quite the contrary, in fact.' Absolutely. It is clear in the late twentieth century, in the age of quantum mechanics and cosmology, that theorists who define what is *possible* often get closer to what actually happens in the Universe than those who merely look and see.

On a more practical front, too, in 1929 the British geologist Arthur Holmes proposed a model of the Earth that resembled that of Fisher in the nineteenth century, although more precise. Holmes knew by now that the Earth's interior was heated by radioactivity, which explained the swirling by convection. Thus, at least in part, he provided the component that Wegener's hypothesis was lacking: a *mechanism* and source of energy, to drive the continents along.

Nevertheless, as the twentieth century wore on, opinion hardened against Wegener until by World War II his support had all but dried up. Some of the world's greatest scientists were simply dismissive. The American palaeontologist and mammal specialist George Gaylord Simpson declared, 'The known past and present

distribution of land mammals cannot be explained by the hypothesis of drifting continents... the distribution of mammals definitely
supports the hypothesis that the continents were essentially stable
throughout the whole time involved in mammalian history.' In
fact, as we will discuss in the next chapter, the 'whole time
involved in mammalian history' is at least 200 million years. The
continents have moved spectacularly in that time.

The tide began to flow towards Wegener after World War II,
when new geophysical techniques came on line and provided the
essential hard data. Of crucial importance was the study of rock
magnetism. Some types of rock, of the kind that are formed by
cooling from a molten state, become magnetised as they cool, and
the direction of their magnetism is in line with the Earth's own
magnetic field. But a series of key studies throughout the 1950s
showed that not all magnetised rocks had the same direction of
magnetism as the present-day Earth. Yet the variations from the
present were not random. They varied consistently, depending
upon the age and geographical location of the rocks.

The conclusion was inescapable. When those ancient rocks
were formed, the land masses of which they are a part were ori-
entated differently with respect to the Earth's magnetic field than
is now the case. Either the world had the same geography in the
past as it has now but the magnetic poles had moved, or else the
poles had stayed roughly in the same place and the continents had
moved.

In the mid-1950s S.K. Runcorn of Cambridge University and
his colleagues showed that the magnetic orientation of rocks from
Europe had changed steadily over time; which meant that in the
Precambrian the North Pole must have been where Hawaii is
now – either that, or Europe had moved relative to the North
Pole. Then in 1960 P.M.S. Blackett from Imperial College,
London, and his colleagues showed from observations in the
southern continents and India that it must be the continents that
moved rather than the pole that wandered. In short, they could
explain their results beautifully if they arranged the big land
masses of the south in one giant continent roughly as Suess had
proposed, and then envisaged them sliding away from each other.
But their results just did not fit the idea of a wandering pole.

There was another complication, again dating from the early
1950s. It became clear, initially from work in Iceland, that every

now and again in the past the Earth's north pole became the south pole, and then flipped back again. This does not materially affect the points I have just been making because the reversal was apparently a quick flip through 180°. That is, the polar axis remained unchanged during these times of flip; there is no question here of poles going on walkabout around the surface of the globe. In the 1960s it became clear that the last reversal took place about 1 million years ago, and the one before that around 2·5 million years ago. In general, these reversals of the Earth's magnetic polarity provide another rich seam of data from which all manner of insights can be inferred.

Also from the 1950s onwards, this time using the newly-developed techniques of echo-sounding and deep-sea drilling, oceanographers began to study the ocean floor more thoroughly than ever before. Thus they showed that the centres of the world's oceans were traversed by ridges of mountains, as high as those on land, and those mountain ranges were in turn cut through by deep faults. The mid-Atlantic ridge was particularly dramatic. It transpired, too, that the rock of the mid-ocean ridges was almost invariably of the same type, or similar, as that of the underlying mantle. Finally, and startlingly, the rock of the mid-ocean ridges was invariably *new* – or at least none was older than the mid-Cretaceous. Yet conventional wisdom assumed that the sea-bed was ancient, and should therefore have contained ancient rocks.

So then, in 1960 (published 1962), Harry Hess of Princeton University put forward what became known as 'the spreading sea-floor hypothesis'. He proposed that new sea-floor was constantly being created in the ridges in the middle of the oceans, as rock from the radio-actively heated mantle welled up from below. The ocean floor, in fact, was 'frozen' mantle. The new-formed floor then spread outwards from the ridge in both directions, towards the continents on either side. When it reached the continental margins, it was shoved down into the mantle again. The surface of the Earth is indeed mobile.

Powerful support for this startling idea – indeed virtual confirmation – was provided by the phenomenon of polar reversal. If Hess's idea was true, after all, then the rock of the sea-bed, underlying the sediment, should get steadily older from the centre to the ocean's edge. The direction of the magnetism of any one piece of the ocean floor would depend on the orientation of the Earth's own magnetic field at the time that piece of floor first exuded from the mantle beneath and cooled into solidity. Since the Earth's magnetic axis reverses every few million years, we should expect to find that the sea-floor, magnetically speaking, was striped. The floor nearest the ridge, newly formed, should have the same magnetic orientation as the present Earth; the floor slightly further from the ridge should be reversed in orientation; and so on. Broadly speaking (the observations are far from straightforward) this does indeed seem to be the case. Modern studies of the ocean floor continue to add to the picture. In particular, the mid-ocean ridges have emerged as truly prodigious mountain ranges. Sometimes they even reach the surface: Iceland, the Azores, and Tristan da Cunha are part of the mid-Atlantic ridge. Every now and again they remind us of their provenance, as magma spurts forth from them.

The complete modern picture began properly to emerge in the mid-1960s, beginning (we may say) with the Canadian geophysicist Tuzo Wilson. Wilson it was who suggested that the Earth's crust is actually divided into a series of 'plates'; he was the first to coin the word 'plate' in this context. Thus he also gave rise to the modern term 'plate tectonics', where the word 'tectonics' is derived from the Greek 'tecton', meaning 'building', or 'construction', and is applied by geologists to the Earth's crust in general.

Nowadays geologists recognise about twenty discrete plates, some very large, some small. Some plates simply form ocean floor, and others, known as 'continental plates', have continents floating upon them. Each ocean plate, as Harry Hess first intimated, acts like a conveyor belt. The back end is constantly re-formed from underlying mantle, as it wells to the Earth surface, generally along a mid-ocean ridge; the front end is recycled as the plate dives back into the mantle again, typically along the edge of a continent, where an ocean plate is thrust beneath a continental plate.

All the features of the Earth's basic structure, and much of its behaviour, are explained by this 'plate tectonics' model. We now see clearly the distinction between the ocean beds and the continents. The plates themselves consist of solidified magma, which is very heavy. The continents are indeed discrete entities: blocks of lighter rock which sit on top of some (but by no means all) of the shifting plates. Where the plates go, the continents must go too. They are like foam on rough water: thrust hither and thither, pushed together and torn apart, but always floating on the heavier material beneath.

Unsurprisingly, the contact and shearing of plates may result in earthquakes – which indeed occur mainly in the 'zones' where the plates are known to meet, such as California, Japan and Azerbaijan. Where plates are shoved together mountains are thrown up, like ripples in silk. The energy of the convection currents in the underlying mantle is prodigious, the mass of the plates is enormous, and the force of the collision, slow though it is, is awesome. With such power, it is not at all difficult to see how mountains can be so casually tossed up, and the strata folded and 'overthrust'. Thus have the Rockies and Andes grown; thus do the Himalayas continue to buckle as the plate that carries India is thrust into the underside of Asia (although the mountains are no longer growing taller as their rise is countered by erosion). But parts of the Himalayas are notoriously unstable as the people of Nepal are only too aware. The continuing upthrust leads to landslides – helped by the erosion that is encouraged by deforestation.

Volcanoes emerge as special cases of the general process that occurs constantly at the mid-ocean ridges, as magma escapes to the surface. There are places in the hot mantle known as 'plumes' where convection currents produce particularly fierce upthrust, and where plumes coincide with weaknesses in the overlying crust and the magma beneath bursts through as larva. Traditional textbooks depict this outflow as 'molten' rock surging from deep within the Earth but, as we have seen, the mantle is not 'molten' in the sense of being liquid. The physics of volcanoes is more subtle than that, as is now revealed by Dan Mackenzie of Cambridge University. The point is that the rock of the underlying mantle *would* be molten – it is certainly hot enough – but it remains in a semi-solid, glass-like state because it is under such enormous pressure from the weight of the overlying crust. When the pressure is released – that is, when the crust is breached – then the rock changes 'phase', from semi-solid to liquid. Professor Mackenzie compares the phenomenon to the fizz of carbon dioxide gas when you take the top off a soda bottle. As the pressure is released, the dissolved gas is able at last to stretch itself, and comes swooshing out. Not surprisingly, volcanoes occur in areas where the crust is being pulled about. Thus there are clear zones of vol-canoes where the crust is under stress, just as there are zones of earthquakes where the plates make contact.

More broadly, the lay-out of the present continents results entirely (or almost entirely) from the movements of the plates since the world began – and over the past few million years they have moved athletically. Exactly where and how they have moved is crucial to our story, for the positions of the different land masses at different times have largely determined the peregrinations of animals and plants around the world, and therefore have largely determined their evolution. So where have they been?

WHERE THE CONTINENTS HAVE BEEN

The plates that bear the continents upon them move only slowly by human standards: from less than a centimetre a year, to several centimetres. But the Earth is about 4·5 billion years old and over that vast time most of the stretches of land that now combine to form the modern continents have travelled over most of the world, splitting from old neighbours as they go and joining to others as if in a global square-dance, sometimes far under the sea and sometimes forced upwards in long-gone mountain ranges that reached greater heights than the Himalayas today. Animals of a modern kind, with hard shells and skeletons forming solid fos-sils, started to appear about 570 million years ago in the eon known as the Phanerozoic. The first period of this eon, the Cambrian, seems extraordinarily ancient; yet it occupies only the last one-eighth or so of the world's history.

In the Cambrian the land masses of the world had a somewhat scattered look. For example, the mass known as Laurentia now forms much of northern North America – but then it was an island that straddled the Equator in the midst of a huge ocean, and it was spun through 90° relative to its present position. Most of present-day North America was then under water, forming part of Laurentia's continental shelf. Siberia, now the epitome of land-locked northernness, was a subtropical island in the southern hemisphere; and again, most of it was under water. The area that now is northern Europe was even further south than Siberia, and again was largely submerged. Part of present-day northern China also floated free, again straddling the Equator, again spun through 90° relative to the present, again largely under water. Almost all the rest was fused into the huge continent of Gondwana.

Throughout the next three periods of the Palaeozoic – through to the Carboniferous – the land masses drifted together, and there was a net movement northwards; by the time of the mid-Permian, around 265 million years ago, almost all the land was joined into one huge continent known as Pangaea ('All Earth'), focused mainly around the south pole but stretching practically to the north pole. Pangaea was hook-shaped, and within the eye of the hook was the then giant sea known as Tethys. Modern-day Africa lay to the bottom of the hook; modern-day Europe lay to the top of it. As the two came together and the eye of the hook closed, Tethys was squeezed to become the Mediterranean Sea.

Figure II.1   Jurassic, 175 million years ago

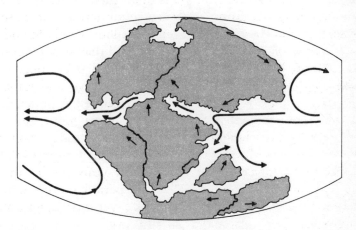

By the early Jurassic period, say 200 million years ago, Pangaea began to break up, and appeared along the lines of how it's shown in Figure II.1. For a time, roughly speaking, there were two land masses – Laurasia to the north, and Gondwana to the south. Laurasia was made up of the land masses that now are North America, Greenland, Europe, and most of Asia; Gondwana contained present-day Antarctica, South America, Africa, Arabia, Madagascar, India, Australia, and New Zealand. The two great supercontinents remained in contact for a time but only by a narrow isthmus between what are now north Africa and southern

Europe; in fact, the isthmus was roughly in the region of present-day Gibraltar. The Tethys filled the space to the east of that isthmus. As the Jurassic wore on, say by about 175 million years ago, India broke free from Gondwana at a place that now forms the coast of Antarctica and began its long existence as an island. It also began its long drift north towards Asia.

Mesozoic India was like modern-day Australia: an 'island continent', travelling north. We do not know what India's island creatures were like, however, or how they might have turned out, because its surface was obliterated around 60 million years ago by the Deccan volcanoes, the biggest known on Earth. India's present land and its continental shelf is formed from Deccan lava.

Figure II.2   Early Cretaceous, 125 million years ago

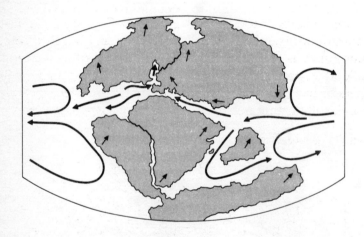

By the early Cretaceous period, about 125 million years ago, the outlines of some of the modern continents can be made out (Figure II.2). Laurasia was now split completely from Gondwana. Greenland still provided a broad link between North America and Scandinavia, so that North America, Greenland, and Eurasia were still one continent. South America was still joined to Africa to its east, along the coast of Brazil, but was clearly beginning to break free; it was still joined to Antarctica to the south, though only by a narrow isthmus. India was now fairly well advanced in its journey towards the south of Asia.

Laurasia remained intact through the Cretaceous but very significant breaks began in Gondwana (Figure II.3): the start of

Figure II.3   Late Cretaceous, 65 million years ago

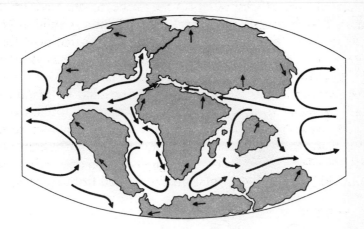

the southern lands of today. By the time the Cretaceous came to an end around 65 million years ago, the land mass that was to become Australia and New Zealand had broken from Antarctica, and South America remained only feebly attached, while Madagascar had split from the east coast of Africa. Note India: still an island, still floating north like modern-day Australia.

Figure II.4   Late Eocene, 40 million years ago

So into the Cenozoic: the time of dominant mammals. In the Eocene and Oligocene the ancient land masses finally began to assume their modern layout (Figure II.4) — although North America, Greenland, and Eurasia continued to form one land mass throughout the Eocene. India finally made contact with Asia around 35 million years ago, soon after the start of the Oligocene. We must assume, however, that the continental shelves of the Indian and Asian plates met long before the land itself, and so initiated the rise of the Tibetan plateau. It rose, and is still rising, quite simply because there was nowhere else to go but up. As we will see, this ripple in the surface of southern Asia has affected the ecology and evolution of all living things throughout the Cenozoic.

South America finally split from Antarctica around 25 million years ago virtually at the start of the Miocene, to begin its long and crucial period as an island continent in which in the manner of islands – like modern-day Australia – it evolved its own unique suites of animals and plants.

Figure II.5   Early Miocene, 20 million years ago

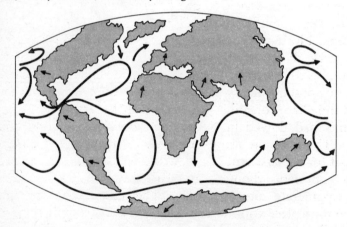

By 20 million years ago, still in the early Miocene (Figure II.5), Laurasia had finally broken up. North America, Greenland, and Eurasia were now separate continents. North America, like South America, was an island – though shortly to make contact again with Eurasia not through its eastern side but through its western, as Alaska was linked intermittently with Siberia via the vast but transient landbridge of Beringia.

Africa had split once more along the Red Sea, and the fragment which thus was almost broken off – Arabia – had joined with south-west Asia. India was now very clearly a part of Asia, and Australia had journeyed well towards the tropics.

Figure II.6   Today

The most large-scale change of a primarily tectonic nature, and one of huge significance, occurred 3 million years ago in the Pliocene. North and South America, two very different islands with very different origins, were joined via the isthmus of Panama, as they are today (Figure II.6). This must have had huge climatic consequences worldwide as one huge ocean, shaped for some time like a dividing amoeba, finally became two. Whatever currents had flowed between them now had to find another route. The collision also brought two very different faunas into contact for the first time – and, as we will see, animals from each of the continents, though particularly from the North, were anxious to migrate into the other. This most recent continental liaison took place within our own history. The family Hominidae was well established when it took place, though living, at that time, in a quite different continent.

In practice, however, the relatively simple picture of joining and splitting land masses had been complicated by rises and falls in sea level. The continental shelves of two shifting continents may butt together long before the bits that appear above the water are contiguous; after the shelves are in contact they may be covered by sea and uncovered again many times in the years that follow. These rises and falls have been particularly significant over the past million years or so because of the ice ages.

A particular example of crucial ecological importance is the landbridge that opened from time to time between North

America and Eurasia: not via Greenland, as in the days before the Oligocene, but by the exposure of continental shelf between Alaska and Siberia. It was across this bridge – the hefty chunk of land known as Beringia – that mammals of many kinds, including human beings, flowed both ways between the two continents during the Pleistocene. Very significantly, too, New Guinea and Australia have been joined and divided from time to time as water has flowed and retreated over the shallow shelf between them – and the present-day islands of Indonesia and Malaysia have in the past been joined to south-east Asia.

In Europe, the Straits of Gibraltar through the past few million years have sometimes been just that (a narrow channel of water) and have sometimes been dry land. When the latter prevailed the Mediterranean would have been all but dry – and at the end of those arid periods the ocean surged back in through the straits in what must have been a truly stupendous waterfall, until the whole vast sea was full again. Further south, in Africa, the Great Lakes have time and again dwindled as the tropics dried in the ice ages, and then grown again. Populations of fish have correspondingly been isolated (as the waters fell and left them divided by pools too shallow to cross) and then reunited. The periods of isolation are ideal for creating new species, as we will see again in later chapters. In Lake Victoria there were until recent years about 300 species of fish from the single sub-group of cichlids (pronounced 'sick-lids') known as haplochromines, while Lake Malawi, for much the same reason, now has more than 500 recognisably different cichlids.

The movements of continents will presumably continue until the Earth finally dies. Exactly what will happen is impossible to predict, at least with present knowledge, though some generalities seem certain enough. Africa will one day split from end to end along the fault line that is now the Rift Valley and Australia will crash into the base of Asia, or perhaps slide along Asia's eastern edge, just as it has been girding itself to do this past 80 million years or so. If it crashes into Asia, mountain ranges big enough to dwarf the Himalayas will appear along what is now the southern rim of China, just as the Himalayas themselves arose 40 million years ago when India first drifted in from the south. But if Australia avoids China it will sweep the islands of Japan before it and shove them steadily northwards until they hit Siberia.

So the understanding has grown: first, from the eighteenth

century onwards, the general realisation that the Earth is dynamic; then in the nineteenth century the acknowledgment of ice, although its full significance has become apparent only in the last few years (and it will hold some surprises yet); then gradual acceptance of the extraordinary notion that the sea-floor is constantly flowing and continents are always on the move.

Once we add the modern understanding of the atmosphere, the whole picture truly starts to come together.

THE ATMOSPHERE

The outermost reaches of the atmosphere are now known to stretch deep into space and to include a recondite assortment of unearthly ethers: single atoms, too energetic to form molecules; atoms disrupted to form electrically-charged 'ions'; particles totally detached from each other and forming inchoate, electrically-charged 'plasmas'. They are all formed from atmospheric gases, as their molecules are bombarded and torn apart by high-energy radiations from the cosmos in general and the Sun in particular.

But closer to the Earth the atmospheric gases are largely cushioned from these damaging rays and for the most part remain intact. Closest to the Earth and extending ten to fifteen kilometres up into the sky is the 'troposphere': this is the 'air', the bit we breathe, whose perturbations account for most of our weather. Above that, stretching outwards to about fifty kilometres, is the 'stratosphere' which is the principal bearer of debris from volcanoes and from nuclear bombs. The stratosphere does contain some recondite disrupted particles, particularly in its upper reaches, but for the most part contains conventional molecular gases.

It is tempting to assume that whatever is present in the greatest amounts is the most important. However, in the troposphere and stratosphere some of the crucial roles are played by gases that are present in amounts so small that the highest of technologies are needed to detect them at all; by unstable ingredients that persist for only a twinkling before they are converted to something else; and indeed at present by exotic ingredients produced by human activities. Our own effect on the atmosphere, and therefore on our own and our fellow creatures' lives, is immense, and yet is largely out of our control. It is also very tempting to assume that the fundamental features of the Earth are a 'given'; that they are as they were destined to be, and shall be ever more. We have already seen that this is not so. Applied to the atmosphere, it is a desperate and dangerous untruth.

Thus, almost 80 per cent of the modern-day atmosphere consists of molecular nitrogen, N_2. This has immense direct importance to life on Earth because nitrogen is an essential ingredient of proteins and nucleic acids; micro-organisms living in the soil and the sea are able to trap or 'fix' this atmospheric nitrogen by turning it into soluble ammonia which then, after further chemical conversion of a very simple kind, becomes food for plants to turn into proteins. Thus, the vast mass of atmospheric nitrogen (there are around a thousand million million tonnes of it) is a huge and vital source of nutrient.

Almost all the rest of the atmosphere – about twenty per cent of the whole – consists of oxygen. Each molecule of gaseous oxygen contains two atoms, and so has the chemical formula O_2. That the atmosphere should contain gaseous, 'free' oxygen is chemically peculiar, for oxygen is extremely reactive and ought simply to disappear as it combines with whatever else is around, notably the world's apportionment of rocks. Indeed, until about 3 million years ago the Earth's atmosphere contained very little oxygen. The only organisms on Earth were those known as 'anaerobic' which respired without its benefit, and would generally have been poisoned by it; in its virtual absence, they thrived in vast numbers and variety. Free oxygen gas could not exist in the atmosphere as more than a rapidly passing trace until bacteria, and then plants, developed the skills of photosynthesis. For in photosynthesis, the energy of the Sun is employed to split molecules of water, which then release the oxygen they contain; the hydrogen from in the water molecules is then attached to atmospheric carbon dioxide to create carbohydrates, from which (with nitrogen and other elements added here and there) all the flesh of plants, animals, and fungi is subsequently constructed. Note in passing that the atmosphere is the greatest food resource of life on Earth: carbon from carbon dioxide is the basis of all organic molecules, and nitrogen the principal extra ingredient of proteins and nucleic acids. Plants and bacteria expropriate these gases, and we and other animals eat what they produce.

As the atmosphere first began to acquire oxygen from the water that was severed by photosynthesis, the oxygen-hating anaerobic organisms retreated to the airless marshes where their descendants can still be found; they left the surface of the world to the oxygen-dependent 'aerobes', among which the plants, animals, and fungi are now the most conspicuous. But oxygen is able to persist as a constant component of the atmosphere only because plants and photosynthetic micro-organisms produce it in such vast amounts; they in turn can survive in the midst of such a reactive and destructive gas only because they have evolved a battery of chemical mechanisms for diverting and suppressing it (including the protective ascorbic acid, otherwise known as Vitamin C). But although the majority of present-day creatures are adapted to oxygen – we cannot live without it – an atmosphere containing free oxygen cannot be taken for granted. It is no more inevitable than is a world with ice at its poles and forests along the Equator. Indeed we may note in passing that the oxygen content of the atmosphere is at present diminishing slightly, though measurably, as we employ it to burn fossil fuels (see *New Scientist*, 12 September 1992, p. 16), and that in times past the concentration has been far higher.

Every other component, save these two, is present in small amounts. But 'small' does not mean 'unimportant', and 'amount' is not the same as 'turnover': 'amount' means the quantity present at any one time, and 'turnover' refers to the quantity that passes through over time. Water vapour and carbon dioxide are present only in minute proportions but both are extremely important in more than one way, and their turnover is vast. Billions of tonnes of each are thrust into the atmosphere every day but billions also disappear, leaving only a small amount present at any one time.

Then there is a whole catalogue of ingredients of a somewhat exotic nature, perhaps to be regarded as 'pollutants'. Some of them are produced naturally, and some by human industry. Some are highly unstable but still have a very high turnover, while some remain in the atmosphere for many years. Ammonia and methane are among the gases produced naturally in huge amounts, but are turned over rapidly and so are present at any one time only in trace. Methyl chloride, which arises naturally from sea-salt, is always passing through. The vapour of chlorofluorocarbons (CFCs) is man-made: CFCs have been manufactured in vast

amounts in recent years for various purposes, of which the chief
is refrigeration. They are being pushed into the atmosphere at a
steady pace and remain there, because they are extremely long-
lived: they are like lead in the body of an urban child, building
up slowly over time, with very little elimination. Then there is
ozone, which is a special form of oxygen: oxygen in which the
molecules contain three atoms, rather than the usual two, and
which is therefore given the chemical formula O_3.

Three of these trace gases are especially important because they
play an enormous role in regulating climate, and therefore to a
large extent determine which creatures live where – and indeed,
whether life is possible at all. The most important by far, in the
past, now, and forever in the future, is carbon dioxide. But two
others whose fates are intimately linked are having an impact at
least for the time being, and their story has many instructive features. These are ozone and the CFCs.

OZONE AND CFCS

The CFC–ozone story provides three powerful lessons that are
highly pertinent to our theme. First, extremely small quantities of
pollutant can have a huge effect. Secondly, even the very best science, brilliantly applied, cannot predict the unexpected; Nature
invariably proves to be more complex than anticipated. Thirdly,
although the trouble is now diagnosed (we hope!), and legislators
for once have acted promptly, there is nothing we can do to stop
the rot over the next few decades. The world has to bite the bul-
let. The processes of CFC infiltration and ozone destruction will
take more than a century from now to run their course.

Ozone, O_3, is the Jekyll and Hyde of the atmosphere. As
Hyde, it is a pollutant at ground level: the acrid by-product of
sparking electric motors, and a hideous and aromatic component
of traffic fumes. But ozone is also generated naturally through the
action of solar radiation upon oxygen in the stratosphere, where
it is concentrated at between 20 and 25 kilometres above the
Earth's surface. This is 'the ozone layer'. Even at its densest, the
layer contains only ten molecules of ozone per million total molecules. But without the layer of ozone – in its Jekyll persona – all
living things would be very different, and it is hard to see how

any could have ventured on to the land.

Ozone is vital to modern life forms because it is extremely good at absorbing and screening out ultra-violet radiation from the Sun. Ultra-violet (uv) is light of short wavelength and correspondingly high frequency – light is a form of electromagnetic radiation, and the higher the frequency of electromagnetic radiation, the higher the energy. X-rays and gamma-rays are electromagnetic radiations of extremely high frequency and are notoriously damaging. Ultra-violet is somewhat less energetic than X-rays, and far less than gamma-rays, and so is not quite so destructive. Yet it can still be lethal. In particular, it is absorbed by molecules of DNA, which it disrupts, inducing genetic mutation which can lead to skin cancer. Even with the ozone layer intact, a small proportion of uv reaches ground level, and an estimated 5 per cent decrease in stratospheric ozone would lead to an additional 100,000 cases of cancer per year in the US alone. Smaller creatures are simply killed by uv – sunshine is a great antiseptic, and the allegedly lethal waters of the Bay of Naples contain fewer live bacteria than some of the bracing seas around cloudy Britain.

Creatures that live in the light of the Sun have various mechanisms to protect them from uv. Human beings have skin pigments. Corals must sit in the sun near the surface of the sea if they are to survive, because they rely on algae within their cells which contribute to their nutrition by photosynthesising. Corals have now been shown to contain extremely effective chemical uv screens, which manufacturers of suntan lotions are seeking to imitate. So too, as a matter of no small interest, do slime-moulds. But as ozone is simply a form of oxygen, it is clear that the ozone layer could not have existed until after the atmosphere began to contain significant amounts of oxygen – which was after living things evolved photosynthesis. Clearly, the very first photosynthetic organisms must have been in something of a dilemma – needing to expose themselves to the Sun, but in mortal danger from ultra-violet, streaming from an ozone-free sky. I have no idea how the trick was pulled. Presumably, uv-protectors were among the first pigments to evolve. It does seem clear, though, that plants and animals could not have ventured on to the land, exposing themselves to the full blast of uv, until the ozone layer had formed.

But now, as all the world knows, the ozone layer is being

punctured, and the principal causes are gases created by human industry, in particular the chlorofluorocarbons, or CFCs. In the long term – that is, after another century or so – this may no longer be a problem. This is one pollutant that could be cleared up; indeed the latest legislation to control CFC production was agreed in Copenhagen in 1992 and could well do the trick. But pollutants like CFCs cannot be purged from the atmosphere overnight and in the next few decades the degradation of the ozone layer could matter a great deal: the holes could spread to parts of the world where crops are grown, for example Canada, and if the world lost the Canadian wheat crop there would be trouble indeed. Already there have been reports that the lichen on which the reindeer of Scandinavia feed ('reindeer moss') is being killed by excess uv.

So what exactly is going on? What and where is ozone, and what for that matter are CFCs, and how do they work their evil way? Well, ozone is formed naturally in the stratosphere in a two-stage process: first, radiation from the Sun breaks down molecules of oxygen into two isolated oxygen atoms ('monatomic oxygen'); then, each single atom is liable to combine with another oxygen molecule to form ozone. In irreducibly simple chemical terms: $O_2 = 2O$; and $O + O_2 = O_3$. As we have seen, the resulting ozone absorbs uv, and as it does so it is warmed. Thus the stratosphere as a whole grows warmer. Because the stratosphere is heated from above, it is warmer than the upper layers of the troposphere below. Thus the stratosphere is less dense than the upper troposphere and has no tendency to sink into it. It remains happily on top of the troposphere and is stable, much to the delight of pilots and passengers of high-flying aircraft. Thus, too, the thin and fragile ozone layer stays where it is.

A huge amount of energy is required to create the total ozone layer around the world: in fact, about 10 million million watts, which is about three times the total energy consumed by the present world population of human beings. If the ozone layer was destroyed we could not even begin to replace it. Only the Sun can do this. But as Joe W. Waters of the Jet Propulsion Laboratory in Pasadena comments in *Engineering and Science* (Summer 1993 p. 3), the ozone once formed is very easy to break down; indeed in concentrated form it is 'about as explosive as dynamite'. We should be grateful that in the stratosphere it remains dilute.

Ozone does disappear naturally from the stratosphere. For example, it reacts directly with ordinary molecular oxygen. But this process is slow, and the ozone lost by this means is constantly replaced as solar radiation generates more. It has become clear since the 1950s, however, that the breakdown can be accelerated by various materials in trace amounts: materials including hydrogen, nitrogen (in certain chemical forms), and the two related elements bromine and chlorine. Each of these materials acts as a catalyst. It is the feature of catalysts that very small amounts can have huge effect. And when the breakdown is catalysed, the loss of ozone can exceed the rate of formation.

Of the four catalytic destroyers of ozone, chlorine has in practice proved to be the most significant. It occurs naturally in the atmosphere in very low concentrations – namely, 0·6 parts per billion (ppb) by volume. Its principal natural form is methyl chloride (CH_3Cl) from sea-salt. But the present level of chlorine in the atmosphere is 3·6 ppb. The additional 3·0 ppb – five-sixths of the whole – comes from CFCs, produced industrially.

That the chlorine in CFCs could damage the ozone layer was first pointed out by American scientists in 1974, but the initial calculations, based on the laboratory knowledge at the time, suggested that the ozone would be depleted only by about 15 per cent over a hundred years. As time passed, the calculations grew even more optimistic; by 1980, the depletion was estimated at a mere five to seven per cent. But the British Antarctic Survey Team had been measuring the ozone layer over Antarctica since 1957 (which was International Geophysical Year) and their measurements of what was really happening showed a very different picture. The ozone over Antarctica dropped dramatically after the mid-1970s. By 1985 it was down to one per cent of normal levels.

But chlorine from CFCs was not thought to be the cause, for laboratory studies suggested on theoretical grounds that chlorine could not remain in the stratosphere in sufficient amounts to do the damage. Other causes were invoked: a change in solar activity, leading to an increase in oxides of nitrogen, which also catalyse breakdown of ozone; or an upwelling of air from below – air that was low in ozone. But then Susan Solomon of the US National Oceanic and Atmospheric Administration organised an Antarctic expedition to test the various ideas and found that neither a change in solar activity nor an upwelling of ozone-poor air could be responsible. Chlorine – CFCs – were indeed the cause. So why had the laboratory chemists not predicted this?

The answer is simple: because nature is more complicated than the laboratory. The basic reason why CFCs break down ozone was clear enough. First, they enter the atmosphere where, being extremely stable, they are not broken down by the sunlight of the troposphere, they do not react with other atmospheric components, and they are not soluble in water and so are not washed out by rain. Instead, over a decade or so, they slowly percolate up to the atmosphere: through the ozone layer and above it.

But then once the CFCs are above the ozone layer they are no longer protected from uv – and uv, in upper stratospheric quantities, does destroy CFCs. Each CFC molecule consists of one atom of carbon, plus one of fluorine and three of chlorine: $CFCl_3$. Ultra-violet releases one of the chlorines. This single chlorine atom is extremely reactive, and reacts with one of the equally reactive ozone molecules. In practice, the chlorine wrests an oxygen atom from the ozone to form chlorine monoxide, leaving behind a molecule of 'ordinary' molecular oxygen. In short: $Cl + O_3 = ClO + O_2$.

But the stratosphere, in the region of the ozone layer, also contains single atoms of oxygen: single atoms formed as solar radiation breaks up molecules of ordinary, bimolecular oxygen. Single oxygen atoms are desperately reactive. Chlorine monoxide, for its part, is desperately unstable. So where ClO meets O there is reaction: the two Os join to form molecular oxygen, and the Cl is released once again. In chemical terms: $ClO + O = Cl + O_2$.

The monatomic Cl, released afresh, is now free to react with another ozone molecule.

Thus, once the Cl is released from CFC, it is endlessly and rapidly recycled in the stratosphere. I say 'endlessly', but fortunately the process does come to an end, for eventually the Cl may react not with ozone but with methane, CH_4, to form hydrochloric acid, HCl. HCl diffuses downwards into the troposphere, meets the clouds, and is washed out of the atmosphere. But before this happens the CFC may stay aloft for a century or more. ClO may also react with nitrogen dioxide, NO_2, to form chlorine nitrate, $ClNO_3$; so here is another theoretical way for it to be rinsed out.

All this, however, was known to the chemists who predicted that CFCs would not have a hugely destructive effect on the ozone layer. So where did they go wrong?

Well, in 1987 James Anderson and his colleagues from Harvard University flew a converted U2 spy plane into the ozone layer over Antarctica and found that when they hit the hole in the ozone layer the concentration of the notoriously unstable chlorine monoxide, ClO, rose dramatically; rose, in fact, to levels a hundred times greater than theory predicted was possible. Something else was going on, therefore: something that ground-level chemistry had not predicted.

That something else was the presence over Antarctica of stratospheric clouds of ice. Within those clouds, using the particles as a substrate, the HCl and the $ClNO_3$ that should have transported the chlorine safely out of the atmosphere stopped to react with each other. They released bimolecular chlorine gas, Cl_2, plus nitric acid which remained locked in the ice-clouds. Solar radiation at that height is easily powerful enough to break the Cl_2 molecules apart to form monatomic chlorine, Cl. Thus the Cl is given a new lease of life. New ozone holes occur in Antarctica in September – springtime in Antarctica – when the first rays of the Sun start to break up the accumulated Cl_2. The ozone over Antarctica bears the brunt of the damage because that is where the ice-clouds form, which frustrate the processes that should remove the chlorine. The stratosphere of the Arctic is not so damaged because it is closer to warming land: the continents of North America and Eurasia. Thus we see that the climates of the two hemispheres are not symmetrical.

The first regulations intended to reduce CFCs, passed in Montreal in 1987, would have allowed levels of atmospheric chlorine to rise to almost 9·0 ppb by AD 2100. The tighter Copenhagen guidelines of 1992 will still allow a rise to more than 4·0 ppb by AD 2010 – less than twenty years' time – but the level will fall to about 1·0 ppb by AD 2100. If we stopped producing all CFCs tomorrow we would not halt ozone destruction, because the last decade's worth that was released has still to work its way up to the stratosphere.

It is possible, then, that present regulations have stopped the rot of ozone in the nick of time. But just think what might have happened if CFCs had been manufactured in quantity in the

nineteenth century. That was a great age of industrial chemistry –
all those tanneries and factories for matches and dynamite – but
the science of the day was conceptual aeons from the modern age
of high-atmosphere chemistry. *Inter alia*, the moderns rely heavily upon very high technology, including probes fixed to
high-flying aircraft that can detect ridiculously tiny quantities of
ClO. The scientists of the late nineteenth century did not even
know that the ozone layer existed, or that it filtered out uv; nor
did they appreciate the destructiveness of uv. Victorian CFC factories, had they existed, leaky as all Victorian factories were,
could have destroyed the ozone layer decades before the science
and technology existed to show what was happening. Once in the
atmosphere, the CFCs could not have been recalled any more
than they can now – even assuming that anyone had guessed that
they mattered. The people of the early twentieth century would
just have stood by and watched each other die, along with all the
plants and other terrestrial creatures. This would have been the
mass extinction to end all mass extinctions, and if intelligent creatures had ever evolved again – after the CFCs had finally
dissipated, and the ozone layer re-formed, and animals crept back
on to land – then they could never have guessed the reason. Well,
perhaps they would have got close – they would have seen that
human beings had once become anomalously populous, and then
had suddenly stopped, and they might have found enough of the
stinking remains of nineteenth-century factories to have inferred
some form of self-destruction.

Of course that did not happen. The invention of CFCs was
delayed. Just in time, atmospheric chemists developed the skills
required to see what was going on. No one who owns a 'fridge
can feel pious about this – we have all made use of CFCs. But it
seems apt to quote the Duke of Wellington's comment on the
Battle of Waterloo: 'It was a damn'd close-run thing.'

However, the loss of ozone could be cured within another
century or so, and the story of CFCs may remain as a curious
morality tale for the history books. Carbon dioxide is unlikely to
prove so tractable.

CARBON DIOXIDE: HERE AND NOW

Carbon dioxide, CO_2, is just a gas, present in the atmosphere in minute amounts, and yet is the principal food of plants: taken up in the course of photosynthesis, and combined with hydrogen, split from water, to produce organic molecules that are the source of plant and animal flesh. It is streamed into the atmosphere as plants themselves respire, and as they die and decompose, and as animals breathe out, and decompose in their turn. The immediate biological importance of CO_2 is therefore obvious. But CO_2 plays another vital, and quite separate, role. It is the principal short-term regulator of Earthly temperature. Like ozone, CO_2 acts as a filter, or rather as a trapper, of electromagnetic radiation: not ultra-violet this time, but infra-red.

Infra-red has a much longer wavelength than ultra-violet, and hence lower frequency and a much lower energy content. When it strikes molecules in material bodies, it is not inclined to break them apart, as uv does. Instead, it merely vibrates them. The vibration of molecules is experienced as heat. In other words, infra-red is warming.

Infra-red is called infra-red because its wavelength is somewhat longer than that of red light; in fact, it is just too long for human beings to see. The wavelength of ultra-violet by contrast is just shorter then violet: just too short for human beings to see (though bees and some other animals can see uv well enough, and many flowers are uv-coloured, however that may look to the creatures who can see it). Most of the radiation from the Sun that actually reaches the surface of the Earth is in the visible spectrum: between infra-red and ultra-violet (which, as we have discussed, is filtered out by ozone *en route*). So the surface of the Earth is warmed mostly by the energy in the visible light.

But once the surface of the Earth is warmed, it immediately starts losing its heat again; indeed, there is a constant flow of heat energy between all bodies, and the temperature at any one time is merely the net effect of heat in versus heat out. But the molecules of the surface of the Earth jettison their heat again in the form of infra-red.

Carbon dioxide intercepts infra-red, just as ozone intercepts ultra-violet, though not in the same way. It does not stop much of the Sun's energy from hitting the Earth's surface, because most of the energy coming from the Sun is not in the form of infra-red but of visible light. But CO_2 does stop radiation from leaving the Earth's surface, because most of the energy *leaving* the Earth is in the form of infra-red. Thus the net effect of CO_2 in the atmosphere is to trap escaping energy, but not to exclude incoming energy. Thus, carbon dioxide in the atmosphere tends to warm the Earth's surface. Greenhouses work in exactly the same way. Hence, carbon dioxide is said to be a 'greenhouse gas'.

At present, as everyone knows, the burning of fossil fuels is causing atmospheric CO_2 to rise. This is 'the greenhouse effect'. It will almost certainly cause a rise of sea-level, just as occurred at the end of previous ice ages – although, as we have seen, there are reasons why such an outcome is not certain, and we need not expect such a dramatic rise as the one that followed the last ice age since most of the ice remaining from that time has already melted. Nevertheless, the rise could be dramatic.

In practice, we could do quite a lot to decelerate the rise in atmospheric CO_2, just as we can do a lot to reduce the rise in CFCs. But, as is the case with CFCs, our control is imprecise, and the most dramatic feasible action will not prevent further changes over the next few decades. In other words, as with CFCs, we are having an enormous impact, but we are not in control. There are two possible ways to achieve reduction (or at least to slow the increase). The first is to burn less fossil fuel, and the second is to plant more trees. One way to reduce the use of fossil fuel is to burn more firewood. Such burning of course releases CO_2; but the CO_2 released is equal only to the CO_2 that the tree providing the wood took up during its own lifetime, so the net effect of burning firewood is zero. Note, by contrast, that when we burn fossil fuel we are releasing carbon into the atmosphere that was trapped initially by the plants and marine animals whose fossilised and undecayed bodies compose that fuel. Hence we are releasing within a few decades carbon that those creatures trapped over many millions of years.

In addition, if the world had a policy of burning firewood, then we should be planting forest specifically for that purpose for the next few decades at least. So long as the planting of trees outstripped the burning, there would be a net reduction in atmospheric CO_2, as the growing trees photosynthesised. Indeed, it has been estimated that an extra forest the size of Arizona could

absorb all the 'surplus' CO_2 that the world is liable to produce in
the foreseeable future. There would be no danger of precipitat-
ing another ice age by this means: if the extra trees were to
remove too much CO_2 then they would stop growing, because
the world would be too cold for them and – more to the point –
the loss of CO_2 would rob them of their food supply.

Overall, then, living things (or the dead bodies of living things
manifested as fossil fuels) play a crucial role in regulating the
amount of CO_2 in the atmosphere – and this in turn is a critical
determinant of Earthly temperature and therefore of climate.

Finally, there are jokers in the modern greenhouse pack. Water
vapour is itself a powerful greenhouse gas. There is not a great
deal we can do about this – except to point out that as the world
grows warmer, evaporation increases, and as the world enters ice
age the air grows drier, and so here we have an example of positive feedback of the kind that helps to determine and complicate
climate. Methane is also an important greenhouse gas. It is produced by the actions of anaerobic bacteria – in marshes, and from
the gut contents of animals. Oddly, human action is increasing
methane too. Cattle are a major source, because as they ruminate
they belch, and their belches are a significant methane source –
and the world's population of cattle is anomalously high because
we have domesticated them. The flatulence of termites is also a
major source; they too are increasing because termites prefer
grassland to forest, and we are felling the forest to make way for
grass so that we can keep more cattle. CFCs are also significant
greenhouse gases – but perhaps that is being put right.

I am sure that this general picture is now very familiar. Even
politicians tend to write about it. Some in Britain seem to regard
the pending greenhouse effect as a bit of a lark: what fun it will
be, they suggest, when dour northern constituencies are warmed
like the Mediterranean. They clearly do not appreciate the possible magnitude: what a rise in sea-level even of a few metres may
mean; what effect a novel climate – changing temperature and
rainfall with no corresponding alteration of daylength – will have
on wild creatures or on crops; or that all such changes are innately
unpredictable. For example, they clearly do not realise that the
direction of sea currents depends upon the distribution of energy
around the Earth. This can have grand effects, as demonstrated by
Hartmut Heinrich's and Geoff Boulton's ideas on the behaviour

of ice. Of particular relevance to Britain is the behaviour of the Gulf Stream, which now brings warmth from the semi-tropics. With a shift in the world's distribution of energy it could go into reverse. Then Britain could be as cold as present-day Baffin Island while the rest of the world – or most of it – basks in the new tropics. The point is not to spread gloom. The point is simply to realise that the Earth does indeed behave in extraordinary ways – and incredulity is no defence.

Over the past decade or so, however, an even grander picture of carbon dioxide has been emerging.

CARBON DIOXIDE: THE GRAND PICTURE

The picture of greenhouse effect can be dramatic, if we take all the implications into account. Yet it does not convey the full significance of carbon dioxide in shaping the behaviour of the world. Two more components need to be added: first, a knowledge of climate history – the *extent* to which atmospheric carbon dioxide has determined climate in the past, and all that depends upon climate – and, second, the extraordinary interactions of carbon dioxide with the rocks of the Earth's surface.

For one thing, it is now clear that the pending (or present) greenhouse effect is not an isolated phenomenon. Theory now suggests that the climate of the past for as far back in time as can be measured has largely been determined by the concentration of carbon dioxide in the atmosphere. Thus Robert Berner of Yale University has produced a computer model to show that over the past 600 million years the concentration of atmospheric CO_2 has correlated at least roughly with the Earth's climate. He infers what the climate was like from the fossil record, using knowledge of, or at least informed guesswork about, the kind of conditions each class of creature would have preferred. The model shows that 500 million years ago atmospheric CO_2 was eighteen times the present value – and 500 million years ago the fossils show that the world was warm. Then the level of CO_2 dropped until the Permian to reach levels similar to today's – and we know that the Permian was cold. CO_2 dipped again in the early Cretaceous, around 120 million years ago – another cold time. Overall, simple physics tells us that if the atmosphere contained no CO_2 at all then the Earth would freeze almost instantly, and irrevocably. If it contained much too much, we would boil like our neighbouring planet Venus.

The grander insight, however, also largely from Berner, is that the carbon dioxide interacts on a massive scale with the oceans and with the rocks of the Earth's surface, and that it is these geological interactions, rather than the respirations of living things, that in the end determine how much carbon dioxide is in the atmosphere at any one time. Indeed we may envisage carbon dioxide like currency: money circulating in a society. Living things shuffle CO_2 between them in the way that consumers exchange cash. But the *amount* of cash that is available for circulation is determined by the government and by the banks. In this metaphor the oceans and ultimately the rocks are the bankers of CO_2. They determine how much is in the atmosphere, for plants and animals to play with, and how much remains under wraps.

Thus in 1983 Berger suggested that at any one time there are Earthly processes at work that remove carbon dioxide from the atmosphere, and others that tend to increase it. Carbon dioxide is removed from the atmosphere – or 'scrubbed', as industrial chemists might say – by rain. Rain dissolves atmospheric CO_2 to produce a weak solution of carbonic acid. Carbonic acid in turn reacts with the common rocks of the land, such as granite, which are silicon-based and contain various metals such as calcium and magnesium. The reaction produces bicarbonates of those metals, which flow away from the land and into the sea. What is left on land is oxide of silicon – alias silica alias sand. The bicarbonates that wash away become integrated with the sea-floor, and as the sea-floor finally dives back into the mantle at its leading edge those bicarbonates are temporarily lost from circulation. Thus is CO_2 gas leached from the atmosphere, and the carbon it contained buried deep within the Earth.

The CO_2 is restored again to the atmosphere as the mantle wells up at the ocean ridges to form sea-floor, and by volcanoes, and as rocks are put under stress and pressure as the sidling of plates forces continents together. Thus tectonic movements have a profound effect on the CO_2 content of the atmosphere, and hence on the climate of the Earth.

I find insights like this quite wonderful. They are conceptually simple but the scale is awesome: it takes a great leap of the imagination to see that such a process is taking place.

The final synthesis, though, comes from elsewhere: from earth scientist Maureen Raymo and Bill Ruddiman. They have explained what for our lineage and for our species is the key issue of Earth history: why the world has cooled over the past 50 million years, during the time that the mammals – including us – were finally taking their modern forms. Raymo's and Ruddiman's idea brings together all the grand notions we have been discussing: the movement of continents; the huge circulations of energy by ocean currents; the interactions of atmosphere and rocks. The key to the whole issue is the plateau of Tibet. This, I suggest, is one of the great insights of the late twentieth century.

TIBET AND THE COOLING OF THE WORLD

The computer model of Robert Berner which described the effect of carbon dioxide upon climate had one shortcoming. The fossils tell us that the Cenozoic began on a tropical note and reached a climax of warmth in the Eocene; that it began to cool as the Eocene wore on; and that the cooling has continued and culminated in the cool Pleistocene, which flickered in and out of glaciations. If falling CO_2 is the cause of the Cenozoic cooling, then the model should show a dip in atmospheric concentration some time after 50 million years ago. But it does not.

The missing component in Berner's model, according to Maureen Raymo of the Massachusetts Institute of Technology, is the Tibetan plateau, with the Kumlun mountains to the north and the Himalayas to the south. The key is India, which broke free from Gondwana more than 180 million years ago, floated north, collided with southern Asia around 40 million years ago, and has been ploughing into Asia ever since like a very slow but immensely powerful locomotive that has overshot its terminus. The land in the path of India has risen to form the Tibetan plateau, and this plateau is, says Raymo, like 'a giant boulder thrust into the atmosphere'. It has absorbed CO_2 from the atmosphere by the processes that Berner described. Indeed it has been big and active enough to scrub much of the CO_2 from the atmosphere of the whole world. This in turn has subjected the entire planet to an anti-greenhouse effect – an 'icebox effect'.

This, then – the rise of the Himalayas – has been the fundamental cause of Earthly cooling since the Eocene, and of all its ecological and evolutionary consequences. The jerkiness of the fall in temperature, as in the Miocene and in the late Pliocene, 2·5 million years ago, is easily explained by the complexity of the planet itself and by the phenomenon of catastrophe. Most obviously, when the temperature cools below a particular threshold the distribution of energy around the world is changed, ocean currents may reverse their flow, and the world takes a sudden, 'catastrophic' lurch into a new stable state. The constant split and reunion of continents also has its effect – as we have seen, the liaison of North and South America 3 million years ago would have stopped all flow between what are now the mid-Atlantic and mid-Pacific. The lurches and reversals of climate since the Eocene are not surprising at all. The overall cooling has been inexorable.

Why did Berner not arrive at this conclusion? Why did he not take the Tibetan plateau into account in his own model? Well he did, of course, but he did not acknowledge its full potential. He assumed that the absorptive effect of rock depended more or less exclusively upon its area. But Raymo and her erstwhile academic supervisor Bill Ruddiman, now at the University of Virginia, concluded from studies that other scientists had carried out in the Amazon that the *topography* of rock – in particular its slope – is very important too. The edges of the Tibetan plateau, and in particular the Himalayas to the south, are steep, and that improves their efficacy as extractors of atmospheric CO_2.

Even so the Raymo model would not work unless the Tibetan slopes were washed with truly prodigious quantities of rain, to bring carbonic acid to the steep rock. But of course they are. The wind that drives against the plateau from the south-east has crossed the Indian Ocean and is heavy with water. As it strikes the mountains it is forced high into the sky. As it rises it cools and as it cools the water that it carries precipitates. This is the rain of the Asian monsoons, which largely determines what and who lives where. The Tibetan plateau as a whole covers less than 5 per cent of the world's land, but it is drained by eight of the world's mightiest rivers, which include the Ganges, the Brahmaputra, the Indus, the Yangtze, and the Mekong, and they between them carry 25 per cent of all the dissolved material that reaches the world's oceans. On its leeside, the plateau of Tibet throws a rainshadow that embraces the Gobi to the north and the Mediterranean and Sahara to the west.

Raymo and Ruddiman thus present a beautifully simple picture which again beggars credence only because of its scale. But there is independent evidence for their idea – for example, in the amounts of various forms of metals such as strontium and osmium that have been washed from the Tibetan plateau over the past 50 million years and are now to be found on the ocean floor. Support comes also from other climate modellers. In 1992, for example, models run at the National Center for Atmospheric Research at Boulder, Colorado, suggested that if southern Asia did not have mountains at the top then the region would be an astonishing 12°C warmer than in fact is the case. The model also shows that the temperature would fall and the rainfall would increase if the land of Tibet was raised even further.

Indeed the main theoretical problem with Raymo's proposed mechanism is that it might be *too* effective. Some calculations show that a CO_2 extractor as efficient as the Tibetan plateau would scrub all the CO_2 from the atmosphere in a few hundred thousand years. Countering this, as CO_2 is removed and the world grows cooler, perhaps the *rate* of the chemical reaction between CO_2 and rock is reduced. Here, then, would be negative feedback comparable with the feedback that prevents the over-efficient removal of carbon dioxide by photosynthesis. It is possible that a new balance has now been struck between the Himalayas and the atmosphere, albeit leaving less free CO_2 than before.

Some scientists do not like the Raymo–Ruddiman model. They argue that it is too *ad hoc*. For my part, for what it is worth, I like it very much indeed. In particular it is in the right spirit of Earth science as it has emerged this past 200 years: just the right blend of boldness and discipline. The maths is there – but so too is that wild streak of romanticism. I love the notion of the rising Himalayas, thrust up by the awesome power of migrating India, soaking half a continent in its monsoon rains, starving another half-continent of rain all together, and cooling the whole world through a trick of esoteric chemistry which, just a couple of decades ago, was unsuspected. Perhaps it is wrong to judge the truth of science by its emotional impact – but that, in practice, is how truth is ultimately judged.

Still, though, we have left a gap in understanding. The Raymo–Ruddiman model explains how the world has cooled since the Eocene, culminating in the bleakness of the Pleistocene. It does not explain why that bleakness has flickered in and out of ice ages. To understand this we need to look outside the Earth.

THE SUN

We should be grateful that the Earth is just the right distance from the Sun: much closer and we would boil, like Mercury; much further away and the ice might stretch from the poles to the Equator. We should be grateful for its spin: without it, one side would cook and the other would freeze. Our position *vis à vis* the Sun is critical. It is not so surprising, then, that small and cyclic alterations in that position critically affect our climate.

That this might be so was first suggested in 1867 and again in 1875 by James Croll – but the thought at that time was put on one side, as is so often the fate of bold ideas in science. Milutin Milankovich then elaborated the notion in the early twentieth century – but again it was put on one side. In the 1970s Milankovich's ideas were refined mathematically by Anandu D. Vernekar and A.L. Berger, and from the 1980s onwards they have become the orthodoxy. Changes in the Earth's position and attitude relative to the Sun are now believed to have had a profound effect on climate – and even to have provided the final spur to the ice ages which have so dominated the past million years. In fact, to anticipate, we should probably envisage the Pleistocene Earth on a climatic cusp: uncomfortably cool to begin with, and nudged into glaciation every now and again by fluctuations in the path and attitude of the Earth.

In practice, the Earth's relationship to the Sun changes in three ways: in its 'orbit', or eccentricity (the path it follows around the Sun in the course of a year); in its 'tilt', inclination, or 'obliquity' (the angle of its axis of spin, relative to the Sun); and in its 'precession' (which can be loosely defined as 'wobble'). Each of these alterations has its own kinds of effects and, because all three kinds of change take place simultaneously, the different effects are superimposed, sometimes building upon each other, and sometimes tending to cancel each other out. Each kind of change works to its own time-scale, quite independent of the others. Milankovich's brave contribution was to show (or begin to show) how these interacting cycles of the Earth's position and attitude would have affected the Earth's climate, and to relate the 'Milankovich cycles' to the ice ages of the past few hundred thousand years. We should look at the three kinds of change in turn.

The Earth's orbit around the Sun, like that of all the planets, is not a circle, as Pythagoras supposed, but an ellipse. Ellipses are like circles with two hubs – foci – instead of one. The Sun is positioned in one of the foci of the ellipse, so that the Earth is closer to the Sun at one end of the ellipse (the perihelion) than at the other (the aphelion).

The shape of the ellipse changes over time. Sometimes the ellipse is almost circular, and at other times it is much 'flatter', more dish-shaped. The total amount of energy reaching the Earth from the Sun in the course of an entire year is the same whether the orbit is (almost) round or is flat – the mean distance from the Sun must remain the same – but the way the energy is apportioned throughout the year is different. With the orbit at its flattest, there can be a 30 per cent difference in the input of solar radiation between perihelion and aphelion. The total cycle of orbital change takes 95,800 years: that is, it takes 95,800 years for the orbit to progress from nearly circular, to dish-shaped, to nearly circular again.

The inclination of the Earth changes too. At present, the tilt away from vertical is 23°44', but it varies between 21°39' and 24°36'. At present, therefore, the Sun is directly overhead at 23°44' latitude north (the Tropic of Cancer) during the northern summer and at 23°44' latitude south (the Tropic of Capricorn) during the southern summer. The total width of the tropics is therefore 2 × 23°44'. Clearly, the tropics grow wider or narrower depending on the degree of tilt – though this, in practice, is not of huge consequence, and the tropics are not much affected by change of tilt. But the poles – or high latitudes in general – are greatly affected. Greater tilt means longer winter darkness, and longer midnight Sun. Contrast between winter and summer is thus enhanced even more when the Earth is more tilted (and it is extreme at the best of times), and so too – which is very important – is the contrast between poles and tropics. The periodicity in the change in inclination is 41,000 years: that is, it takes 41,000 years to go from a tilt of 21°39' to 24°36' and back again.

Finally, the Earth wobbles as it spins: the phenomenon of pre-cession. The effect is generally explained by analogy with a spinning top, which never spins quite upright, for its axis of spin always describes a cone around the vertical. Precession matters, because it means that different parts of the Earth are pointed towards the Sun at different points on the orbit. Thus, there will be times when the northern hemisphere is enjoying its summer – that is, is inclined towards the Sun – when the Earth is at perihe-lion, and times when the north is tilted to the Sun when the Earth is far from the Sun, at aphelion. At present, northern summer occurs with the Earth at aphelion, but 11,000 years ago (at the time known as the Younger Dryas) northern summer occurred during perihelion. The periodicity of precession (the time the axis takes to work through a complete cone) is 21,700 years.

Just as a theoretical exercise, consider the kinds of things that might happen when we start to put these three sources of varia-tion together. Note, first, that the three periods of change – of eccentricity, inclination, and precession – have nothing to do with each other: 95,800 years is not a simple multiple of 41,000 years, or of 21,700. This means that, in theory, any combination of orbital position and tilt is possible. Note, too, that the various changes affect different parts of the Earth differently. Low lati-tudes (towards the Equator) are affected mainly by variations in the Earth's orbit, and by precession: whether a given hemisphere is pointing at the Sun during perihelion, or aphelion. By contrast high latitudes (towards the poles) are affected mainly by changes in obliquity (tilt). Note also – again – that the two hemispheres are not mirror images of each other. They can be affected differ-ently. Depending on which hemisphere is inclined towards the Sun at which point in the orbit, it can transpire that seasonality (the contrast between summer and winter) will be exaggerated in one hemisphere but reduced in the other.

The Milankovich cycles also clearly affect the degree of differ-ence between the amount of radiation falling at the poles and the Equator, and this in turn affects the build-up of polar ice. For whether or not ice can form at high latitudes depends only in part on how cold it is. It also depends on how much water (precipi-tation) is falling at high latitudes.

In short, when the effects of the three Milankovich cycles are superimposed upon each other, as in reality is the case, then the ramifications and the possibilities seem endless. Yet reality is even more complicated because the effects of the Milankovich cycles are superimposed on other events: changes brought about by tectonics, and changes in the atmosphere. It does seem, however, that the constant flip from ice age to interglacial throughout the Pleistocene is related to the Milankovich cycles. In particular, the roughly 100,000-year periodicity of those cycles corresponds with the roughly 96,000-year cycle of orbital change – and the fluctuations of the past 130,000 years (the late Quarternary, which includes the Holocene and the late Pleistocene) may also reflect the 41,000-year oscillation in tilt.

We may ask why the Milankovich swings did not apparently trigger ice ages at intervals since the beginning of time. The answer seems to be that before the Pleistocene the world was usually too warm to be pushed easily into ice age. But it cooled throughout the Cenozoic and by the time of the Pleistocene was in a hair-trigger state, poised to freeze. From time to time, Milankovich cycles pushed it into glaciation – not (to repeat) by changing the total amount of radiation reaching the total Earth in the course of a year (for that would be impossible), but more subtly by changing the places on the Earth's surface where the radiation impinged, and the timing of that impingement, thus varying the contrasts between winter and summer, tropics and poles, and northern and southern hemispheres.

So that is how the world works most of the time. There is, however, one more unworldly influence which, from time to time, throws everything into turmoil and on at least five occasions has wiped out huge swathes of animals at a stroke.

THE JOKER IN THE PACK: ASTEROIDS

That the Earth has been struck by asteroids in the past is not in doubt. No planet or moon can escape their impact. At the very least they remind us that the Earth is not an island but part of a hostile, or at least indifferent, Universe. The questions are whether those asteroids have really been as influential as some scientists maintain; whether, as some believe, they strike at regular intervals; and, if their impact is regular, when we can expect the next.

The physics of asteroids, like that of plate tectonics, is awe-some. They are in effect large meteors – and large might easily mean a solid mass with the same diameter as, say, an English county. Movement in space is relative. The Earth hurtles through its orbit at around 12,000 kilometres an hour. Speed has little meaning until different bodies come together. So imagine a body that was the size, say, of the Isle of Wight or Manhattan, hitting us with a speed relative to us of around 20,000 kilometres per hour: a perfectly plausible scenario. We might envisage the soft-est possible landing   it would have a good chance of hitting the Pacific Ocean – but that would make no difference. It would hit the Pacific like a brick in a puddle – or, rather, it would bore through, vaporising as it went.

Such an impact is bound to have a significant, indeed a tremendous, impact on climate. Even if a large asteroid struck the deepest part of the deepest ocean it would throw up more debris than can be imagined, like a super-volcano. Such debris would surely create the mother of all nuclear winters, blotting out the Sun for decades. On the other hand, the energy of impact has to be dissipated somehow, and in practice would be transposed into heat. So perhaps the world is cooled after such impacts, or per-haps warmed – or perhaps hovers between uncomfortable extremes as contradictory forces fight it out.

That asteroids might have such an influence was first suggested informally in 1980 by the Californian physicist Luis Alvarez. He looked at clay dating from around 65 million years ago, when the Cretaceous was ending and the Tertiary was beginning. This of course was the transition between two great eras, for the Cretaceous is the last period of the Mesozoic and the Tertiary is the first of the Cenozoic.* This time of transition is known as the K/T boundary, where 'K' stands for *Kreide*, which is the German for Cretaceous, and 'T' means Tertiary. Anyway, this clay – a layer that had been laid down within only about a thousand years – proved to contain about 300 times more of the rare metal irid-ium than did the surrounding limestone. The uninitiated might say, 'So what?', but in practice this kind of thing is not too easy

*Please note that the Cenozoic era is divided into two periods: the Tertiary and the Quarternary, each of which is equivalent to Mesozoic periods such as Cretaceous and Jurassic. The intervals that are more generally referred to in this book – Eocene, Pliocene, Pleistocene, etc. – are *epochs*: sub-divisions of the Cenozoic periods. All is made clear in Figure I.1.

to explain away. Indeed, said Alvarez, the most likely explanation
is that the iridium was brought in by an asteroid.

It was of course at the end of the Cretaceous that the dinosaurs
came to an end. The most likely cause of their decline – in fact
the only one that is truly plausible – is a shift in climate. The
question is, was an asteroid responsible for that shift?

There are problems with this idea. If, for example, such an
asteroid had simply caused a giant nuclear winter then we might
have expected the dinosaurs to die out within a few years – effectively over one long winter weekend. In practice they clearly
declined over several thousand years and many were living after
the time that the iridium was laid down. But there is much support for the notion that an asteroid was at least involved, and
there is even a possible site, in the Caribbean. Dave Raup and
Jack Sepkoski of the University of Chicago further suggest that
asteroids have been a regular feature of Earth history and were
probably responsible in large part not only for the demise of the
dinosaurs but also for many other episodes of widespread extinction, including the five great 'mass extinctions'. In fact, say Raup
and Sepkoski, if you look closer at the fossil record then you find
'minor' mass extinctions occurring at intervals of 26 million years.
For it happens, they say, that every 26 million years the Earth's
orbit crosses that of a belt of asteroids which, like the planets, cir-
culates around the Sun. If Raup and Sepkoski are right, then we
are due for another impact, and another mass extinction of unpredictable extent, in 13 million years' time. We will just have to
wait and see.

So that, in outline, is how scientists now explain the behaviour
of our planet and its history. I think it is interesting, but why does
it matter?

WHAT CAN WE LEARN FROM HISTORY?

In practice, all lessons drawn from history must be general, for the
first, ironical lesson of history is that nothing, including climate,
ever happens in quite the same way twice. The world was often
warm in the past and it will be warm again in the future, but the
weather will be different – because the continents are not in quite
the same place as they were before, and the mountains are not

quite the same height, and the currents of the sea have found a new position and the Earth is tilted slightly differently, and there are bound to be new combinations of temperature and daylength and temperature and rainfall, while the contrasts will be greater or lesser between winter and summer and the northern hemisphere and the south. In short, whatever is happening at any one time is unique.

But the broad lessons are cogent nonetheless. History tells us that the world is capable of extremes, and it tells us too that those extremes are inevitable. Though we may have plenty of time to live our lives and spread our civilisations and our species, we all of us live in the gaps between disasters. It tells us, abundantly, not to be too incredulous. It is difficult to believe that the mountains of today must once have been beneath the sea yet this has been commonplace knowledge for at least 200 years. It seems astonishing to cover a continent with ice and lower the sea by 150 metres but this has clearly happened and could happen again. The shift of continents is ridiculous and the consequent rise of the Rockies and the Himalayas defies belief and yet the evidence is there; so too is the evidence for the icebox world that the Himalayas have created. Asteroids are a fact of living in the Universe – and *something* killed the dinosaurs.

We learn, too, that the behaviour of the world is extraordinarily complex. In this brief chapter I have outlined the major forces that shape our planet and its landscape, and the list is not overwhelming. Atmospheric chemistry, topography, the tilt and orbit of the Earth: we should be able to cope with all that. But as the components interact the complexities multiply. The oceans are the year-by-year brokers of climate, for they hold much more heat than the labile rocks of the continents and through their currents they shift the heat from one part of the Earth to the other. How and where those currents move depends in part on the distribution of energy around the Earth – where for example the sunshine is falling – and also on where the continents happen to be at the time, and whether the ocean surface is being invaded by vast cold icebergs which sit on the surface because the water they contain is fresh and upset the whole rhythm of the sea because the coldest water ought to be underneath, and so may reverse the currents on their own account.

The heat and moisture of the oceans is translated into weather by the atmosphere, and thus the whole saga of currents and upsurges that are seen in the ocean is acted out again on a far more rapid timescale. But we can add even more to all this. For example, the fact that ice will act like a mirror and reflect the warming radiations of the Sun back into space means that as ice fields spread when the cold times come they increasingly reject the source of heat and so create a positive feedback loop that makes the world even colder.

Finally, we must add the mathematical principles of catastrophe and chaos. Catastrophe tells us that forces acting smoothly may produce sudden changes. A slowly cooling world may suddenly freeze. A warming ocean current may suddenly decide to take its favours elsewhere. Chaos tells us one thing that has already become evident: that a combination of apparently simple forces can produce an horrendously complicated outcome. But the theory of chaos adds a rider which is not obvious: that the outcome is literally unpredictable – there is nothing in the system at any one time that can tell us precisely how things will be in some future time. Perhaps the most chilling lesson of all to emerge from the ideas of chaos is that little things really can have huge consequences, because of the ways in which one thing leads to another. Thus it is that the puny industries of humankind – our fossil fuels that generate CO_2 and refrigerants that send CFCs to infiltrate the atmosphere – are affecting the prospects of all life on Earth.

The awesome complexity and the innate unpredictability do not stop climatologists worldwide from trying to understand and forecast the weather, both in the short term and the long. It is worth doing, for there is nothing more important to the economy of human beings or the ecology and evolution of all our fellow creatures. And it is not entirely forlorn because the predictions, though never cast-iron, can in theory and practice approach greater and greater degrees of certainty. Without the climatologists we would know nothing of the pending greenhouse effect – and that knowledge alone justifies all the effort. Without the palaeoclimatologists, the moderns would have nothing solid to go on.

So now we should see how the climates and the continental movements of the past have influenced living things; especially the ones who, as things turned out, proved to be our ancestors.

3

The Dance Through Time

Old-style palaeoanthropologists liked to suppose that the present-day human species, *Homo sapiens*, represents some kind of ultimate. Thus in 1933 Robert Broom, who discovered the early hominid now known as *Australopithecus robustus*, suggested that after the appearance of human beings 'there was no further need for evolution' and felt it was 'very doubtful if a single new genus had appeared on earth in the last two million years'. And as Roger Lewin comments in *Bones of Contention* (Penguin Books, London, 1987, p. 42) Broom's opinion 'was unusual only in the very forthright way in which it was stated'. Other leading authorities of the day, including Henry Fairfield Osborn in America and Sir Grafton Elliot Smith in Britain, were 'close spiritual fellow travellers with Broom'. Such a view of evolution is in the tradition that Misia Landau described as myth-making – and not of the kind that is acceptably heuristic. Broom's belief in evolution was founded in mysticism – a conviction that evolution must move towards some destiny; that this destiny is *us*, made in the image of God; and that God, having achieved this much, can now retire with a clear conscience.

To modern biologists such ideas are terrible nonsense, and I am inclined to suggest that they are mildly blasphemous. If there is a God, then I am sure He would find such conceit most irritating, and also the implication that He can now put Himself out to grass. In reality, other species *have* appeared since us, including quite a few plants which can produce instant novelty, of true species status, simply by a doubling of chromosome number. More to the point, our own species almost certainly will not last forever. We may ourselves be transmogrified into other forms, or if we simply go extinct then we can expect that whatever remains will radiate (diverge to form new species) in all kinds of directions. If the only animals left by the time we disappear are rats, cows, chickens, and cockroaches then they for several million years will have a field day, their descendants refilling some at least of the niches now occupied by tigers, elephants, parrots, and wasps.

In short, we should see evolution not as a mechanism that was designed to lead to us or even – more broadly – as something that happened in the past. It is happening *now*. We are part of it. We ourselves have evolved and, like all living things, have been affected by the evolution of other creatures and are affecting them in our turn. To understand how and what we are and what effect we are having we should see ourselves as part of a process – or, more graphically, as latecomers to a global party that has been in progress for at least 3·5 billion years, since life first began, and will continue until the death of the planet itself. It is a fabulous party, with billions of participants from all walks of life; with riotous games with rules that lie deep beneath the mêlée; with giant quadrilles that span entire continents and take tens of millions of years to unfold – what Elisabeth Vrba of Yale University has called 'the dance through time'. It is a party, furthermore, that takes place upon a shifting stage as outlined in Chapter 2 – a stage which itself is crucial to the action.

In this chapter and the next I want to explore the party that human beings have joined, and at which we have become such noisy guests; to see who else is there, and what they do, and to seek the rules that underpin the turmoil. To do this properly we need to go back further than our allotted 5 million years. We should ask what was happening before the hominids arrived, for only then can we judge our effect, and indeed understand how and why we came to the party at all. We do not need to retreat through the whole 3·5 billion years. But it is appropriate to look at the emergence of the primates – the group, or order, to which the Hominidae belongs – and, even more broadly, at the rise of the class of mammals of which the primates in their turn are a part. There are historical lessons here that are pertinent now. This exploration takes us back to the end of the dinosaurs, which disappeared suddenly from the Earth 65 million years ago after 150 million years of world 'dominance'.

THE IDEA OF EVOLUTION

Modern understanding of the party's rules began with Charles Darwin (1809–82), who in 1859 published his seminal *On the Origin of Species by means of Natural Selection*. There he showed, once and for all, that present-day creatures had evolved into their present forms, and provided the first plausible explanation of the means by which they did so. Darwin was extremely astute but many of his immediate followers were less so and they, rather than Darwin himself, developed a version of his ideas that now seems crude but is widely perceived as traditional 'Darwinism'. But as the twentieth century has progressed, much of that crude superstructure has been stripped away while refinements have been added to produce a new but still essentially Darwinian view of nature (which in fact in many ways is closer to Darwin's own, pure perception). I get the impression that many non-biologists still equate 'Darwinism' with the somewhat coarse overstatements of the immediate post-Darwinians, and have come to believe that the moderns have in large part rejected Darwin. That simply is not the case. What might be called the mainstream of modern biology is still emphatically Darwinian. To illustrate the difference between the old and the new — and to advance our exploration of our own history — it is worth looking at the demise of the dinosaurs and at the rise of the mammals through the eyes of both the 'traditional' post-Darwinians and the moderns.

DINOSAURS, MAMMALS, AND EVOLUTION: THE OLD VIEW

Many biologists who followed Darwin felt that the rise of human beings to the top of the heap needed virtually no explanation. Darwin's great contribution, after all, was first to establish that living things do indeed evolve — that they were not simply placed on Earth in their present form — and then, crucially, to establish the mechanism of evolution — 'by means of natural selection'. His concept of natural selection was rooted in one piece of late eighteenth-century economic theory, and two simple observations. The economic theory was due to the English cleric and economist Thomas Malthus (1766–1834) who in 1798 first published *An Essay on the Principle of Population*. Malthus argued that the human population increases exponentially, but that the human food supply can be increased only arithmetically. 'Exponentially' means increasing by a fixed proportion of what was there before; since what was there before gets larger and larger, steady proportionate increase implies that the growth becomes faster and faster.

'Arithmetically' implies growth by a fixed absolute amount: there is no increase in the speed of growth as time passes. Since population does grow faster and faster, and resource does not, population must eventually outstrip resource.

Darwin perceived that this generalisation of Malthus must apply to all species. All creatures, even the ones that breed most slowly, such as elephants, must tend by this process to outstrip their resource. Therefore there must be competition between them to survive – or, in Darwin's words, a 'struggle for life'. But he also observed that within any creatures of the same kind – elephants, cats, oak trees – there is variation. It follows that some of the variants must be better adapted to the prevailing conditions than others – or 'fitter', where 'fit' has the Victorian meaning of 'apt'. The ones that were most apt, or fit, were the ones that were most likely to survive and leave offspring of their own. Hence, in the words of post-Darwinian biologists (though not of Darwin himself), there is 'survival of the fittest'. In other words, said Darwin, the prevailing conditions – the environment – effectively *select* the creatures that will survive and reproduce, in the same way that a pigeon-breeder favours the birds that conform to the ideals of the show-bench. The pigeon-fancier's art is called 'artificial selection'. The analogous process in nature may be called 'natural selection'.

With this idea firmly in place post-Darwinians found no difficulty in explaining the 'ascent' of human beings. First, effortlessly, they conflated the concept of 'fit' with the idea of 'superior'. So they were able to argue that human beings have prevailed simply because we are better. So, more generally, is the primate order to which we belong: indeed the term 'primate' was coined by Carolus Linnaeus in the eighteenth century when he first set out to classify all living things, and it means 'first'. Linnaeus called other animals 'secundates'.

More generally still, the mammals as a whole were viewed as superior. The fossil record showed that the dinosaurs disappeared suddenly around 65 million years ago, and that the mammals then very rapidly filled all the niches that they had hitherto occupied, and a few more besides. Indeed the period since the dinosaurs, known as the Cenozoic, has clearly been the 'age of mammals' (with the birds playing a very conspicuous supporting role). Again, the reason seemed obvious. The dinosaurs were dolts which had outgrown both their strength and their wits, given to lolling in shallow seas since they could no longer support their own weight and freezing passively to death when the climate took a turn for the worse. The mammals, by contrast, are fast-moving, quick-witted creatures which make their own body heat and could chew the dinosaurs to death as they lay torpid under cloudy skies. The mammals, in short, are a superior caste. Natural selection was bound to favour them; among the mammals, selection was bound to favour the primates; and among the primates it was bound to encourage the magnificent creature who in those days was invariably called 'Man' (which indeed is the literal meaning of *Homo*).

Later in this book, very unfashionably, I will argue that this view of things is not quite so gross as most biologists now suppose. I will suggest that some animals are indeed 'superior' to others, and that this superiority does correlate to some extent with survival, and hence that there is 'progress' in evolution. But I will also argue that 'superiority' has to be defined extremely carefully, and that 'progress' absolutely does not mean 'destiny'. Thus I will maintain that some evolutionary outcomes really are more likely than others (and it is idle to suggest otherwise) – but no historical path traced by evolution can be considered inevitable. Hence, despite my defence of old-fashioned notions of progress and superiority, I agree absolutely with all those modern biologists who argue that it was not the mammals that ousted the dinosaurs, but time and chance – and indeed that the dinosaurs could be with us still and might have 'dominated' the Earth until the Earth itself finally died. In short, we are lucky to be here. So let us look again through modern eyes.

DINOSAURS, MAMMALS, AND EVOLUTION: THE MODERN VIEW

The traditional view of the death of the dinosaurs and the subsequent rise of the mammals contains a number of flaws. First there is an awkward detail of fact which was known perfectly well to the Victorians: that the lineage of reptiles that evolved into mammals (known as 'synapsids' or simply as 'mammal-like reptiles') is at least as old as the lineage that led to the dinosaurs. Indeed those reptiles show the first mammalian tendencies as long ago as the Carboniferous, which ended 290 million years ago; from the time of the Permian – more than 245 million years ago – the mammal-like lineage can be clearly discerned; and in the Permian and Triassic, the lineage became numerous. So the mammal-like reptiles flowered *before* the dinosaurs were established.

Mammals differ from reptiles largely in details that are not preserved in fossils – in their 'warm-bloodedness', their possession of hair, in suckling their young and, I would say, in their heavy reliance upon olfaction (which means they are particularly smelly, and responsive to smells). But some features that are diagnostic of mammals *are* preserved in their bones: in particular, the lower jaws of reptiles and other non-mammalian vertebrates are compounded from several bones, whereas the lower jaws of mammals are built from only one. The one-bone structure is stronger than the multi-boned arrangement (and may enable the mammals to eat more, with less wear and tear) and the extra bones that were no longer needed to form the jaw were evidently modified to form the chain of bones that transmits sound through the mammalian middle ear. Here in passing is a marvellous example of evolution's opportunism.

The point, though, is that the peculiar jaw structure of the mammals enables us to trace their transition from mammal-like reptiles through the fossil record, and we can be sure that *bona fide* mammals had appeared by the mid-Jurassic, say 170 million years ago – a time when the dinosaurs were only just reaching their peak. Then for more than 100 million years these mammals – true mammals – played second fiddle to the dinosaurs. During that time they must have evolved enormous genetic diversity, and, as we will see, the main branches of modern mammals were clearly discernible long before the dinosaurs disappeared. But so long as the dinosaurs remained, the mammals were ecological also-rans, none bigger than a polecat. They emerged and radiated only after the dinosaurs disappeared, like genies wakened from a thousand-year sleep. Their initial radiation in the early Cenozoic was spectacular – there were huge mammalian carnivores and herbivores as big as modern rhinos by the time of the Eocene – but that radiation had to wait until the dinosaurs unscrewed the lid. The notion that the emergent mammals inevitably outwitted the dullard reptiles as soon as they got into their stride simply does not stand up.

In the age of dinosaurs the birds put up a slightly better showing than the mammals. They clearly evolved from a line of dinosaurs and the first true bird, *Archaeopteryx*, dates from the late Jurassic (somewhat *after* the first mammals). Some – notably the ancestors of modern gulls and auks – flourished in the Cretaceous. Modern gulls are prone to harass anything that flies and we can imagine Cretaceous proto-gulls hassling the pterodactyls (although we cannot assume that they got the better of them!).

We may also question whether mammals are indeed 'superior' to reptiles in general. A key difference between *modern* reptiles on the one hand and mammals and birds on the other lies in their control of body temperature. Modern reptiles rely for body warmth on external energy (the Sun) and on heat generated as a by-product of muscular activity. They are sometimes said to be 'cold-blooded' – although a better term is 'poikilothermic', which emphasises simply that their temperature is variable. By contrast, mammals and birds can generate heat internally just to keep themselves warm, and so maintain a core body temperature of around 40°C, which is close to the optimum for biological systems. They are colloquially called 'warm-blooded' – but 'homoiothermic' is the preferred term, stressing the constancy of body heat rather than absolute temperature.

When homoiotherms and poikilotherms are in competition, it seems obvious that the homoiotherms have the advantage: after all, homoiotherms can be active when it is cold, while poikilotherms often tend to be torpid. But all is not so simple. For a start, many poikilotherms clearly can be active in cold conditions – for example the fish and krill which operate happily in Arctic seas, or the lizard-like tuataras which run about on their New Zealand offshore islands on freezing nights, leaving the biologists who study them in severe danger of frostbite. True, most of the modern poikilotherms that we are now familiar with, from tortoises to snakes, do prefer warmth, but this is clearly not invariable.

Then again, so-called poikilotherms in general employ a range of strategies for maintaining constant temperature whatever is happening outside: from basking in the sun, like tortoises and butterflies, to whirring the wings like bees, or lying with the tail immersed in a warm tropical river, like crocodiles.

What really counts, however, is that poikilotherms for the most part heat themselves up for free. A combination of sunshine and normal movement gives them all the warmth they need. By contrast, animals committed to homoiothermy commonly use 90 per cent of their food energy simply keeping warm. Indeed, many homoiotherms are obliged to compromise or abandon their 'warm-bloodedness' just to save energy. Some, like armadillos and sloths, allow their temperatures to vary in a somewhat reptilian fashion, while hibernating mammals tend simply to cool down, as bats do by day and hummingbirds do by night. The important thing is that poikilotherms get by on far less food – so a crocodile that can bring down a wildebeest may eat no more than a goose may do. The problem for homoiotherms is not simply to find enough food for one individual, but to find enough to support an entire, viable, self-sustaining population.

Thus we find that in habitats where food is limited – such as deserts and small islands – poikilotherms have often prevailed and in many cases still do. You will find no leopards on small islands but you will find flourishing populations of big lizards and sometimes of snakes. Thus the largest living lizard of all is a monitor that lives on the small island of Komodo in Indonesia, and is known as the Komodo dragon. It is big enough and fast enough to ambush and eat a goat – or a human being. Australia, which is both an island and largely desert, also has huge monitor lizards known as goannas; its most formidable predator ever was the giant goanna known as *Megalania* which was up to seven metres long and weighed about two-thirds of a tonne – about eight times the weight of a modern Komodo. In the Pleistocene, Australia also had land crocodiles, such as *Quinkana*, which lived in Queensland. That *Quinkana* lived on land is suggested by its tail, which was rounded (not flattened to form an oar, as in aquatic forms), while its claws were modified into hooves. At three metres long, *Quinkana* was not huge by crocodilian standards but it was quite bit enough for most prey. Indeed it seems highly likely that such reptiles inhibited the evolution of truly impressive marsupial carnivores in Cenozoic Australia just as the dinosaurs apparently suppressed mammalian development worldwide through the whole of the Mesozoic.

As a twist in the story, Robert Bakker from the University of Colorado argues that the dinosaurs were not 'cold-blooded' at all but were perfectly good homoiotherms, like mammals and birds. Specifically, he points out that dinosaur bones show the close-packed pattern of blood vessels which denotes rapid bone growth – and such a structure is typical not of poikilotherms but of homoiotherms. Probably, too, flying reptiles such as the pterodactyls had insulating fur.

But even if the dinosaurs were poikilotherms, they would not have slumped into cold-blooded torpor overnight. For, above all, they were large, and big animals are like storage heaters: they take a long time to cool down. In any case, it is clear now that the dinosaurs were not uncomplicated layabouts. Some that were once supposed to be too heavy for unsupported life on land are now known to have trekked happily across deserts. Some were obvious sprinters. Many lived in herds like cattle or elephants. Many were excellent parents.

In short, modern biologists tend to argue that the dinosaurs were not innately 'inferior' and they were not simply brushed aside by the mammals. Instead modern theory has it that around the end of the Cretaceous, at the K/T boundary, there was a dramatic change of climate. The precise cause is unknown but the leading candidate is an asteroid, perhaps of around ten kilometres in diameter – one of those which, as Dave Raup and Jack Sepkoski suggest, are liable to strike the Earth every 26 million years. As noted, there are problems with the impact theory, notably that the dinosaurs clearly died out over a period of at least several thousand years, whereas a single crash would presumably have led to a sudden die-off. But mounting evidence supports such an event.

At present, however, it is not clear whether this hypothetical but likely impact brought about a dramatic cooling, or a warming. Common sense suggests cooling, as debris would have been thrown into the stratosphere. This also fits in with the traditional notion that dinosaurs would not have coped with cooling as well as mammals would, because of their alleged poikilothermy. Others argue, however, that the world is not so simple and *inter alia* that the massive energy of the asteroid's impact would have 'burned' surface rock and thus released carbon dioxide and so provoked a period of greenhouse warming. So perhaps sudden cold was followed after a few years by egregious warmth. Certainly the first epoch of the Cenozoic, the Palaeocene, seems to have been warm while the subsequent Eocene seems to have been as hot as the world has ever been, with tropical forests pressing towards the poles. Indeed I wonder whimsically whether the real problem of the dinosaurs was not an inability to keep warm but to stay cool. Perhaps the irony is that dinosaurs were homoiotherms, as Robert Bakker suggests, but that they lacked the methods of cooling that mammals have, and in particular the ability that many of us have to sweat, which is a profligate and potentially dangerous way to cool because it squanders so much body water but is highly effective nonetheless.

If it is the case that excessive warmth rather than extreme cold killed off the bulk of Mesozoic reptiles, then this would account for the lack of cold-adapted reptiles in the modern world. Only the ones that were best adapted to warmth survived the events of the K/T boundary. If this were true, then the present-day lack of cold-adapted reptiles would not be a matter of physiology – an innate inability of poikilothermic reptiles to survive the cold – but simply of history. Neither need we be surprised that Australian dinosaurs survived Cretaceous ice ages. Perhaps the whimsical notion that dinosaurs disliked heat more than cold has some mileage.

But whatever the precise cause of their passing, it is clear that the extinction of the dinosaurs has profound implications for our understanding of evolution. Some feel that because the crude, late Victorian explanation of dinosaur extinction does not work, it shows that 'Darwinism' itself does not work. After all, if mammals replaced dinosaurs just because a meteor and a change of climate wiped the dinosaurs out, then what price natural selection, and the idea that the environment chips away to produce the best adapted lineages?

However, other biologists (including me) argue that Darwin's view of evolution by means of natural selection is alive and well, and absolutely deserves its status right at the heart of modern biology. All that is wrong is the over-zealous and simplistic application of Darwin's ideas. To get a true feel for what has gone on – for the rules of the evolutionary party – we must tell the Darwinian story with greater subtlety, as indeed Darwin did himself, and also add a few twentieth-century refinements. Chief of these refinements has been the transformation of 'Darwinism' into 'Neodarwinism', a term which in this context implies the fusion of Darwin's ideas with those of Gregor Mendel.

NEODARWINISM

Darwin himself knew full well – it bothered him until his dying day – that, as it stood, his idea of evolution by means of natural selection was incomplete. It fails completely unless creatures of any particular kind give birth to offspring which are like themselves. After all, there would be no point in nature selecting horses that were particularly swift unless those swift horses produced offspring which, like themselves, were swifter than the rest. On the other hand, his theory also depends upon the notion that the offspring of any one creature are variable: without variety, there is nothing to select between. These observations seem incompatible – for what mechanism of heredity could on the one hand produce offspring that closely resemble their parents, and yet produce offspring that demonstrably differ both from their parents and from each other? For a long time, indeed, Darwin toyed with the mechanism proposed by the earlier, French biologist Jean Baptiste Lamarck (1744–1829) – the notion that offspring inherited characters that their parents had acquired in their own lifetimes. He even began a book about it. But he seemed to know in his bones that it was not right and was easily talked out of it by his friend and adviser Thomas Henry Huxley.

Did he but know it, however, his problem was solved in principle in his own lifetime by the Austrian monk Gregor Mendel (1822–84), whose work on heredity in garden peas and other plants began the science now known as genetics. But, alas, Mendel's work was effectively ignored and (despite speculation to the contrary) there is no evidence that Darwin knew of it. Indeed, the force of Mendel's ideas was not realised until the early twentieth century; 'genetics' is a twentieth-century word. The fusion of Darwin's ideas with Mendel's – a fusion commonly known as 'The Modern Synthesis' – was achieved from the 1920s to the 1940s and produced neodarwinism. Neodarwinism is one of the intellectual triumphs of the twentieth century and represents the essence of modern biology.

Mendel's explanation of heredity, looked at in retrospect, is delightfully simple. It is easy to forget how confusing the facts of heredity really are when that explanation is lacking – how it is, for example, that a family of brown-eyed people can suddenly produce a blue-eyed child (but never vice versa!), or how it is that some extremely unpleasant disorders, such as cystic fibrosis, tend to run in families (but only erractically) while some (like haemophilia) affect one sex far more than the other. Yet this and much else is explained just by applying the very simplest of

Mendel's notions. If you are *au fait* with basic genetics then please skip the next few paragraphs.

Mendel's first great and crucial insight was that each feature (or 'character') of each creature was 'determined' by some discrete 'factor' – a factor which in twentieth-century parlance is called a 'gene'. In practice, each individual possesses a pair of genes for each character, one inherited from the mother, and one from the father. Each parent passes on to each offspring only one of each pair of genes, in her egg or his sperm. The complete set of genes in any one individual is its 'genome'. Mendel's second crucial insight was that each gene within each species could exist in more than one version, and each version nowadays is called an 'allele'. 'Allele' is a very useful and much underused word which ought to be in common parlance and is not – a pity. Thirdly, Mendel perceived that some alleles are dominant over others. Put the three notions together (with just a few extra refinements) and almost everything you need to know about heredity is explained.

Thus we say that human beings are different from carrots because they have different genes. Carrots have genes to make chlorophyll, and human beings do not. Human beings have genes to determine eye colour, and carrots do not. Humans and carrots do in fact have some genes in common – for example those that make various fundamental enzymes involved in respiration. But on the whole, the genomes of carrots and those of humans are compounded from quite separate sets of genetic ingredients.

On the other hand, it is clear that my genes are different from yours. If it were not so then we would be identical, give or take a few battle scars. But we are both human, so we both have the same kind of genome. What is the difference? Simply that although we have basically the same set of genes (those that befit a human), we have different versions of those genes. Where you may have an allele that gives you blue eyes, I have an allele for brown eyes, and so on. In practice, biologists speak of the 'genetic variation' within species, or within populations. It would be far less confusing to speak of the 'allelic variation' within populations or species, and the 'genetic difference' (or similarities) *between* species.

Those, then, are the basic Mendelian ideas. Neodarwinism now seeks to impose Darwin's notion of 'evolution by means of natural selection' on to a Mendelian framework. The result, again, is delightfully simple.

We have merely to envisage the reality of life: that almost all animals, and most organisms of all kinds, practise sex, which means that they swap genes with each other. In fact, a 'species' is commonly defined as a group of creatures that can mate successfully with each other – which means they can swap genes – and thereby produce 'fully viable' offspring. For example, asses and horses are considered separate species because their offspring – mules – are sexually sterile, and hence are not 'fully viable'.

A population is simply a subset of a species: a group of creatures from any one species who happen to be in contact with one another. All of us are members of sexually-reproducing populations, and we can therefore say that each of us partakes of, and contributes to, the collective 'gene pool' of that population (though it should more accurately be called the allele pool). We can also say that we are members of 'lineages', a lineage being a population (or a gene pool) that unfolds through time, generation by generation. Since all human beings are members of the same species our genomes all have the same basic structure: the same basic array of genes. In general, none of us can contain more than two allelic variations of any one gene; yet any one gene in any one population may in theory exist in the form of dozens or even hundreds of different alleles. The alleles in the population pool are like books in a central library. Each of us is allowed to possess a selection of the books at any one time – but only a selection. But it is a private library: to be a member of a species is to be a member of a club, able to borrow alleles of the genes that collectively belong to the club, but forbidden or at least inhibited from borrowing genes from other clubs.

On the whole, and within limits, a species (or population) benefits if the alleles within its gene pool are as various as possible. First, if there is little variation in the population as a whole then each individual will tend to inherit more or less the same alleles for each gene from its mother as from its father. Individuals who inherit similar alleles from each parent are said to be highly 'homozygous', which in effect means they are 'inbred'. Inbred individuals tend in general to be more feeble than 'heterozygous' individuals who inherit different alleles from each parent and benefit from a version of what Darwin called 'hybrid vigour'. Second, populations that contain a great deal of allelic variation are much more able to adapt to changing circumstance than populations that are more uniform – as Darwin said, variation is the raw material on which natural selection can work. The amount of allelic variation within a population (or in the species as a whole) largely determines its chances of long-term survival in a changing world.

In the neodarwinian view, the net effect of natural selection is perceived in the gene pool as a whole. Thus, natural selection favours individuals who carry particular alleles that confer advantage. The individuals who have such an advantage are more likely to live long enough to reproduce, and they will leave offspring who also carry that advantageous allele. Over time, as natural selection continues to operate, the advantageous allele will become more commonly represented within the population – or more 'frequent' as biologists say. Contrariwise – unless the population is simply increasing in size – individuals who do not carry the advantageous allele will be squeezed out. Hence the effect of natural selection over time is to *change the composition of the gene pool*.* Over time, some genes become more frequent, and some become less frequent, and some will be squeezed out altogether. After many generations of such change the population will be altered so much that members of it would no longer be able to interbreed with members from the original population even supposing that the original ones were still alive. Hence the population would have changed so much that it had given rise to a new species. The idea that lineages can transmogrify into new species was one of Darwin's key contributions – and one which, at the time, gave rise to some of the fiercest controversy.† But the mechanism of neodarwinism shows how this is possible.

In practice, the basic pool of alleles (the gene pool) is constantly

---

*Nowadays, most biologists agree that natural selection operates at the level of the gene; genes spread through populations if they have the means to further their own replication. This is the notion behind Richard Dawkins's 'selfish gene'. In practice, however, genes tend to survive best if they bring advantage to the individual of which they are a part, and the net effect of natural selection, albeit working on 'selfish genes', is to change the frequency of the alleles in a gene pool, just as neodarwinism suggests.

†Ernst Mayr points out that the heresy was not against God but against Plato, who had suggested that each species represents an 'ideal', and that ideals were sacrosanct. Some who accepted the general idea of evolution by means of natural selection rejected the idea that species barriers could be broken, and some who accepted that the barriers could be broken rejected the mechanism of natural selection. In short, responses were complicated. See Mayr's *Toward a New Philosophy of Biology*, Harvard University Press, Cambridge, Mass., 1988).

added to. First, alleles themselves alter – that is, they *mutate* to form novel alleles. Most of these variations are disadvantageous (mutations are random, like kicking a television set) but some of the novelties remain in the pool and sooner or later some of them come in useful. Such mutations are the prime source of the 'variation' which Darwin required as a basic strut in his original theory. Second, gene pools are added to by *introgression* – that is, populations which may have been separated for some time and have evolved along different lines may sometimes – I believe more often than biologists often suppose – be brought together again. Then there will be matings between individuals from each population, to produce a flow of genes from one gene pool to the other, with each pool then enriching (or polluting) the other. North American ruddy ducks brought to Britain have been making their own way to Spain where they are currently showing introgression in action as they mate ('hybridise') with the native white-headed ducks. I also think it is highly likely, as many palaeoanthropologists do, that at least some introgression occurred in Europe between the first modern European people – our own ancestors – and the neanderthals whom the moderns replaced.

But in addition, of course, alleles are constantly lost from the gene pool. Some are eliminated by natural selection but many are simply lost by chance. Thus, as Mendel said, each individual parent possesses two alleles of each gene but passes on only one of each pair to each offspring; unless the parent has a huge number of offspring there is a good chance that it will fail to pass on at least some of its alleles to *any* of its children. Most alleles are possessed by many individuals in any one generation and so are likely to be passed on, despite that possible source of loss. But rare alleles – by definition – are possessed by only a few individuals, and there is a good chance that they will not be passed on at all. Loss by such means is called 'genetic drift'. Clearly, the smaller the population becomes, the rarer any one allele will become, and the greater the chance that the rarest alleles will not be passed on at all. Thus in small populations genetic drift is a major force, and small populations rapidly lose genetic (or allelic) variation. But we have commented that it is good for a population to be genetically varied. Small populations are more vulnerable than large populations at the best of times and the rapid loss of genetic variation within them, leading to inbreeding in the short term and to loss of flexibility in the long term, can provide the *coup de grâce*.

Note finally that evolution by natural selection is inveterately opportunist. Natural selection is obliged to act simply upon the gene pool as it finds it at the time: upon a pool of alleles that has been shaped by the selective forces of the past, and has been enriched (or polluted) by chance mutations and introgressions, and depleted by the hazards of drift. Natural selection does not create: it does not conjure appropriate mutations to order.* It is like a sculptor, chiselling a block of marble, unable to improve the substance of the stone, able only to remove and never to add – stuck, in short, with what the quarry was able to provide. This is one reason why nature can produce some bizarre forms, and some apparently bizarre solutions to problems – like, for example, using spare jaw bones to make bones for the mammalian middle ear. There is also an important philosophical connotation: natural selection can shape the lineage *only to cope with the pressures of the moment*. It does not look ahead. It cannot create half-way, apprentice creatures with an eye to greater things in the future. In the Miocene there were small, three-toed horses, grazing the newly-spreading grass. They coped with their surroundings as well as natural selection could manage with the gene pool available, and they did what the environment required of them. They were not a rehearsal for the Arabs and thoroughbreds of today. By the same token, the ancient *Homo erectus* were their own people. They were not a prototype for us.

That, then, is the essence of neodarwinism. And that, so most biologists agree, is also the essence of modern biology. Natural selection operates to change the frequency of the genes in each gene pool, and hence in the end to produce qualitative change, although at the same time the forces of chance act both to provide new alleles (by mutation and introgression) and to remove others (by genetic drift).

The theory is excellent. But to understand what really happens in nature we have to look at the component notions more closely. Key among these is the much misunderstood concept of competition.

---

*In fact there is evidence that some bacteria are able to undergo mutations in a directional way, producing genes appropriate to the task in hand. But this is a very special ability described only in certain bacteria and is not typical of living things as a whole and certainly not of animals and plants.

THE CRUCIAL BUT COMPLEX ISSUE OF COMPETITION

To Darwin, the notion of competition was crucial. He implied that constant competition – unremitting pressure from other creatures – led inexorably to change. But many modern biologists question this. First they say that when you look at nature you do not often see overt competition. Most of the time the various creatures seem to rub along well enough – like people in a football crowd, who interact up to a point but apart from a little passing abuse have little impact on each other. There is little to justify Tennyson's pre-Darwinian vision of 'nature red in tooth and claw'. These modern biologists also doubt whether the competition that is discernible actually leads to adaptive change. Sometimes the fossil record shows that animals remain unchanged for millions of years even though they are presumably engaged in constant contest. Sometimes, contrariwise, competition seems simply to lead to obliteration. So what is really going on?

THE NATURE OF COMPETITION

What, first of all, do creatures actually compete *with*? Well, consider that beautiful and versatile African antelope, the impala. In the dry season it eats mainly grass, in the wet season mainly browse (the leaves of bushes and trees). All year round it may be preyed upon by leopards. In the breeding season both sexes must find mates. Some biologists apply the term 'competition' sparingly, and regard 'predator-prey' relationships as a special and separate case. But it seems neater simply to admit that in practice impalas (like all animals) must 'compete' with a whole range of other organisms in order to stay alive. The competition in part is *inter*-specific (between species): so impalas compete with grasses and trees, which on the whole would prefer not to be eaten, and adorn their leaves with spikes and toxins; with other herbivores, from gazelles to rhinos, that also eat grass and browse; and with leopards which seek to eat them. There is also competition with their own kind: *intra*-specific. The males in particular may fight for mates – and all impalas must compete with others both to find food and to escape from leopards. The leopards for their part have their own suite of competitors.

Note, in passing, that the competition takes two completely different forms. Sometimes impalas must indulge in an out-and-out
fight – when males battle for mates or females attempt to drive
predators away from their young – and sometimes they merely
strive to outshine the others, for example as they flee from leopards. The first kind of contest is comparable with, say, a boxing or
tennis match, where you win by undermining the opponent; the
second is more like a race or a game of golf, where neither competitor should interfere directly with the other, but both 'compete'
with the environment. The two are conceptually different. In
short, 'competition' in nature is a complicated business.

Yet it seems undeniable that impalas and leopards do compete
with each other; so if Darwin is right, and competition really does
drive evolution, then we should expect the fossil record to show
that leopards have grown steadily stronger and more agile, and
impalas ever more swift. In practice, however, as Elisabeth Vrba
points out, the record shows no such thing. The two animals have
evidently remained more or less unchanged for the past 3 million
years. This is a long time: time enough for our line, the hominids,
to change from virtual apedom into us. So what is going on?

There are two points. The first we have noted: that leopards
are only one of many problems faced by impalas, and vice versa.
Every creature in the wild has to keep many balls in the air. Thus
an impala might in theory evolve tremendous fleetness of foot,
but if it did it might thereby sacrifice some of the strength of
shoulder and weight of horn needed to beat off rivals in the fight
for mates. It might on the other hand develop an enviable ability
to digest coarse vegetation. But if it did it would come into competition with zebras, or acquire a huge belly which would
compromise its fleetness. In short, the real impala in the real
world has to compromise, and its present size and shape allows it
to balance one need against another. Indeed because the pressures
are so various, different pressures are liable to prevail at different
times. Thus at times impalas may not be pressured by lack of
food, because leopards may check their numbers before this
becomes a problem. But at other times the lack of food may
indeed be keeping them in check – and then the leopards merely
take the surfeit. Whichever way you look at it, the two beasts
clearly rub along well enough. In this case natural selection is not
operating to produce change.

However, the example of the leopard and the impala does not tell the whole story. Africa has changed in the past 3 million years, and the fact that leopards and impalas have not is in part a tribute to their individual versatility. Impalas are indeed more adaptable than most herbivores and leopards can live anywhere. But, apart from climate, their habitat has been more or less left alone – except for the steady encroachment of evolving hominids. But nowhere on Earth can ever be left alone indefinitely. Sooner or later something changes. Some time or other there is bound to be a change of climate that is too extreme even for impalas, or for one reason or another faunas and floras which hitherto have been separated will be brought together. Then there is a new ball-game. Then the phenomenon of competition takes on a whole new aspect as the various creatures vie to exploit the new ecological opportunities and to come to terms with new neighbours.

COMPETITION AND INVASION

When a foreign species or group of species is thrust into a novel environment this is called 'biological invasion'. Since members of the genus *Homo* have been the greatest invaders of all – they, plus the many creatures they have carried around the world with them – it is salutary to look at some examples. I have chosen three: two brought about by human beings and one by the tectonic movement of continents.

My first example is very straightforward: the flood of creatures that Europeans have taken to Australia over the past 300 years or so, that are now playing havoc with the native creatures. Domestic cats jumped from Dutch ships in the seventeenth century and are still working their way across the continent, laying waste the small marsupials as they go. Foxes, brought in for sport, joined them in the nineteenth century. In the twentieth century the huge cane toad was brought from Central America to clear pests from the sugar-cane fields of Queensland and is now chewing up native reptiles and amphibians state by state. A different kind of competition is provided by rabbits, imported for food and sport in the nineteenth century and now transforming landscapes, and water buffalo, now obliterating delicate wetlands in the Northern Territory by their wallowing and trampling. The impact of the cat on the native marsupials has sometimes been taken to illustrate the innate superiority of a placental mammal over mere marsupials. But it seems much more sensible to observe that Australia, for all its vastness, is an island, and island creatures commonly are not adapted to the depredations of continental-style predators. Marsupials themselves have sometimes been successful invaders in lands dominated by placentals – look at the opossums in North America.

The second example, also generated by human beings, seems more complicated. Britain's native squirrel is the bushy-tailed red; it used to be called the 'common squirrel'. Then in the 1820s grey squirrels were introduced from North America. Decade by decade the grey squirrels spread and the 'common' reds retreated and are now found only in a few special retreats in England, although they still do well in Scotland. But whereas cats in Australia are known to kill small marsupials there are no convincing records of grey squirrels attacking reds. So why have the newcomers flourished while the natives have faded?

Well, two British biologists have finally provided the answer, and it is strikingly undramatic. It simply seems that grey squirrels enjoy a slightly more catholic diet. Red squirrels prefer the seeds of conifers and are reluctant to eat very much else. But greys will eat other things and in particular have a greater predilection for acorns (perhaps because they cope more easily with tannins – though this is speculation, and not part of the original study). So in any one piece of woodland in any one year, grey squirrels have a greater chance of surviving. That is, they have a better chance of building a viable population and therefore – crucially – of pulling through in difficult times. Thus, over time, the greys inexorably spread, and the reds inexorably retreat.

The third and final example is of one of the greatest invasions of all time: the exchange of creatures between North and South America when those two continents came together in the Pliocene. This is the Great American Interchange.

In outline (there are more details in Chapter 4) South America evolved several huge suites of unique species during its tens of millions of years as an island continent. These included an amazing selection of marsupials, of which the present-day creatures are but a shadow, while the edentates, which are now represented by armadillos, sloths, and anteaters, produced some truly fabulous forms including the tortoise-like glyptodonts and the giant sloths. South America also produced several entire orders of ungulates (hoofed animals) which are only very distantly related to the ungulates we know today, although they imitated most of the body forms of the moderns, including those of rhinos and elephants. A few of the early South Americans are still with us – for example the armadillos – but the only ones whose ancient forms would still truly seem familiar today are the New World monkeys, which must have lived on the South American land mass even before it finally broke away from Africa.

Following the clash with North America, some of the South Americans went north – including the armadillos, glyptodonts, giant sloths, and the ancestors of the modern marsupial opossums, which are the only wild marsupials in present-day North America. But a great many more passed from north to south, including cats (the ancestors of modern jaguars and pumas), dogs, bears, horses, camelids (the ancestors of the modern llamas and vicunas), elephants, and deer. North America's rhinos had already disappeared during the great cooling of the Miocene.

After the northerners invaded, many of the southerners – including most of the marsupials and most of the unique South American ungulates – disappeared. It looks as if they simply could not compete with the swifter and brainier northerners – as if the shortcomings of the cosy southern islanders were exposed by the street-wise and more continental invaders from the north, just as modern bandicoots are now succumbing to cats. Thus the Great American Interchange has long been presented as *the* classic example of competition in general, and of the superiority of the modern mammals in particular.

But Elisabeth Vrba has provided a brilliant alternative explanation of the events that followed the interchange. To be sure, the northerners flourished in the south, while the southerners largely disappeared. But there is no reason at all to suppose that the northerners were innately superior. Neither, she says, need we suppose that there was any overt 'competition' between the northern immigrants and the southern natives.

For consider, says Dr Vrba, what else was happening in the period about 3 million years ago, when the two continents collided. The world as a whole was growing cooler and drier – a fact that is crucial to our own evolution in Africa. Indeed the cooling helped to bring the two Americas together, because as global temperature goes down polar ice builds up and sea-level falls. But the animals of North America were not adapted to the cold. They had evolved in warmer times. So what did they do? They moved towards the Equator. And where is the Equator? In South America: roughly along the Amazon. On the other hand, it would have made no sense at all for the southerners to go north, *away* from the tropics to which they were adapted.

But why did the southerners who stayed where they were so often go extinct after the clash? Well, tropical Brazil was itself severely affected by the cooling, drying climate. The rainforest retreated and grass encroached to produce a grassland-woodland mosaic. So the southerners found that their favoured rainforest was depleted – but they had to stay where they were because there was nowhere else to run. So they died out. But such a mosaic was precisely the kind of country that the northerners had previously experienced. So they were happy enough with the new-styled Brazil. They had simply followed their favoured habitat southwards.

Thus the northern immigrants survived while the southern stay-at-homes died out, yet we need suppose no direct conflict between them. What brought the southerners to an end was a change in climate. The hypothesis is that they would have died out – or at least suffered severe set-back – even without the northern invasion. The northerners merely occupied the spaces left by the retreating southerners. It *looks* as if the northerners swept the southerners aside, but that is an illusion. By the same token, to revert to our earlier example, it *looks* as if the mammals pushed the dinosaurs out, but all they did was jump into the void that the dinosaurs had left. Both the Pliocene South American mammals and the dinosaurs worldwide were eliminated by outside forces that had nothing to do with the creatures who succeeded them. They were actually eliminated by a change of climate. But the animals that did survive the American interchange evolved to form new suites of creatures – and this is just as true of the edentate glyptodonts and giant sloths that emigrated to the north as it is of the northerners that made new homes in the south.

If, says Dr Vrba, the Equator ran through Massachusetts, then the entire scenario might have been reversed. The northerners would have stayed at home and died in their beds, while the southerners marched north. Then, perhaps, biologists would now be concluding that the South Americans were biologically superior to the northerners.

These examples, I suggest, show how competition really works. And the lessons that emerge are directly applicable to our own species, and the effects we have had upon others.

Note, first of all, that competition takes different forms at different times. When animals are given a chance to settle down, they come to terms with each other, just as the leopard and impala have so obviously done. Then indeed they may remain side by side, unchanged. But when the system is shaken up – when the climate changes, or different suites of creatures are brought together – there is a new fraughtness, as the animals strive to come to terms with the new conditions and with each other. Such periods in practice may last forever, as the fortunes of different groups continue to fluctuate over time. But in general the periods in which competition is obvious and bloody are short-lived. Soon the Australian marsupials that are simply unable to cope with cats will have gone, and those that are left will adapt to cats just as impalas are adapted to leopards.

But the example of the red and grey squirrels shows that competition can be devastating, and yet be covert. American greys wiped out the British reds so subtly that it has taken biologists more than a hundred years to find the reason. From this example two principles emerge that illustrate mechanisms of competition which, I believe, are far more typical than those of the depredations of cats in Australia. For to explain the replacement of reds by greys we merely need to invoke a general principle which may be seen as a component of game theory (discussed further in Chapter 6). This principle is that of 'pre-emption': once a creature has taken over a particular territory or ecological niche, then it is extremely difficult for another creature to turf it out. This may seem to conflict with our examples of biological invasion but in fact successful invasions are rare compared with the failures; it is simply that when they do succeed they are often spectacular.

So, in the squirrel example, we can imagine a scenario in which there are plenty of pine trees and a few oaks, in which the red squirrels compete very well with any greys that are present. But in one particular year the pines may fail to set much seed – it

happens to all populations of trees at some times. Then the reds
are forced to move out. But the greys stay on, sustained by the
acorns. While the reds diminish, the greys multiply. The following season the pines may set seed again and the reds might seek
to return – but in practice they cannot because the greys never
left and are already in residence. Their presence pre-empts the
reinvasion of the reds. There is no overt conflict – the reds do not
even try to get back, because they perceive that the territory is no
longer available. Over time, through this ratchet effect, the reds
retreat and the greys expand but never a blow is struck. I am sure
that this same mechanism – simply staying in residence when
other creatures are obliged to move out – largely accounts for the
observed ability of human beings to spread around the world
while other creatures retreat. Our versatility gives us the same
kind of pre-emptive edge for we can occupy places at times when
other species cannot.

Indeed this same principle of pre-emption, applied on a
grander scale, explains why the mammals remained as also-rans
for 100 million years while the dinosaurs held the stage. To be
sure, a modern lion dropped by some meddlesome time-traveller
into dinosaur country might have done very well. There were
plenty of efficient dinosaur predators but lions could surely have
held their own. But because the dinosaurs already prevailed, there
was no opportunity for lions to evolve. For modern lions were
preceded by ancestral lions, and before ancestral lions there were
big clumsy predators that simply lacked the agility, cunning, and
social organisation of the modern beast. Those cumbersome predecessors could not have competed with the dinosaurs. Indeed
they never even had a chance to appear. No big mammalian
predator of any kind could get a look in until the dinosaurs had
gone, and the niches were left vacant. By the same token, as
already noted, big lizards and crocodiles may have inhibited the
evolution of big marsupial predators in Australia in the Cenozoic.
Taken all in all, then, 'competition' is a complex set of phenomena and one to which animals respond in a variety of ways.

In practice, however, only four options are open to animals
and plants when they are challenged by outside stresses. Clever,
or otherwise versatile, creatures may simply modify their behaviour, as pigs or leopards or human beings may do – or the foxes
and crows that are now adjusting to life in cities. Or they may

move into new territory, either by active migration or by dying out in one place and spreading into another. This of course depends on opportunity. Thus the shrews of Europe were pushed south during the cooling Pleistocene until they ran out of land and some species finally disappeared in southern Italy and Greece; but North America's mammals were saved from a similar fate in the cooling Pliocene by the timely arrival of South America. If a behavioural change is insufficient and emigration is impossible, then animals may exercise the option suggested by Darwin: they may undergo adaptive, evolutionary change. If that is impossible for whatever reason, then they may simply go extinct.

But when are animals able to evolve in the face of pressure, and when are they simply wiped out? This question is crucial to our own evolution, and to our impact on other creatures.

STRESS, EVOLUTION, AND THE VITAL MATTER OF POPULATION

As Darwin pointed out, no population can change unless it contains a variety of individuals from which the natural pressures can make their selection. Without variety, there simply are no options. In these neodarwinian days we know that the necessary variety results from a varied gene pool.

To provide such variety, two conditions must be fulfilled. First, the individuals within the population must be genetically varied. Modern studies of DNA show that wild populations of animals may differ hugely in the degree of genetic variation. Thus it transpires — serendipitously — that the Indian rhinos that live in the national park of Chitwan in Nepal are extremely varied genetically, even though there are only a few hundred individuals. Evidently they converged on the park from a vast area of Asia, and brought their variety with them. By contrast, studies in the 1980s revealed that all the cheetahs of Africa were as similar to each other as peas in a pod. At some time in the past the world's cheetah population must have been extremely reduced, and stayed at a low level for some time. Then there would have been rapid loss of variation through genetic drift, until the remaining animals were practically uniform. Animals that lose genetic variation by such means are said to pass through a 'genetic bottleneck'. By good luck the tiny population of cheetahs multiplied again, but the inheritance of genetic uniformity remains.

This brings us to the second point: quite simply, big populations can contain more allelic variants than small populations. To be sure, some small populations – such as the Chitwan rhinos – may be very varied, but if there were tens of thousands of those rhinos instead of a few hundred we could expect even more variation.

Thus we see that small populations of animals lose out in all ways. Just because the numbers are low, small populations are more easily wiped out than big ones by purely physical means: an epidemic, a fire, an exuberant hunting party. But in addition, small populations are at a huge genetic disadvantage. First, they cannot contain as much genetic variation as large populations, and so lack the genetic wherewithal to make evolutionary change. But second, as already noted, small populations lose genetic variation much more rapidly than large ones do by the chance process of genetic drift. Because of drift, a small but genetically various population (such as the Chitwan rhinos) can degrade into a genetically homozygous and uniform population (as in modern cheetahs) within a few generations, if the population remains at a low level.

In fact, modern genetic theory allows us to define the sizes of population that are needed, in theory, to resist various kinds of pressure. In general, any population of animals that remains consistently at fifty individuals or less is almost bound to be wiped out sooner or later simply by accident – anything from an epidemic to a failure in one generation to produce enough offspring of the appropriate sex. At present the population both of Javan and of northern white rhinoceroses is less than fifty. To have a reasonable chance simply of surviving in the wild, populations in general need to be maintained at at least 500. But to contain enough genetic variation to enable evolution to continue in the genetic, neodarwinian sense, a population must generally be sustained at at least a thousand.

The ecological and conservational implications are obvious. Elephants in Asia for example generally need about ten square kilometres each – so 10,000 square kilometres are needed to sustain Asian elephants in truly viable numbers. Tigers, as top predators, need even more space: anything between ten and a hundred square kilometres *each*. A truly viable population needs up to 100,000 square kilometres: the size of a small country. That kind of area just is not available. At present, tigers in the wild are simply hanging on. But we see, too, how easily we can explain our own impact on other creatures. It is not necessary to wipe out every last one in order to drive them to extinction – we merely have to reduce the population below viable numbers. But viable numbers are surprisingly high and, in the case of large animals, an extraordinary amount of space is required.

Population size also affects an animal's evolutionary fate. As we have seen, if a population is very small (less than a few hundred) then all but the smallest pressure is liable simply to wipe it out. If, on the other hand, the population is huge – many millions – then it is hard to see how neodarwinian change can occur at all. After all, we cannot say that a gene pool has altered irrevocably until some of the alleles have been cast out altogether. Any change of frequency that falls short of total elimination is merely a fluctuation, which all lineages undergo as the generations pass. It seems to follow that neodarwinian change can occur only if the population is middle-sized. This, I will suggest later, has great implications for the emergence of our own lineage – and for our present-day evolution, or the lack of it.

It also seems to me (though I have not heard the matter discussed) that variations in size of population help to explain why it is that evolution sometimes seems to proceed slowly, and sometimes quickly. For when a population is doing well, it grows. Eventually, I suggest, it gets to a size at which neodarwinian change is no longer likely, because there are no alleles rare enough to be shuffled off. But when some new pressure builds up the population may start to drop. Eventually numbers fall to a point at which the rare alleles start to be weeded out. Thus the gene pool undergoes qualitative change, which is the essence of neodarwinian evolution, and natural selection ensures that it changes in ways that increase its 'fitness'. So then the population expands again, and the process of change comes to a halt. If, however, the pressure is too great, then the diminution continues until the population is no longer viable, and then it decays rapidly to extinction. Hence, I suggest, a rise and fall in population, which itself is a reflection of fitness, also helps to regulate the pace of evolutionary change. We could say that such a mechanism helps to ensure that lineages change when they need to change (when the pressure is reducing their populations) and to stay the same when they are doing well (and their populations are large).

The need for populations to be large also explains why, when habitats are under stress, some species disappear while others expand. A million years ago the world contained at least a dozen species of elephant (and probably many more) and now it contains only two. But one of the two that remains occupied virtually all of Africa until recent decades, and the other extended from Pakistan to China and the islands of south-east Asia. What has happened, I suggest, is that over the past few million years various pressures (including the rise of *Homo*) reduced most of the elephant species to numbers that were simply unviable, and they disappeared. But the surviving species were then able to spread into the elephant territory that was vacated. Thus one effect of pressure is to reduce the number of species – though not necessarily to reduce the total biomass, because the remaining ones expand. Reduction of the population below viable numbers is again the root cause.

In short, over the past 130 years Darwin's original vision of evolution has been modified by a broader view of what 'competition' really entails, and by adding the ideas of genetics, but the overall effect has been not to threaten but to enrich the original concept. The third and final area of enrichment is in the matter of timing.

TIMING

Darwin never supposed that evolutionary change always occurs at the same pace. Enough fossils were known in his day to show that some lineages have changed quicker than others, and that any one lineage may alter rapidly in some periods and more slowly in others. But he does imply that the 'struggle for life' is a constant, nagging force, which suggests that the creatures themselves must constantly be modified to stay ahead of the game. Furthermore, he supposed that evolutionary change is bound generally to be slow. Hence Darwin's original view of evolution is generally said to be one of 'gradualism': slow but inexorable change.

Modern studies of a fossil record that is much more complete than in Darwin's day suggest that this need not be the case. On the one hand we now know that evolution can, at times, be astonishingly rapid. Thus in the interglacial period between the last two ice ages, around 120 million years ago, the North Sea encroached into western Europe to create the English Channel and the Channel Islands (although it retreated again, temporarily, during the last ice age). Red deer were trapped on the island of Jersey and, as is typical of island animals, they became dwarfed. Astonishingly, fossil studies by Adrian Lister at Cambridge University now show that, simply by natural selection, their body weight was reduced to *one-sixth* of the original in a mere 6,000 years (*Nature*, vol. 342, 1989, pp. 539–42). Contrariwise, long fossil sequences of marine snails now show that some lineages remained virtually *un*changed for hundreds of millions of years.

With such examples in mind, Stephen Jay Gould and Niles Eldredge suggested in the early 1970s that the slow-but-steady change known as 'gradualism' is not the normal pattern of things. Instead, evolution has a tendency simply to shudder to a halt – until the system is given a jolt and the lineages rapidly evolve into some new form. They called this stop–go pattern 'punctuated equilibrium'.

In the light of much that has already been said in this chapter, we can see why this might well be so. Often, after all, it pays an animal to stay the same. Impalas and leopards, for example, are coping very well with life, and change could upset their respective apple-carts. The South African biologist Hugh Paterson has suggested another reason for staying the same. All creatures that breed sexually (which is most of them) must recognise each others' mating signals. Thus male crab spiders impress other crab spiders by waving their palps, while male bustards jump up and down to display their vigour. At the chemical level, eggs must recognise sperm from the appropriate species and the stigmas of plants must recognise suitable pollen. The fact that all creatures must communicate with others of the same kind if they are to reproduce and spread their genes implies that they should beware varying too far from the norm, unless there is special reason to do so. The need to be recognised, in short, is another reason why natural selection should favour the creatures that stay the same.

Thus a generalisation emerges: that *natural selection favours change only when the advantages of changing outweigh the advantages of staying the same.* I have also suggested that the rate of evolutionary change is affected by population size: populations that are very large –

which implies successful – seem resistant to change.

Elisabeth Vrba has developed the general notion of punctuated equilibrium into a grand vision of evolutionary change which she calls 'the turnover pulse hypothesis'.* She has looked not simply at single lineages but at entire suites of different creatures in whole ecosystems: notably at the fossils of bovids (mainly antelope) in Africa over the past 10 million years or so. She finds that in general *all* the species tend to stay much the same until provoked by some outside event, when they all tend to change more or less together. 'Turnover' implies change, and 'pulse' implies a distinct period of alteration imposed on a background that is generally quiet. She also suggests that the outside event that usually produces such general alteration is a global change of climate. Thus fossil and geological evidence suggests that the whole world cooled dramatically about 2·5 million years ago. The bovids of Africa changed accordingly; in particular, the gazelles appeared. At about that time, too, the genus *Homo* made its first tentative appearance.

I would like to add a suggestion of my own, which is that plants are sometimes able to subvert these climatic pulses, and this is of prime importance since plants ultimately provide the animals with their food and much of their shelter, and largely determine what kinds of animals can live. Of course, plants are subject to climate. We see this clearly as the world cooled during the Cenozoic, and Eocene forest gave way to Miocene grassland (with occasional resurgence of forest in periods of temporary warming). But plants also have a significant tendency to do their own thing whatever the climate is doing. In particular, it seems that the flowering plants, the angiosperms, first appeared in the Jurassic, and became widespread and varied during the Cenozoic. Unlike the rise of the mammals, this radiation of angiosperms did not apparently depend on the loss of some previous life form, and did not follow any discernible change of climate. The flowering plants simply appeared, and having appeared they continued to spread. As they did so they created a quite new kind of environment: in particular, a canopy of angiospermous trees which both in their chemistry and in their geometry (the shape and lay-out of

---

*Elisabeth Vrba's idea of 'turnover pulse' derives in large part from the general notion of punctuated equilibrium as first made explicit by Stephen Gould and Niles Eldredge. The speculations concerning the influence of population size on the rate of evolutionary change are my own (which means that Dr Vrba should not be blamed for them).

the branches and leaves) were different from anything that had gone before. It was in this new environment, cut off from the essentially terrestrial world of the dinosaurs, that our own ancestors developed: the first essentially arboreal primates. The primates, in fact, are one of the few groups of modern mammals (the others being the edentates and marsupials) whose ancestors must have existed in recognisable form long before the dinosaurs disappeared. I suggest that the rise of the angiospermous trees, *occurring independently of global climatic events*, allowed this to happen.

These, then, are the ideas of Darwin as modified and enriched by later thinkers. I would like to suggest, however, that Lamarck, whom Darwin superseded, does have something important to say to us – though it is not the thing for which he is generally remembered.

LAMARCK REVISITED

I mentioned earlier that Darwin toyed for a time with the hereditary notions of Jean Baptiste Lamarck, and was then persuaded to reject them. That has been the fate of Lamarck: to be rejected, and indeed often ridiculed. But although Lamarck said some things that were wrong and should be cast aside he also said other things which, I believe, are of profound significance but are generally overlooked. The babies have been thrown out with the bathwater.

Thus in 1809 – he really was a pioneer – Lamarck published his *Zoological Philosophy* in which he not only promulgated the idea that creatures evolve but also proposed four laws of evolutionary change. The fourth is the law of 'inheritance of acquired characteristics'. It proposes that creatures inherit the features developed by their parents during life. So, for example, a blacksmith who developed big biceps would produce children with big biceps, and a giraffe which stretched to reach the uppermost branches would produce offspring with long necks. This is the law for which Lamarck is remembered and which is, unfortunately, wrong. Such a mechanism could not operate unless information from the muscle cells could somehow be transmitted to the sperm or eggs, and in the 1880s the German biologist August Weismann (1834–1914) pointed out that there is no such transmission. The germ (reproductive) cells and the somatic (body) cells developed independently. *Ergo*, 'inheritance of acquired characteristics' was a non-starter. Gregor Mendel's ideas then delivered the *coup de grâce*.

But another of Lamarck's laws – the second – has much to commend it. This proposes that 'the population of a new organ in an animal body results from a new need that continues to make itself felt'. Most modern biologists accept, as Darwin said, that giraffes acquired their long necks by natural selection: that is, ancestral giraffes had necks of varying length but the ones that survived the best and produced most offspring were the ones with the longest necks. There is no reason to suppose that the parents' straining necks influenced the gametes – as Weismann said, this cannot happen.

So *why* did natural selection favour long necks in giraffes? And why not in hippos? To put the matter anthropomorphically, giraffes had already 'decided' to earn their living by feeding from the tops of trees. In animals feeding from the tree-tops, Darwinian natural selection would indeed favour those with the longest necks. But, I suggest, the 'decision' to feed in the tree-tops is made to meet what Lamarck called the 'need that continues to make itself felt'.

This idea seems to me of crucial importance in understanding evolution, in explaining why lineage after lineage has shown the ability to shift dramatically from one way of life to quite another, and back again. For example, all the lines of herbivorous megareptiles in the Mesozoic evolved from carnivorous ancestors. It is clear too (as discussed in the next chapter) that the modern ungulates, which are the hoofed animals and are generally herbivorous, shared a common ancestor with the carnivores. And in the Palaeocene there were creatures with the potential to go either way. *Andrewsarchus* is one such. It was the biggest terrestrial meat-eating mammal of all time (about four metres long) and had jaws like a crocodile, but it also had hooves.

A look at some modern animals shows how this kind of shift might come about. Thus bears are basically meat-eaters, within the mammalian order Carnivora. But in practice all bears are somewhat omnivorous, and even polar bears will eat some vegetation if given a chance. At least two bears, the giant panda (which clearly is a bear) and the spectacled bear of South America have evolved into virtual vegetarians. Indeed, giant pandas subsist almost entirely on bamboo although they clearly remember their carnivorous roots and can be lured into traps by the smell of roast pork. Contrariwise, many apparently committed herbivores are more omnivorous than they look. Recently in a nature reserve red deer acquired notoriety by biting the heads off ground-nesting birds. Apparently the deer lacked calcium – and most animals display a remarkable ability to identify what it is that they lack, and to seek it out. I was also told in India by excellent field biologists that elephants sometimes acquire a taste for flesh. 'Doc' Krishnamurthy of the Bombay Natural History Society, a veterinarian acknowledged as India's greatest hands-on authority on Asian elephants, tells how he once tried to rescue from a river an Asian elephant bull which munched contentedly upon a decaying antelope as the waters rose fatally around it. There are well-attested tales, too, of man-killing elephants occasionally becoming man-eaters. One bull reputedly returned to the shallow grave of his victim and dug her up, to continue his interrupted meal.

Thus we see that many animals are behaviourally versatile – which implies that the same animal is capable of acting many different roles. Between them, these roles provide the *variety* that Darwin perceived as the essential raw ingredient of evolution. *Each* of those roles is exposed to its own particular set of selective pressures, and if the conditions are right then any one of those roles, after a few generations of selection, could evolve into a new kind of creature. Thus if elephants that had a taste for flesh were marooned on some hypothetical island where there was more animal matter than vegetation (on which, for example, passing whales had a particular tendency to strand themselves) then natural selection might eventually transform them into committed scavengers. But the crucial point is that *natural selection could not transform elephants into scavengers unless they had a taste for scavenging in the first place.* This idea seems to me an extremely important one – and it derives from Lamarck. It conforms with his *second* law, which rephrased in the language of Darwin states that creatures tend to put themselves in a position in which natural selection can start to work on them.

This principle seems to me of profound significance in the evolution of human beings. For we are supremely versatile. Our early ancestors in Africa offered to the anvil of natural selection a whole range of possibilities. If our ancestors had been set in their ways like, say, duck-billed platypuses, then they simply would not have provided natural selection with interesting raw materials, and we would still be duck-billed platypuses. Thus we – like all animals – have to some extent shaped our own evolution. We have not done this consciously. But, like giraffes, we have put ourselves in a position in which natural selection could shape us in particular ways.

A SUMMARY: NATURAL SELECTION AND TIME AND CHANCE

This has been a brief summary of the way the game of life has been played. Charles Darwin first outlined the rules in a plausible form and later authors, from Gregor Mendel to the modern ecologists and palaeontologists, have added refinements. It is clear, now, that the evolutionary machine is not a smoothly-oiled and self-motivating engine. Still less does it run on any metalled track, towards any stated goal. I will argue in Chapter 9 that evolution does, in fact, 'progress', which is an extremely unfashionable idea. But to progress should not imply a 'destiny': the progress is not in any direction that can be foretold.

Overall, indeed, the evolutionary machine is a ramshackle and patchwork affair. Left to itself it is liable simply to shudder to a halt. All the creatures on board would be quite content to stay the same. In general it lurches into life again only when provoked. But fortunately (if we think evolutionary change is a good thing), the Earth and the Universe as a whole will always provide provocation sooner or later – a change of climate, collision with some formerly alienated continent, or the importunate arrival for whatever reason of some novel suite of animals and plants.

During these periods of change many creatures are lost. For one reason or another, they simply lack the wherewithal for suitable adaptation. They may lack the necessary genetic variation – perhaps because there simply are too few of them to embrace the necessary variety. They may lack the versatility of behaviour which would enable them to explore new ways of living, and put themselves in a position in which natural selection can act upon them. Or the new pressures may simply be too great or too rapidly applied and snuff them out before they have a chance to change.

But some of the creatures in these times of change will respond by altering in ways that increase their adaptedness, their fitness. These will be the ones that have the right genetic wherewithal and the potential for suitable behaviour and are in the right place at the right time.

Overall, there are plenty of conditional clauses. Evolution by natural selection clearly can produce a huge variety of creatures wonderfully adapted to an enormous variety of habitats. The evidence is all around us. But it works to no plan: it just follows its nose, does what the conditions at the time require, and is obliged to build only on what was there before. Time and chance play a huge part. But for a change of climate 65 million years ago, the dinosaurs would be with us yet; they may well have remained, still as recognisable dinosaurs, until the end of the Earth. Our ancestors, the primates, appeared long before the dinosaurs had gone, but if the dinosaurs had survived they could forever have been confined to the trees.

So those are the rules of the games at the global party. It is time to introduce our fellow guests.

4

Fellow Creatures

At this moment we may be sharing the planet with 30 million other species. That is a guess, for only about a million or so have been named, but preliminary studies suggest that for every species that is known, there are about thirty others living in the canopies and roots of tropical forests. If all 30 million had been described, and you recited their names at speed – a second for each – then it would take you a year to get through them all, assuming you did not stop to eat or sleep.

Yet all we see today is a soupçon of what has been. For every present-day species of animal there have been thousands in the past. The mammals of today are a shadow of former glories – even though they include some of the most beautiful and extra-ordinary creatures that have ever lived. Thus, the fossil record suggests that throughout the Cenozoic each species of mammal has lasted for an average of around a million years before going extinct or evolving into something else. Since the Cenozoic has lasted 65 million years then commonsensical but slightly esoteric maths suggests that for every mammal species that exists at present there must have been thirty or more in this era. Add the mammals of the Mesozoic which shared the planet with the dinosaurs, and we may reasonably guess that for each mammalian species of today there have been at least fifty in times gone by. Now there are about 4,300 mammalian species on Earth but the total that have lived since the group began can hardly be less than 200,000: not as many, but in the same league, as the known inventory of present-day beetles.

So today there are five species of rhinoceros in one family while the fossil record reveals at least 200 in three families; and whereas the present-day rhinos are all tank-like and much of a muchness, some of the ancient rhinos ran like small ponies, some were more hippo-like than the hippos, and one, *Paraceratherium*, which lived from Pakistan to Yugoslavia in the Oligocene, was built like a massive giraffe, stood six metres *at the shoulder*, and was the biggest land mammal that has ever lived, dwarfing the biggest elephants. Today there are two species of elephant but over time

Figure IV.1: A Note on Names and Classification

All creatures seek to classify the other creatures that surround
them in some way or other, even if it is a simple 'things that can
be eaten' versus 'things that might eat me'. Human beings have
been playing this game for as long as humanity has existed, though
the oldest known formal attempts to classify all creatures date
back to the Greeks. Modern methods of classification began with
the eighteenth-century Swedish biologist Carl Linnaeus (1707–78).
But Linnaeus sought only to reflect what he took to be the
orderliness of the Creation – the mind of God. Today, most
'systematists' (biologists interested in classification) seek to
devise groupings that reflect true relationships – that is, creatures
in the same group are supposed to have descended from a
common ancestor. This approach rests on the idea that living
things have indeed *evolved*, which was not firmly established until
Charles Darwin's *Origin of Species* of 1859.

Biologists universally acknowledge the basic 'unit' of living things
as the 'species'. A species is generally taken to be any group of
creatures that can breed together successfully, to produce 'fully
viable' offspring (that is, offspring that are just as fit and fertile as
their parents). Modern horses and domestic dogs are obviously
different species since they cannot interbreed. When horses and
asses mate they can produce 'hybrid' offspring, but they still count
as separate species because the hybrids, known as mules, are
sexually infertile and hence are not fully viable.

When animals are extinct, and known only from their fossils, it is
of course impossible to judge directly whether any two types could
or could not have mated successfully together. Then the
palaeontologist has to define the species more or less exclusively
on the basis of appearance. This is generally acceptable but there
is obvious scope for error, since we know from living examples that
some true species can vary greatly in anatomy, while some groups
of creatures look very similar but in fact do not breed together and
so form different species. For example, there are different species
of living gazelles, bush-babies, possums, mice, and owls that are
almost impossible to tell apart by eye, and yet do not interbreed.

Groups of species that are obviously very similar but are
nonetheless distinct are grouped together in the same 'genus',
plural 'genera'. Thus all living horses, zebras, and donkeys are
placed together in the genus *Equus*. By the convention devised by
Linnaeus, each creature is given two names – the 'generic'

followed by the 'specific' – which together form the name of its particular species. Thus the modern domestic horse is *Equus caballus*, the African ass (which is the one that is commonly domesticated) is *Equus africanus*, the plains zebra is *Equus burchelli*, and so on. Formal scientific names may be called 'Latin' names although the Latin is often simply invented and many of the roots are Greek.

Three further conventions are worth noting. First, when the Latin name is presented formally it is *always* written in italics, with the generic name beginning with a capital letter and the specific starting lower case. Thus *burchelli* is spelt with a small 'b' even though it derives from somebody's name. Secondly, when it is clear what genus is being talked about, the generic name can be presented simply as the initial letter: as in '*Equus caballus* and *E. africanus*'. Thirdly, zoologists sometimes find it convenient to subdivide species into races, otherwise known as subspecies. Then a third name is added, as in *Equus burchelli burchelli*.

Different but related genera are grouped together in 'families', families are combined in 'orders', orders are combined to form 'classes', classes are grouped to form 'phyla' (singular 'phylum') and phyla are grouped to form 'kingdoms'. Thus the genus *Equus* and various related types (such as the three-toed *Hipparion*) are grouped in the family Equidae; Equidae is linked with the rhinoceroses and tapirs (and some extinct groups) in the order Perissodactyla; the perissodactyls are grouped with other warm-blooded furry creatures in the class Mammalia; the mammals are joined with reptiles, fish, and so on in the phylum Chordata; and the chordates are combined with worms, snails and the rest in the grand kingdom Animalia, the animals. Any one of these categories can also be further subdivided or grouped together to give, for example, 'infraclass' or 'superorder' or 'suborder'. Thus the Perissodactyla are combined with the Artiodactyla (the cattle, deer, and antelopes) and some other orders to form the superorder Ungulata, the hoofed mammals. Finally, it has sometimes proved necessary to invent even more subcategories – thus the grouping 'cohort' may be interposed between infraclass and superorder, while families may be divided first into subfamilies and then into 'tribes', before further subdivision into genera. Any group of any size is called a 'taxon', plural 'taxa'.

The 'higher order' groups (family, order, and so on) are always written formally in Roman type, but beginning with a capital letter, as in 'Chordata' or 'Mammalia'. But they can be referred to informally in lower case, as in 'chordates' or 'mammals'. The names of plant families tend to end in '-aceae' (as in Chenopodiaceae, the family of Good King Henry) or '-ae' (as in Labiatae, the mint family) or '-eae' (as in Gramineae, the grasses). Botanists then refer informally to the families in various ways, as in 'chenopods', 'labiates', or just plain 'grasses'. But the names of animal families always end in '-idae'. Zoologists therefore refer informally to members of a particular family just by shortening the name. So 'equids' obviously refers to members of the Equidae; 'pongids' are the Pongidae – the family of chimpanzees, gorillas, and orang-utans; and 'hominids' are members of the human family, the Hominidae.

In addition, members of a particular genus can be referred to informally by adding '-ine'. So *Homo sapiens* (our own species) and *Homo neanderthalensis* (the neanderthals) are both 'hominines'. The extinct genus *Australopithecus* is almost certainly the ancestor of *Homo*, and is also placed in the Hominidae and is therefore also a hominid. But members of the genus *Australopithecus* are not hominines. They are australopithecines.

One final point. A taxon that includes the common ancestor of a group of creatures plus *all* its descendants, and no other creatures, is called a 'clade'. Thus the class Aves is a clade because it contains all the birds that have ever lived, including the presumed ancestor of them all which was *Archaeopteryx* (or something very like *Archaeopteryx*). But the class Reptilia is not, strictly speaking, a clade, because the reptiles gave rise both to the birds and to the mammals. To qualify as a clade, 'Reptilia' would have to be taken to include Aves and Mammalia. This would mean that you, and I, and sparrows, as well as snakes and dinosaurs, are all reptiles. But in practice most biologists recognise the need to compromise, and retain the term 'Reptilia' even though it is not properly a clade. The integrity of the group is preserved by introducing the concept of 'grade': that is, an animal is placed in the Reptilia if it is a descendant of the first reptile, and if it also retains obviously reptilian features such as a scaly skin.

there have been at least 150. Today there are four species of
hyaena but almost seventy are known from the past. Today there
are 200 known species of primate – apes, monkeys, and 'prosimians' such as lemurs and tarsiers – but the total estimated from the
past is around 6,500. Today there is only one species of hominid
– us – but since our family first appeared in the late Miocene
there have been at least twenty (see Fig. IV.1).

Not just species but entire groups of mammals have disappeared: entire orders of tank-like creatures from the Eocene;
gone are the relatives of the horse, the uintatheres; the two
unique orders of ungulates (hoofed animals) from South America,
the litopterns and the notoungulates, which between them emulated most of the forms of the ungulates on other continents; and
the creodonts which were the first large specialist mammalian carnivores, before the true Carnivora group – the cats, dogs, bears
and their ilk – got under way. Orders that now are sadly reduced,
such as the edentates which now manifest as small tree sloths and
armadillos, once were glorious, with the immensely successful
giant sloths and tortoise-like glyptodonts bestriding both
Americas. Other modern groups that enjoyed much better times
in the past include the Perissodactyla (now represented by rhinos,
horses, and tapirs); the camel family that once included the long-
gone oreodonts which for a time were the most numerous large
animals of North America; the bizarrely-horned deer-like protoceratids; the pronghorn 'antelopes' or antilocaprids, once a superb
and varied family but now down to one species (although they
have fared better than the protoceratids who have gone altogether); the marsupials, now known best for the kangaroos and
koala, but among others once including bear-like forms in South
America; an array of sabretooths resembling the sabretoothed cats;
and the hornless but rhino-like diprotodonts of Australia.

These creatures of the past did not necessarily do the things
that their modern relatives do today. Animals are obviously
obliged to obey the laws of physics and those that live on land are
especially prone to gravity, so they cannot be any old size or shape
they choose – pigs will never fly and although I have heard of an
elephant in Sri Lanka that allegedly jumps, elephants will never
soar like a gazelle unless they undergo some vigorous evolution
and re-emerge in a quite different guise. In practice, indeed, animals on land conform to a rather small number of basic

engineering designs which work, known as 'ecomorphs'.

A quick or even a leisurely survey of present-day mammals might suggest that each lineage has more or less commandeered its own particular ecomorph, as if it was somehow destined to take that form and no other. Thus the only existing practitioners of the giraffe-like ecomorph, with Eiffel-Tower necks for browsing from the heights of acacias, are the giraffes themselves.

But giraffes did not invent the giraffe-like ecomorph. Among the very first in fact was the giant rhino, *Paraceratherium*. The giraffe family (Giraffidae) arose from deer (Cervidae) and while *Paraceratherium* was being a giraffe the giraffids themselves resembled moose, which is the largest of the living deer; the modern okapi shows the general form, though it lacks the bulk and the candelabra antlers of some earlier giraffids. Others that have played at being giraffes include several long-necked camels and at least one of the South American litopterns. In general, a giraffe is a reasonable thing to be and there is no reason why giraffes should have a monopoly on that way of being. By the same token, the hyaenas which now specialise in crushing bones (apart from the perversely peg-toothed aardwolf which contrives to subsist on termites in South Africa) have in their time aspired to be chasers and harriers – like dogs. So too, on occasion, have bears. Dogs in their turn have at times played at bone-crushing like hyaenas – and perhaps it was a bone-crushing dog that kept the hyaenas out of North America when the opening of Beringia apparently gave them a chance to spread themselves.

In short, the notion that dogs are 'meant' to be like dogs and giraffes were destined to be giraffes is giving way to the realisation that anything can be anything – or, more precisely, that most big lineages at some time have explored a wide array of ecomorphs and that most ecomorphs have at different times been essayed by a wide array of lineages. The arrangement we see now – giraffes with an exclusive claim to steeple necks and hyaenas as the world's specialist bone-crushers – is just the way things happen to be at the moment.

It is the case that modern-day teachers of biology and publishers of children's books are somewhat obsessed with zoogeography. Zoos at this moment are being redesigned to present 'The Asian Centre' or 'The African Experience'. Well, there is something to be said for zoogeography. The idea of the animal and plant 'community' is not entirely fatuous because many creatures have co-evolved – have been shaped by each other's presence – and there are many interdependencies. Zoogeography has an aesthetic element, too: antelope, lions, and cheetahs give the African savannah its 'character' while feral camels and water buffalo simply look out of place in Australia which has been the land of marsupials (and honey-eaters and goannas and banksias and grevilleas) for 40 million years.

But a preoccupation with zoogeography can be misleading. Elephants now are creatures of the tropics but their relatives have lived almost from pole to pole – from islands north of Siberia to the south of South America. Marsupials today are represented in North America only by the opossums which came in from South America during the Great Interchange. But marsupials evidently *arose* in North America 120 or so million years ago, when the dinosaurs still had several chapters to run. The rhinos now seem inveterately African but they came much later to Africa than to other continents. They too arose in North America. The large mammals of North America now consist largely of Eurasian immigrants which arrived recently via Beringia and yet North America is the birth-place of many a fine group which has long since left: the perissodactyls as a whole and the camelids, as well as the marsupials. Elephants may well have arisen in Africa but the modern family of elephants, the Elephantidae, apparently arose in Asia. But the Elephantidae spread all over the world (not least in the form of mammoths) and the genus to which the modern Asian elephant belongs, *Elephas*, arose from a group that had migrated back to Africa.

Tapirs today are found only in South America and south-east Asia while lions are found in Africa and in one tiny pocket in north-west India. How come? Did God plant them there, like a whimsical gardener? Not at all. Tapirs and lions (and batallions of other creatures too) have in their time spread throughout Eurasia (and North America) and the populations we see now are remnants. Tapirs left Europe and North America a very long time ago but lions lived in Europe, Asia Minor, and deep into China in historical times. How else would Androcles have pulled a thorn from a lion's paw, or David killed the lion that attacked his sheep? Perhaps those stories are not literally true (though there is no good reason to doubt them) but they are based on a fact: the fact that lions are just as able to be European as they are to be African.

The generalisation emerges that zoogeography expresses no deep principle but simply reflects the way things happen to be at the moment. Most of the groups of larger animals have in their time been *everywhere* (except of course Australia, which so far has guarded its island status). They have been motivated to move by changing climate and allowed to move by seas that conveniently drained from time to time (as the Mediterranean has done) and by land-bridges that obligingly appeared (as did Beringia and the isthmus of Panama). Their peregrinations stop only when they run out of habitat — for example, the shrews that were driven south in the ice ages through Spain, Italy, and Greece were finally snuffed out when there was nowhere further to run. We think that animals 'belong' where we happen to have found them but usually they are just passing through.

Add the dimension of time, then, and we no longer see a landscape of creatures with each one doing its allotted thing in its allotted space. Lineages such as pronghorns and elephants that now contain just one or two creatures can be seen to include entire suites. While some animals, for instance platypuses, may be stuck in ecological and genetic grooves, most of the more vigorous types are trying on each others' hats, yesterday — or tomorrow — being giraffes or hippos or sabretooths where today they are content to be rhinos or phalangers. And while these suites of creatures are swapping roles and reclaiming them again, when the opportunities arise they trek the entire surface of the globe: cascades of animals migrating, radiating, moving on or drifting back from whence they came. Over just a few centuries they may flit across a continent like a city park and in practice they have had millions of years to play with.

I intend to look at 'us' in the next chapter, and for the rest of this book. But for now I want to look further at the kind of world our family joined in the Miocene, and our genus entered in the Pliocene and began seriously to influence in the Pleistocene. Before introducing our fellow players in more detail, it is worth looking more closely at the concept of ecomorph. It helps us to see what our fellow creatures are actually trying to do — and why we are different.

THE IDEA OF THE ECOMORPH

For animals that live in the sea the physical problems of life have to do with the properties of water: with its mass, its viscosity, and its adhesiveness, which is felt in particular by very small animals. But they are spared the full rigours of gravity. Thus unless an aquatic creature chooses the life of a swimmer – in which case it must generally be torpedo-shaped – it can take almost any form, and so it is that the free-floating creatures of the plankton can be wonderfully bizarre, with waving feathery gills and spicules and yolk sacs stuck on wherever they happen to fit – or so it may seem to the land-bound naturalist. But on land, the constant reality of gravity ensures that animals must conform to the rules of civil engineering; the bigger and heavier they become, the more critical are the parameters. After all, anyone can make a garden shed. But only a master craftsman can build a cathedral that will stay standing. For homoiothermic land animals, too, the physics of heat comes into play. Thus gravity and thermodynamics between them determine that, on land, body size, shape, and lifestyle are bound to be intimately linked.

Each ecological niche tends to require creatures of a particular body form – a particular 'ecomorph' – and every lineage that aspires to exploit that niche must adopt that form. It is because there have been many more lineages than there are feasible ecomorphs that 'convergence' has been such a powerful theme in evolution: like it or not, all creatures that aspire to live in a particular way find themselves subject to particular physical laws which must be respected and which largely determine what form they take.

In broad terms – the broadest possible – some animals have elected to survive by being big, and some by being small. 'Big' and 'small' seem purely relative terms but because the laws of physics are as they are these parameters in fact impose some absolutes. Gravity alone would ensure, for example, that a creature on land that weighed much more than a hundred tonnes could not move – except perhaps as some slithering mass. In practice, then, land mammals have rarely been smaller than present-day pygmy shrews and only a few giraffe-like rhinos have been bigger than today's elephants. Within this range, though, what are the advantages and drawbacks of being any particular size?

THE SNAGS AND BONUSES OF BIG AND SMALL

On the face of things, it pays to be big. In general, large size means greater strength and – broadly speaking – more speed over the ground for creatures that need to run. Big predators can in theory catch a greater range of prey, while big prey can out-face a greater range of predators. Big males are more likely to defeat their rivals and win more mates. And, for thermodynamic reasons that are discussed below, big homoiothermic animals have a much lower metabolic rate than small homoiotherms, and pro-portionate to their weight they need much less food than do small creatures, or they can manage on food of much lower quality.

Yet there are snags. Large size may be a bonus in winning mates but taking the time to reach a large size can be risky: for example, male natterjack toads in Britain leave more offspring if they breed at two years old when they are small than they do if they wait another year until they are big, and risk dying along the way. Big homoiotherms do need proportionately less food than small ones, but in absolute terms they obviously need far more. Elephants eat thousands of times more than mice. Big carnivores can in theory catch a greater range of prey but it actually does not pay them to catch anything too small – so a tiger, like a weasel, generally finishes up catching things that are roughly its own size. In general, a whole range of niches that are open to small animals, from the canopy of forest to life underground, are closed to big ones. Worst of all perhaps in the long run is that within any given area populations of big animals are bound to be smaller than those of small ones, and this makes them vulnerable to extinction.

The advantages and disadvantages of smallness are simply the converse of the above. The biggest advantage for the small ani-mal is the number of niches available – the bark of trees, a crack between the rocks. A single haystack can contain a viable popu-lation of mice while viable numbers of elephants need a large county. The chief disadvantage for the small animal is its extremely high metabolic rate. Small homoiothermic animals such as shrews must eat every few hours or die and all small ani-mals need food of high quality and concentration: either insects or seeds (which are plant food at its most concentrated).

Having 'chosen' their size, however, big or small animals find

themselves subject to physical laws which shape their bodies and
their lives in particular ways.

LENGTH, VOLUME, AND SURFACE

Size is a matter of geometry and in particular of the relationship
between linear dimensions, volume, and surface area. If you double the linear dimensions of a flat plane then you increase its area
four times. If you double the linear dimensions of a solid body
(length, width, and height) then you increase its volume – and
therefore its mass – eight times. More generally, surface area
increases in proportion to the square of the linear dimension, so
a three-fold increase in height and width increases area nine
times. But volume increases in relation to the cube of linear
dimensions – so a three-fold increase in linear dimension gives a
27-fold increase in volume and hence in mass. Thus it is that a
fish one foot long may weigh a pound, which is big enough when
tailed and gutted to give the angler a pleasant tea. But a fish of the
same kind that is two feet long weighs eight pounds and can feed
the family for several days. A three-footer is a monster.

Because fish are supported by water they can increase their
length with impunity without altering their body shape. Water
can support an eight-pound body as easily as a one-pound one –
or indeed can support a whale of a hundred tonnes. But animals
on land have no such freedom. When an animal gets above a certain size – above that of a rabbit, say – the multiplication of
volume and mass that accompany even a modest increase in
height and length begin to make themselves felt. Body forms that
serve small animals perfectly are unacceptable in a big one.

It is for this reason that small mammals in general, whatever
their genetic provenance, conform to the 'generalised mammalian
form'. This is seen nowadays in the weasel and rat: long-bodied,
short-legged. The notable point, though, is not the shortness of
the legs but their attitude. Small mammals hold their legs bent: a
position that gives them permanent spring, the constantly coiled
potential to twist, turn, and take flight on the instant. High-class
squash players and young boxers similarly stand with bent legs, for
the same reason. Ageing pugilists stand straight-legged, hoping to
make up in 'ring-craft' what they no longer possess in strength.

Big animals, with their volumetric increase in weight, are obliged like ageing boxers to stand straight-legged. Above the size, say, of a coypu, land mammals have legs like stilts. So long as they remain middle-sized then the stilt-like legs can be relatively thin, as in a gazelle. But as linear dimensions increase further the proportions must change. Doubling height and length increases body weight eight-fold – but it increases the cross-sectional area of the limbs only four-fold. Tripling height and weight gives a 27-fold increase in weight but only a nine-fold increase in limb thickness. But limb thickness largely determines limb strength. Hence as linear dimensions and body mass increase the limbs must thicken disproportionately to keep up with the body mass. So gazelles may have needle-like legs but the related eland has legs like a bull, and elephants have legs like Doric pillars. Note, incidentally, that coypus have bent legs while domestic cats, which are no bigger than coypus, have legs like stilts. But then, evolutionarily speaking, coypus are big mice while cats are miniature lions.

From such general body forms further refinements follow. Thus very big animals must also have big heads – at least if they are homoiotherms, and need to eat a lot. Big head means big weight: the head of a white rhinoceros weighs as much as an entire Jersey cow. But again, head weight increases relative to the cube of linear dimension while the thickness – and hence the strength – of the neck increases relative only to the square. So a big animal with a big head cannot afford the sinuous neck of the weasel, even if it wanted such a thing. The simple solution is to settle for a short neck, like a modern rhino or an elephant.

But the short neck raises problems of feeding. If a rhino had long legs it could not reach the ground. Hence huge mammals often have short pillar legs to go with their short bullish necks. This produces a general body form that might for the sake of brevity be compared to a tank – and as we will see, the modern rhinos are only one of many mammalian lineages which, over time, have adopted the tank-like ecomorph. The 'small tank', with relatively thinner legs – effectively shaped like a Regency sideboard – is perhaps the commonest large mammalian ecomorph of all: seen in creatures as diverse as pigs, tapirs, oreodonts, and bears. When in doubt, natural selection has it, be a Regency sideboard.

Tank-like animals face problems of defence. Their feet must be planted four-square to the ground and their necks are short. Their heads, suspended at convenient predator height, seem terribly exposed. So it is that tank-like animals often have face-armour. The rhinos we know, and other armed leviathans we will look at later. The unarmoured state of the marsupial diprotodonts must have left them particularly vulnerable.

There are other ways out of tankish problems, however. One is to leave the neck short but extend the nose and upper lip to create a trunk: essentially a fifth limb that can provide dexterity in an *ad hoc* manner after the rest of the body has been converted into a kind of gun carriage. With a proboscis, tankish animals may grow tall – and trunk and height together bring the canopy into reach. This is the approach of the proboscideans, which include the elephants – but the elephant ecomorph has also been adopted by several long-gone non-proboscideans from South America, and it is at least possible that the proboscideans reinvented trunks more than once. An ancient proboscidean known as *Moeritherium* was nothing like as tall as the later elephants but had the beginnings of a trunk. Modern tapirs show the same trend – and so do black rhinos with their prehensile upper lips.

Another solution for big mammals, of course, is to produce a long neck and to hold it more or less upright like the Eiffel Tower – or, more accurately, like a flagpole – by supporting it with guys (tendons) firmly anchored to huge protrusions of the thoracic vertebrae. A long neck for a large mammal is clearly a big commitment but the Eiffel-Tower morph has been adopted nonetheless by many different creatures – camels, rhinos, and South American litopterns as well as giraffes.

Many middle-sized and large herbivorous mammals, particularly those that live in open country, need to be able to cover large distances, and since such rewarding prey inevitably attracts a suite of predators it often pays them to run at high speed. Hence many have adopted the 'cursorial' mode. The relevant physics here has to do with centrifugal forces and momentum. Animals have legs rather than wheels and as they run they need to reverse the direction in which the leg moves: power stroke backwards, recovery stroke forwards. If the feet and forelimbs were heavy the change of direction to begin the recovery stroke would render them unstable, or at least waste energy. In practice, then, in

cursorial herbivores the bones that are furthest from the body –
equivalent to human forearms, hands, and fingers – are elongated.
The accompanying muscle is reduced to a minimum and the
muscles that move the limb, on the upper-arm, thighs, and buttocks, are packed as closely to the body as possible. Thus the
weight, primarily that of the driving muscles, is as close to the
body as possible. Again the compact, light-limbed cursorial form
has been reinvented many times: by deer, antelope, the antilocaprids, the protoceratids, some ancient rhinos, and of course by
horses which, with their mighty buttocks and ultra-reduced feet,
show the form to perfection.

Small animals, as already outlined, tend to be much of a muchness. The mammals of the Mesozoic must have been extremely
varied genetically – which presumably is one reason why they
were able to diversify so rapidly and dramatically once the
dinosaurs left them to it – but in general shape they all looked
much like modern tree-shrews which, broadly speaking, resemble
large mice (although they are quite unrelated to mice, and may be
more closely related to primates than to shrews). Nonetheless, the
huge strength—weight ratio of small animals gives them latitude
for experiment which is denied to the bigger ones. Thus a range
of small mammals have rediscovered the ecomorph of the glider,
culminating in the powered flight of the bats: and it may be that
the microbats (such as pipistrelles and vampires) are unrelated to
the megabats (such as fruit bats) which would mean that mammals
invented powered flight more than once.

In general, if you want to be big you really do have to make
concessions, which in rhinos include keeping all four feet on the
ground most of the time and in horses include the loss of four toes
from the primitive pentadactyl limb (which mammals originally
shared with all the other tetrapods, right back to the amphibians).
Little animals by comparison are 'over-engineered'. Relative to
their body weight they have strength to burn. Crucially, they
have been free to retain the standard five-toed limb, for they did
not need to evolve feet like pegs or plinths that could withstand
huge forces. And of course there was one particular group of
small mammals which simply made a virtue of its generality:
abandoning few or none of the primitive features but simply
building upon them. These small generalised mammals bit by
bit produced a form whose five-fingered limbs could grip – a

creature that exploited its smallness to explore the trees, particularly the angiospermous trees which came into prominence in the
Cretaceous. These small generalists, which eschewed the dramatic
solutions of the big and diverse ground-dwellers, became the primates. Some of those primates did grow bigger later, and
invented a range of quite new ecomorphs – including the brachiating apes (that is, creatures that progress by swinging arm over
arm, as exemplified by modern gibbons). The brachiating apes in
turn produced the only truly convincing bipeds that the mammals
have yet provided, which is the family Hominidae.

But we will come to this. For now we should look at the other
great ramification of body size: metabolic rate. As a generalisation
it is supremely relevant. In the context of the steadily cooling
Cenozoic, which in the Miocene caused huge areas of forest to
give way to grassland, it is crucial.

METABOLIC RATE AND THE PARTICULAR RELEVANCE OF GRASS

The basic issue here is again the relationship between linear
dimension, surface area, and volume. Homoiothermic animals
such as birds and mammals generate body warmth for the sake of
it – burning energy for no other purpose but to provide heat.
Poikilotherms such as fish and reptiles also generate body heat but
only as a side-product of muscular activity. That, at least, is a reasonable working generalisation. In either case the amount of heat
generated is related to the volume of the animal: more flesh can
generate more heat. But the amount of heat *lost* is related to the
surface area. Body volume increases to a much greater extent relative to linear dimensions than does surface area. So small animals
have a relatively high ratio of surface area to body volume, and
big animals have a very low ratio of surface area to body volume.
It follows that little animals cool down much more easily than big
ones. It is also the case, of course, that the centre of a mouse is far
nearer to the surface than the centre of an elephant. All this, of
course, everyone knows instinctively: tiny cups of social coffee
cool down far quicker than big working mugs.

For small poikilotherms, the relatively high surface area can
work to advantage. A lizard well-placed in the sun can heat up in
seconds. But for small homoiotherms, seeking to retain a body

temperature above the ambient, the high surface area is a night-mare. They need to generate huge amounts of heat relative to their body weight. To do this, they need an extremely high meta-bolic rate. Indeed the metabolic rate of a mouse is about a thousand times greater than that of an elephant. Dr Michael Brambell, director of Chester Zoo in the north of England, cal-culates that if an elephant had the metabolic rate of a mouse then you could fry an egg on its back.

Because small homoiotherms need to generate so much heat, they need to eat high-energy food. Thus they eat insects or worms, as insectivores do, or seeds, as small rodents typically do. If they ate low-energy foods, they simply could not consume or process enough in a day to keep themselves going. It happens to be the case, however, that the most abundant food by far on land is the green leaf. It also happens to be the case that green leaves, which in general are watery and shot through with fibre, contain very little energy relative to their bulk.

Hence in homoiothermic herbivores we see a very clear eco-logical cut-off between the small creatures and the large ones. The small ones cannot subsist on leaves, and the large ones can. The smallest specialist leaf-eating mammals are rabbits. The small-est specialist leaf-eating birds are grouse, which eat the young leaves of heather. Smaller mammals and birds will of course eat some leaves but if they tried to subsist on them they would starve.

Creatures bigger than a rabbit, then, have access to the great-est and most ubiquitous food source of all: the green leaf. We have already noted some of the benefits of being large. But for a homoiothermic herbivore, the ability to make use of the greatest of all terrestrial bonanzas is surely the most important. The poten-tial rewards for large mammalian herbivores are huge. And, of course, where there are large herbivores there is likely to emerge a commensurate suite of large predators.

But subsistence on leaves is not straightforward. The point is not simply that the ratio of energy to bulk is low. Equally trou-blesome is that most of the energy in leaves is in the form of fibre, the most common component of which is cellulose. But no ani-mal is known to produce enzymes that are able to digest cellulose. Rumours that snails can do so seem to have been exaggerated. In general, animals that aspire to digest cellulose and hence to release the energy that it contains must employ the services of bacteria and other microbes which live in their guts and do the digesting for them.

Thus it is that mammals that contrive to subsist on leaves fall into three broad categories. First there is the giant panda, a formerly carnivorous bear which has evolved to live mainly on bamboo but, perversely, still has the small gut of a carnivore and retains no worthwhile colonies of gut microbes and therefore cannot digest cellulose and therefore has to make do on the sugar in the bamboo leaves and therefore has virtually no energy to spare and hence is among the most spectacularly lethargic of all mammals.

The second and third categories are the *bona fide* leaf-eaters that do retain microbes in their guts to break down cellulose. The more obvious strategy, adopted by a wide range of lineage, is to house these microbes in the hindgut: either in the colon or in a diverticulum at the start of the colon known as the caecum. Elephants are hindgut digesters. So too are rabbits, koalas, and all the perissodactyls, such as the rhinos and horses.

The last possibility is to retain the digestive microbes high up the gut – in fact in a modified stomach. Such 'foregut digestion' is a harder trick to pull evolutionarily (not least because conditions in most animals' foreguts do not generally favour bacteria) but mammals have nonetheless achieved it several times. Kangaroos are foregut digesters, with stomachs modified to contain appropriate microbes. But the best-known and ecologically most influential foregut digesters are among the artiodactyls. The camels and their relatives use a form of foregut digestion. So too do the ruminants, which have evolved a stomach with four chambers, one of which – the rumen – is a huge fermenting vat, an *in situ* compost heap. Rumination has proved the most successful mechanism for digesting herbage. Two families of ruminants in particular – the bovids (antelope, cattle, sheep and goats) and the cervids (deer) – have become the most diverse and widespread large mammals on Earth.

In general, foregut digestion is somewhat more efficient than hindgut digestion. The basic reason is simple: in foregut digestion the nutrients that are released from the cellulose then have to pass through the small intestine, where there is plenty of opportunity for further digestion and absorption. Hindgut digesters have already by-passed the small intestine by the time the cellulose is broken down. Rabbits overcome this problem by eating their own droppings, and giving the semi-digested vegetation a re-run. The droppings of horses are similarly nutrient-rich, but horses leave them for others to consume. Jonathan Swift was notoriously coprophobic and in *Gulliver's Travels* he elevated horses – 'Houyhnhnms' – to the highest status precisely because their droppings are inoffensive. Compared with most, they have suffered little decay.

In general, too, as we have seen, big homoiothermic animals are more efficient than small ones: that is, they need less food per unit of body weight. Big hindgut digesters can therefore compete well enough with big foregut digesters, but in the middle-sized range the foregut digesters have the edge. In the modern world we find that the biggest mammalian herbivores of all are in fact hindgut digesters – the elephants, rhinos, hippos, and horses. Yet I can think of no living ungulate hindgut digester that is smaller than a tapir, which even in its smallest wild forms is a big animal. On the other hand there is a huge range of small to middle-sized ruminants, including most of the antelope, sheep, goats and deer. And then there is a range of small hindgut digesters, including the koala whose remarkable caecum and equally accommodating liver enable it to cope with the abundant but uncompromisingly vicious leaves of eucalyptus, shot through as they are with fibre and toxic oils.

Crucially, there is a hierarchy of digestibility among leaves. Roughly this corresponds to the difference between grass and the leaves that grow on trees and shrubs. Animals that eat the latter are 'browsers', while grass-eaters are 'grazers'. In general, in the wild, good browse is the most nutritious; specialist browsers such as giraffes do extremely well on the tender leaves of acacia. Wild grass tends to be viciously fibrous, and indeed contains spicules of silica like needles of glass, but it has become awfully abundant, and where it grows it is easy to consume. Hence there is a classic contrast between the pernickety gourmet browsers, such as giraffes, and the mass gourmandisers of grass, epitomised by the barrel-bodied horses and the grazing ruminants, especially cattle, sheep, and a range of big antelopes such as eland and wildebeest.

As we saw in Chapter 2, the world has cooled throughout the Cenozoic as the Himalayas rose and leached the carbon dioxide from the atmosphere. The cooling happened in jerks – and even when the cooling was steady the vegetation responded in jerks as successive suites of plants were pushed beyond their thresholds of tolerance. The Miocene was the watershed, as the warm wet forest of the early Cenozoic gave way, over huge and rapidly increasing areas, to cool dry grassland. This was when the grazers truly took over from the browsers; the ruminants of various sizes and the big grazing perissodactyls came into their own, and the browsing forest generalists went into relative decline. Our own family, the Hominidae, entered this newly grass-covered world in the late Miocene although it did take them several million years to graduate from forest, through open woodland, into truly open country.

Being a grazer on the ever-more extensive open plain carries further implications. In such spaces it helps to be able to cover large areas, and to do so quickly, especially when harassed by the specialist predators that evolved alongside. Hence the cursorial mode evolved. Food is abundant but the dangers are great – and both are factors that favour sociability. So the grazers of the plains typically roam in herds while their forest relatives, including roe deer and duikers, are often solitary or move in small groups. Thus there is a chain of consequence: global cooling leads to grass and open space, and grass and open space favours the sociable grazers such as the bovids, deer, and the big cursorial perissodactyls, the horses. That is how the world is at the moment.

So much for the ground rules of the game: the nature of the world stage, and the ecomorphic roles that the animals play upon that stage. It is time to look briefly at the players themselves.

A LIGHTNING SKETCH OF OUR FELLOW MAMMALS

Figure IV.2 is a list of the main mammalian groups from the time of their origins in the Triassic, but in particular as they have unfolded since the Cretaceous. Earlier versions of this book now mouldering in my files contain accounts of all of them; but even the broad-brushed versions, taken order-by-order, were almost as long as this entire book is supposed to be. There are just so many of them.

So the following account is highly selective. It omits all creatures that live in the sea, from seals to whales, and gives extremely

Figure IV.2: A Simplified Classification of the Mammals   ⋆ = extinct

	infraclass	cohort	superorder	order	suborder	family

CLASS:
MAMMALIA
  SUBCLASS:
  PROTOTHERIA
 	
  SUBCLASS:
  THERIA
				MONOTREMATA (duck-billed platypus)		

	TRITUBERCULATA⋆			PANTOTHERIA⋆ (ancestors both of metatherians and of eutherians)		
	METATHERIA			MARSUPIALIA (the marsupials)		
					DIDELPHOIDEA	
						DIDELPHIDAE (American opossums)
						BORHYAENIDAE⋆ (borhyaenids)
						THYLACOSMILIDAE⋆ (sabretooth South American marsupials)
					DIPROTODONTA	
						THYLACOLEONIDAE⋆ (sabretooth 'marsupial lion')
						MACROPODIDAE (kangaroos)
						DIPROTODONTIDAE⋆ (diprotodonts)
						PALORCHESTIDAE⋆ (marsupial equivalent of giant sloths)
	EUTHERIA (commonly referred to as 'placental mammals')					
			EDENTATA (edentates)			
				XENARTHRA (armadillos, sloths, anteaters, glyptodonts)		
				PHOLIDOTA (pangolin)		
			EPITHERIA (includes most living mammals)			
				INSECTIVORA (insectivores: hedgehogs, shrews, moles)		
			GLIRES			
				LAGOMORPHA (rabbits, hares)		
				RODENTIA (mice, rats, squirrels, porcupines etc.)		
			ARCHONTA			
				DERMOPTERA ('flying lemurs' or colugos)		
				CHIROPTERA (bats)		
				PRIMATES		
					PROSIMII ('primitive' primates including lemurs and tarsiers)	

infraclass	cohort	superorder	order	suborder	family
				ANTHROPOIDEA	
					CEBIDAE (New World monkeys: woolly, spider etc.)
					CALLITRACHIDAE (New World monkeys: tamarins and marmosets)
					CERCOPITHECIDAE (Old World monkeys: vervets, baboons, macaques, etc.)
					HYLOBATIDAE (gibbons)
					PONGIDAE (chimps, gorillas, orangs)
					HOMINIDAE (humans, australopithecines)
		FERAE			
			CREODONTA* (creodonts)		
			CARNIVORA ('true' carnivores)		
				FISSIPEDA: MIACOIDEA* (the earliest true carnivores)	
				FISSIPEDA: FELOIDEA (cat-like carnivores)	
					VIVERRIDAE (civets)
					HYAENIDAE (hyaenas)
					FELIDAE (cats)
				FISSIPEDA: CANOIDEA (dog-like carnivores)	
					MUSTELIDAE (weasels, otters, badgers)
					CANIDAE (dogs)
					PROCYONIDAE (raccoons)
					AMPHICYONIDAE* ('bear-dogs')
					URSIDAE (bears)
				PINNIPEDIA (seals, sealions, walruses)	
		UNGULATA (hoofed animals)			
			ARCTOCYONIA* (very primitive ungulates: 'condylarths')		
			DINOCERATA* (uintatheres)		
			EMBRITHOPODA* (arsinoitheres)		
			ARTIODACTYLA (even-toed ungulates)		
				SUINA	
					SUIDAE (pigs)
					TAYASSUIDAE (peccaries)
					HIPPOPOTAMIDAE (hippos)
				TYLOPODA (tylopods)	
					MERYCOIDODONTIDAE* (oreodonts)

infraorder	cohort	superorder	order	suborder	family
					PROTOCERATIDAE* (protoceratids)
					CAMELIDAE (camels, llamas)
				RUMINANTIA (ruminants)	
					TRAGULIDAE (chevrotains)
					MOSCHIDAE (musk deer)
					CERVIDAE (deer)
					GIRAFFIDAE (giraffes)
					ANTILOCAPRIDAE (pronghorns)
					BOVIDAE (cattle, antelope, sheep, goats, goat-antelopes)
			ACREODI* (Andrewsarchus)		
			CETACEA (whales and porpoises)		
			PERISSODACTYLA ('odd-toed' ungulates)		
				CERATOMORPHA	
					RHINOCEROTIDAE (modern rhinos)
				ANCYLOPODA* (chalicotheres)	
				HIPPOMORPHA	
					PALAEOTHERIIDAE* (palaeotheres)
					EQUIDAE (horses)
					BRONTOTHERIIDAE* (brontotheres)
			HYRACOIDEA (hyraxes)		
		MERIDIUNGULATA* (South American ungulates)			
			LITOPTERNA* (litopterns)		
			NOTOUNGULATA* (notoungulates)		
			ASTRAPOTHERIA* (astrapotheres)		
			PYROTHERIA* (pyrotheres)		
		TETHYTHERIA			
			PROBOSCIDEA		
				MOERITHERIOIDEA* (Moeritherium)	
				DEINOTHERIOIDEA* (deinotheres)	
				ELEPHANTOIDEA	
					GOMPHOTHERIIDAE* (gomphotheres)
					MAMMUTIDAE* (mastodonts)
					ELEPHANTIDAE (true elephants, including mammoths)
			SIRENIA (dugong and manatees)		
			DESMOSTYLIA* (desmostylians)		

short shrift to the rodents and bats, even though they are of enormous ecological importance and between them include about half of all species of living mammals. In fact it focuses upon the large terrestrial mammals which shared our history and have helped to shape our evolution and our ecology. They in the main are the marsupials and xenarthrans (the edentates); the hoofed mammals that are broadly categorised as 'ungulates'; the carnivores; and our own group, the primates.

But peruse Figure IV.2 if you would and note the broad relationships between the groups. It is not really surprising that the various ungulate orders should be distantly related to each other: that is, that the extinct meridiungulates from South America should have shared a common ancestor both with the perissodactyls (such as horses and rhinos) and with the artiodactyls (such as cattle, deer, and camels), and indeed with the proboscideans who nowadays manifest as elephants. The probable relationship between proboscideans and sirenians, which now include dugongs and manatees, is somewhat more unexpected. It is positively intriguing that somewhere back in the Cretaceous all these various ungulate or quasi-ungulate groups apparently shared an ancestor with the cetaceans – the whales and porpoises. It is a real surprise to find, as anatomists and palaeontologists have done, that the ungulates and cetaceans in turn show many similarities with the carnivores. In the same way, our own group, the primates, show obvious similarities both with the insectivores and with the bats. The point, though, is the one discussed in Chapter 3: that evolution is opportunist, and must begin each new radically different group – species, family, order – with a probably somewhat eccentric representative of whatever animals are there already. Thus herbivore can give rise to carnivore and vice versa, and unless the organs (or even the underlying genes) are irretrievably lost then hoof may become claw and claw may become hoof. Evolution ducks and weaves.

In the sketch of our fellow mammals that follows I would ask you to note six points in particular. First, there are broadly different ways of being a mammal. Cats, horses, and human beings are variations on a single theme – but the platypuses, marsupials, and creatures such as the armadillo demonstrate that creatures very different from ourselves also belong in the class of mammaldom.

Second, and most intriguingly, see how every different lineage has striven in its time to do many different things, and explored many different ecomorphs – and that most ecomorphs have in their time been enacted by many different lineages. Many different creatures have been tanks like the modern rhinos. Many have been giraffe-like. Several quite unrelated groups have adopted the mode of the proboscidean. This radiation of lineages and swapping of roles is an important feature of what Elisabeth Vrba called the 'dance through time'.

Third, note the way that some 'conservative' groups sometimes give rise to groups that become highly 'adventurous' – and vice versa: some groups that begin by being highly varied finally produce just one or a few lines that really take off. Thus the conservative tapirs produced the adventurous rhinos, and our own pre-hominid ancestor produced both the conservative chimps and the highly variable hominids. But, then, out of the adventurous rhinos only one group – the tank-like rhinoceratids – came through. And the only hominid to emerge from the array is ourselves.

The fourth striking theme is the change of fortunes: how some families or even entire orders have disappeared altogether, for example the unitatheres and the chalicotheres, the oreodonts and the protoceratids, the creodonts and the nimravids, the diprotodonts and the borhyaenids, and all the vast array of South American meridiungulates. Note, correspondingly, how many modern groups are sadly depleted from former days, for instance the perissodactyls and the proboscideans. And note finally that you cannot tell at any one time which will succeed at later times. Those piggy relatives of the camels, the oreodonts, were the dominant herbivores in North America for tens of millions of years and now they are gone completely. On the other hand the bovids (antelope, cattle, sheep, and goats) have triumphed in the past few million years as, of course, has the genus *Homo*. But fortunes change. The point is salutary.

Fifth, note how mobile the various creatures have been: that many groups have bestridden the entire globe (though usually missing out on Australia) and that where an animal lives today often bears no relationship at all to its place of origin or to its previous excursions. This restless globetrotting is the second aspect of the 'dance through time'.

Finally we may perceive the host of fine creatures which are now long gone yet survived until the emergence of *Homo*, and indeed of our own species *Homo sapiens*. In later chapters I discuss whether this is simply coincidence or whether, in fact, our own ancestors pushed those animals into oblivion.

Let us begin our survey, then.

AN OVERVIEW OF THE MAMMALS

The great class of mammals is divided broadly into two – two quite different ways of being: a primary division that must have taken place in the Jurassic, when the dinosaurs were at their height. The group that have come through, and dominate, are the Theria, which nourish their unborn offspring in the womb via a placenta. The other group, the Prototheria, lay eggs. The only prototherians that remain today are the monotremes – and there are only six species of them: the duck-billed platypus of Australia and five echidnas from Australia and New Guinea. But the prototherians were ecologically significant in the distant past and more recently there lived a platypus as big as a sheep. Now the monotremes remind us that mammals did indeed evolve from reptiles and show what the half-way stage might have been like: for they suckle their young in true mammalian fashion but the laying of eggs is truly reptilian.

The therians in their turn are divided into three groups of which one (the Trituberculata) is extinct and is simply the ancestor of the other two. The two surviving groups are the Metatheria, alias the marsupials, and the Eutheria, which contains all the rest – whales, bats, horses, dogs, rhinos, cats, us, lemurs, mice, armadillos, and what you will. These two great groups probably divided from each other in the early Cretaceous, perhaps as long as 120 million years ago. So we see again that the ecological 'Age of Reptiles' was also the age in which the mammals laid out their own ground-rules.

ALTERNATIVE MAMMALS: THE MARSUPIALS

Ecologically, these days, the marsupials are the lesser group, confined to Australia and New Guinea, and South America, with a few errant types (the opossums) in North America. They live in New Zealand (possums and wallabies) only as introductions, imported by Europeans. But the marsupials seem to have arisen in North America – or that, at least, is where the oldest fossils are – and spread by routes that are not altogether clear but presumably involved a trip through Eurasia into Gondwana, when Australia was still a part of it. There are fossil marsupials in Europe and Africa and one bonus of the possible greenhouse effect will be to facilitate palaeontology in Antarctica which should reveal a great many more. It seems, though, that the principal home of present-day marsupials, Australia, is historically an outpost.

Marsupials have all too often been presented as also-rans. Nowadays many are taking a terrible bashing in Australia at the hands of introduced eutherians such as the cats and foxes which kill whole suites of the smaller ones or the water buffalo and sheep that transform entire landscapes; the South American types are supposed to have suffered at eutherian hands after the collision with North America in the Pliocene, which allowed the Great Interchange. But as we have seen, *any* kind of animal is liable to suffer when faced for the first time with a ready-made predator or competitor from another continent. In many instances marsupials do extremely well in competition with eutherians, as the opossums have done in North America, and as many Australian natives do today. Possums in Sydney and other cities are among the world's great feral animals, like the raccoons of North America and the foxes of urban Britain. I was once startled half to death by a possum that leapt from a dustbin outside the Sydney Opera House.

In fact, marsupials should be seen not as inferior mammals but as following an alternative way of being a mammal. Like the eutherian mammals, they do nourish their young briefly in the womb via a placenta and then suckle them with milk after birth. The key strategic difference between the two groups lies in the emphasis given to each stage. Thus for marsupials the phase *in utero* is cursory. The babies are born as virtual embryos and the burden of infant nutrition is taken by lactation – for which purpose they are generally cosseted in pouches. Eutherians generally split placental and lactational feeding more evenly, and give birth to more advanced babies (although some, for example those of bears, are remarkably tiny at birth). But in the extreme and unpredictable climate of Australia the emphasis on lactation brings great advantages, for if drought sets in then the joeys in the pouch simply die as the milk dries up and the mother can start again in better times. Eutherian embryos, on the other hand, often cling on like parasites and sometimes, if the bad times roll during pregnancy, both the mother and the foetus perish. The marsupial strategy is harsh, but realistic.

Marsupials may also seem somewhat limited in form – that is, in their range of ecomorphs – compared to eutherians. But that too is not quite fair. Although there are no marsupial whales or even giraffes or elephants and the gliders are not quite in the same league as the eutherian bats, when looked at over time the marsupials are far more various than is now apparent.

For example, present-day marsupials seem low on predators. But until the 1930s Australia had a dog-like marsupial: not the modern dingo, which is a true dog from Asia, but the Thylacine or Tasmanian 'wolf' *Thylacinus*. Thylacines are placed in the family Thylacinidae. At least five other families of marsupial have produced predators that between them have matched at least some of the eutherian otters, dogs, bears, and cats – so there is convergence both between marsupials and eutherians, and between different families of marsupial. South America was the home of the extremely varied family Borhyaenidae. One of them, *Borhyaena*, was bear-like and had flat, bearish feet – although it also oddly had a long heavy tail. It presumably hunted by ambush. Another borhyaenid, *Cladosictis*, was otter-like: from the late Oligocene to the early Miocene it must have dashed through the undergrowth after small mammals and reptiles and plunged in the rivers after fish. The marsupial yapok, *Chironectes*, of the opossum family Didelphidae, still lives an otter-like life in the Andes.

Two different marsupial families produced creatures the size of leopards or even bigger, that for all the world resembled sabre-tooth cats, or at least did the same job. The more cat-like were from the South American family Thylacosmilidae of which the best-known type is *Thylacosmilus*, which lived from the late Miocene to the early Pliocene. *Thylacosmilus* had lost its incisors and, as in sabretooth cats, its canine teeth formed long blade-like slashing teeth. Like the sabretooths, too, *Thylacosmilus* was robust and muscular – built for ambush and clinging. On its lower jaw it carried horny flanges that apparently protected the projecting sabres when not in use, like a sheath, and may also have served as permanent sharpeners. In contrast to the sabretooths, the canine teeth of *Thylacosmilus* grew continuously like the incisors of rodents (a fact that can be inferred from the structure of the roots, which remains 'open' in teeth that continue to grow but is closed in those which, like the teeth of humans, reach their allotted size and then stop).

Thylacoleo of Australia, in the family Thylacoleonidae, shows a quite different approach to the sabretooth genre. It, too, was leopard-sized. But unlike *Thylacosmilus* or the cats its sabres were formed from its incisor teeth. Peculiarly, too, it had huge thumbs that bore commensurately enormous claws. Presumably it used these to grip its prey – kangaroos? diprotodonts? – as it brought its killing incisors into play. The nearest living relatives of *Thylacoleo* are the modest phalangers. *Thylacoleo* itself died out only at the end of the Pleistocene, about ten thousand years ago. Perhaps it was helped to extinction by the first aborigines.

The marsupials have also invented an ecomorph: that of the Macropodidae or kangaroos – for although the eutherians include some small bipedal hoppers there are no big ones. Macropods probably evolved their bounce in Australian tropical forests where they needed to negotiate the tangled undergrowth. Such forests are now largely confined to Queensland but in the past, as the world's climate shifted and Australia changed latitude, they have raced in a body over almost the entire continent. 'Raced' is hardly an exaggeration, for the great forests of Queensland have probably not been in the present location for more than 8,000 years (and neither, for that matter, has that ecological miracle the Great Barrier Reef, for it is a post-ice age phenomenon). Today the red and the great grey kangaroos of the genus *Macropus* are the biggest macropods but there were giants in the past including *Procoptodon* of the Pleistocene which stood three metres tall – an astonishing 10 foot. *Procoptodon* had a short face like a rabbit but also extraordinarily large hind feet, each of which, as in ostriches, had only one functional toe (the fourth).

Until recently, too – the latest types may have been contemporaries of the first aborigines – Australia harboured a suite of giant wombat-like creatures (although they are not closely related to wombats!) of which at least one, within the genus *Diprotodon*, had the size and form of a modern rhino. Australian children are brought up with the legend of the bunyip: a large but amiable and mournful beast that is supposed to roam the outback – the equivalent of the Tibetan's yeti and the Loch Ness monster of Scotland. But the bunyip may not be a fable at all. It may be a true folk memory of *Diprotodon*, transmitted generation to generation by the aborigines. *Diprotodon* died out only a few thousand years ago and folk-tales can last easily as long as that. Other marsupials have resembled mice and gerbils, many were like raccoons, and several marsupial families produced members that are, or were, very like European moles. The whole order today includes 282 species but over time there can hardly have been fewer than 30,000, and probably there were many more. Among the many extraordinary creatures that remain are the koala, kangaroo, yapok, wombat, quoll, and opossum, but the world has clearly lost some magnificent representatives – including many in human times.

Marvellous though the marsupials are, however, it has to be admitted that the eutherians are even more various, although the present types are only an arbitrary sample of what has gone before. Note, first, from Figure IV.2, that the eutherians are further subdivided into two main groups: the xenarthrans, or edentates, now sadly reduced to tree sloths, armadillos, and anteaters; and the epitherians, which include horses, bears, whales and the rest. The edentates, like the marsupials, have had a much more glorious past than is apparent now – and, like the largest marsupials, the later ones encountered our own ancestors and suffered at their hands.

THE EDENTATES

The edentates are tremendously diverse. The living types are the tree sloths, armadillos, and anteaters, dumped together in the single order 'Xenarthra', with the pangolins in their own order, the Pholidota. 'Xenarthra' means 'foreign joint'. All other mammals, from giraffes to pipistrelles, have a statutory seven vertebrae in the neck but the xenarthrans have one or more extra ones. No one knows whether the edentates are really a single lineage, a true 'clade' (see Figure IV.1), or whether they represent several different major subdivisions of mammal that have nothing much in common except their unlikeness to epitherians.

But it is clear that they are sadly faded compared to former glories. The xenarthrans evolved in South America, apparently in the Palaeocene, and several of them successfully invaded the north when the Panama bridge was established in the Pliocene. The living edentates are all fairly small – none larger than an anteater – but there are two major extinct groups which included some giants. The first of these are the giant sloths, which first appeared in South America in the Oligocene. Giant sloths are also known as 'ground sloths' and artists commonly depict them standing on their hind feet like kangaroos and slashing at the vegetation. However, their hind legs are stumpy and bent and equipped with huge claws, and seem most unsuited to standing or walking. I suggest, therefore, that giant sloths were in fact arboreal, just like their extant relatives, and that they used their hind legs and claws as grappling hooks. The only reason for doubting this is that giant sloths were so large. But so are grizzly bears, which are excellent climbers – and there are plenty of enormous trees in the Americas. In fact, the traditional scenario that places giant sloths on the ground seems to me to make no sense at all.

Oddly, the diminutive tree sloths which are still with us today were apparently the *ancestors* of the giant sloths, and have outlived their more adventurous scions. Yet for 30 million years or so giant sloths were highly successful. They did well in North America after the North met the South. They abounded in Florida and their fossils are found well up into California. In both continents they died out only after human beings arrived – possibly they too were victims of the new invaders. Nearly fifty different genera are known which means that over time there must have been scores of species and as the epochs passed some types grew bigger and bigger. Biggest of all was *Megatherium* from Pleistocene Patagonia, Bolivia, and Peru which was six metres long including the tail which it presumably used as a prop while it fed. *Megatherium* must have weighed three tonnes – as much as a fair-sized Asian elephant.

Another giant, *Neomylodon*, survived almost until the present day and samples of its skin can still be found. The skin, too, is uniquely edentate, for beneath the shaggy hair it is studded with plaques of bone. So as if they were not formidable enough, with their massive arms and slashing claws, giant sloths also wore a kind of chain-mail.

Indeed edentates more than any other mammal have had a taste for armour. The armadillos still have, of course, though none today can compare with some of their giant forebears from the Pleistocene. Most armoured of all, however, were armadillo relatives known as the glyptodonts which flourished in South America from the early Miocene, about 20 million years ago. Like the giant sloths, the glyptodonts are known to have produced some fifty genera.

The glyptodonts were the mammals' answer to the giant tortoise. Like giant tortoises they probably lived in semi-desert and so were obliged to graze in extremely open territory. Thus they needed protection against predators for which, otherwise, they were sitting ducks. After all, the only other strategies for desert herbivores are to run away like antelopes, or duck beneath the surface like ground squirrels, or hide and hope the danger will pass, like baby plovers. But for an armadillo relative, these are not options. Presumably – like modern edentates – glyptodonts would have allowed their body temperatures to fluctuate more than somewhat, which would have helped them in a poor, desert economy.

The biggest glyptodont of all was *Glyptodon* which grazed on the plains of Argentina in the Pleistocene and was 1·5 metres tall and 3·3 metres long. Its huge globular 'shell' was fashioned from a mosaic of bony plaques like a golf-ball. Glyptodonts also had a powerful armoured tail which, at least in *Doedicurus* from Pleistocene Patagonia, was whimsically tipped with a ball of spikes like a mediaeval fighting mace. The last glyptodonts died out only 15,000 years ago and they feature in the legends of Patagonian Indians just as diprotodonts seem to have been remembered in the folk history of Australian aborigines. So here are yet more creatures (to add to the diprotodonts, giant kangaroos, and giant sloths) that could have been victims of our own ancestors.

But the bulk of modern mammals are epitherians. These are hugely diverse and the following account is egregiously curtailed. In fact I can deal with only three main groups: the ungulates, the carnivores, and the primates.

THE UNGULATES

Three main groups of 'ungulates' prevail today: the perissodactyls which carry their weight on their middle toes, such as horses, rhinos, and tapirs; the artiodactyls, including the pigs, hippos, camels, and ruminants, which bear their weight equally on third and fourth toes (and hence are 'cloven-hoofed'); and the proboscideans, represented by the elephants. But over time there have been at least sixteen separate orders of hoofed mammals which thereby qualified as 'ungulates'. All of them are vaguely related yet they are distinct enough to be hived into three huge superorders (as shown in Figure IV.2). Those superorders also include some creatures that have lost their hooves or even their feet altogether – such as the sirenians and the whales, and the long-gone, bottle-bodied, maritime desmostylians. The ungulates are also related, distantly but unmistakably, to the carnivores. Some of the earliest ancestral types – such as the huge and irredeemably hideous *Andrewsarchus* with its vast head and crocodile jaws – were probably meat-eaters and scavengers, and yet had hooves. *Andrewsarchus* has from time to time been shuffled from order to order.

Between them the ungulates have explored an enormous range of ecomorphs, most of which still have their representatives: rhinos show us what it is to be a tank, tapirs, pigs, cattle and sheep are standard sideboards, many quite different living ungulates are cursorial, while giraffes, camels, and elephants demonstrate a further range of big, specialist forms. For good measure, the tiny hooved hyraxes which in the Bible are called 'cavies', and indeed resemble big guinea-pigs, are ungulates too: perhaps related to perissodactyls as Richard Owen suggested in the nineteenth century, but perhaps more closely akin to elephants, as some have suggested since. Hyraxes were not always as small as they are now, for they had pig-sized relatives in the past that were far more obviously ungulate. The ungulates have also lost one complete morph: that of the chalicotheres. They were big perissodactyls with appropriately horse-like heads but they apparently stood on their hind legs like giant sloths and hacked at the vegetation with huge claws that were uniquely bifurcated, each one resembling a toasting fork. One of the South American ungulates, *Homalodotherium*, was also giant-sloth-shaped. It seems odd that a form that was so clearly favoured – it was adopted by at least three unrelated groups and was highly successful for millions of years – is no longer represented at all.

Overall, the living and extinct ungulates demonstrate beautifully the principal themes of this chapter: that any one lineage may adopt many morphs; that any one ecomorph may be explored by many different lineages, which arrive at the same conclusions via quite different genetic routes; that there are spectacular changes of fortune, so the triumphs of today may be the disasters of tomorrow; and that any one lineage may, over time, race over the surface of the globe so that where it lives today may bear no relation to its origins or previous peregrinations. Ungulates indeed may be more mobile than most because, after all, mobility is one of their specialities. Finally, we may note that many extinct ungulates were clearly flourishing until they confronted our own ancestors.

There are too many groups to treat one by one. Instead I shall just pick a few ecomorphs and lineages that illustrate the themes. First – a common ecomorph.

A PLETHORA OF TANKS

The tanks we know today, *par excellence*, are the remaining five species of rhino; but in their time at least half a dozen orders of ungulate, plus some marsupials, have essayed the tankish form.

The earliest ungulate tanks of all were the uintatheres, such as the late Eocene *Eobasileus* from North America which stood 1·5 metres at the shoulder and was three metres long and massive with it. On its head *Eobasileus* carried six bony protrusions like the knobbly 'ossicones' that nowadays adorn the heads of giraffes – two on the nose, two between the eyes, and two high on the forehead. In its upper jaw it bore dagger-like canine teeth, proving (as do gorillas, pigs, Indian rhinoceroses, and primitive deer) that carnivores have no monopoly on big canines. But the arsinoitheres were even bigger – for instance *Arsinoitherium* of early Oligocene Africa. They too were very rhino-like, carrying massive twinned horns side by side on their noses. But rhino horn is made from keratin, the hard protein produced in the skin that is also the stuff of nails and hooves. Arsinoithere horns were hollow bone. Like uintatheres, arsinoitheres bore a pair of ossicones high on their heads.

Then there were two groups of perissodactyls which were more closely related to horses than to rhinos – and yet were more rhino-like in form. First there were the brontotheres, such as *Brontops* of the lower Oligocene which stood 2·5 metres high and again had protective and aggressive horns on its head. Then there were various members of the palaeotheres which achieved extraordinary variety in their briefish run in the Eocene and early Oligocene, and included some forms that were horse-like, some tapir-like, and some that were tankish. Thus there have been close relatives of the horse that were very like modern rhinos, and some ancient rhinos that were like horses, while (less surprisingly) both horse-relatives and rhinos have produced more generalised, tapir-like forms. There have also been several tanks among the South American ungulates – including the stocky *Toxodon* which was nearly three metres long. Toxodon survived until the Pleistocene, and may have fallen foul of the first human invaders.

Finally, the marsupial diprotodonts of Australia were three metres long and also robust. They survived for 10–15,000 years after the first people arrived in Australia. Whether those aborigines finally saw them off remains debatable – but the rapid decline of the modern rhinos shows how easily such big animals can be pushed aside when the pressure is on.

Taller creatures with big noses to compensate may be seen as variations on a tank.

ELEPHANTS AND ELEPHANT LOOK-ALIKES

Elephants belong to the order Proboscidea which of course takes its name from the nose. Now it is reduced to just two closely related species in two genera – the Asian elephant *Elephas* and the African *Loxodonta* – but since the order's first appearance in the Eocene it has embraced at least 160 species in forty-four genera and perhaps many more. Furthermore, the elephants represent only one proboscidean suborder out of three.

The oldest proboscideans are the moeritheres which arose in the Eocene as pig-like creatures in northern India. They are probably ancestral to the other proboscideans although the best-known genus, the tapir-like *Moeritherium* which occupied Egypt in the Eocene and early Oligocene, lived alongside modern-looking elephants in Africa for several millions of years and so it cannot be their ancestor.

Then there are the curious and wonderful deinotheres (such as *Deinotherium*) which appeared in the early Miocene and died out towards the end of the Pliocene after a successful run in which they remained almost unchanged for 20 million years. In general form they resembled modern elephants – except for their extraordinary tusks, which were only in the lower jaw and pointed downwards rather than forwards or upwards. Perhaps the deinotheres used them for digging or for stripping bark.

But the ultimately successful group, which in their time have spanned all continents except Australia and have had a huge ecological impact from the Arctic to the tropics, are the suborder known as Elephantoidea. Both the living genera belong to just one elephantoid family, the Elephantidae, but there are two extinct families that in their time were of huge ecological significance. The oldest and most curious are the Gomphotheriidae. Some of the gomphotheres resemble modern elephants in general body form, and even in their heads, but some of the earlier types had long lower jaws which contained tusks just as the upper jaws did – so their heads were long like an anteater's but bristled with protruding teeth. In yet other types known as the amebelodonts the lower tusks became broad and flattened, thus forming the whole lower jaw into a giant shovel, presumably for rooting out aquatic vegetation. Gomphotheres reached North America via Beringia and then pressed on into South America when the opportunity arose in the Pliocene.

The second elephantoid family are confusingly called the Mammutidae – confusingly, because the name sounds like 'mammoth' but in fact refers to the mastodonts. Again they are very elephant-like in general form but their grinding teeth are quite different in structure. Mastodonts also reached South America via North America and some biologists have claimed that the genus *Cuvieronius* survived there until several centuries after Christ. The claim is highly contentious, however.

The last of the three elephantoid families, the Elephantidae, have huge grinding teeth which are unique among mammals. There have been scores of species and subspecies of all shapes and sizes, some very hairy like the mammoths and some almost naked like the modern types; some with curly tusks (including the mammoths), others with tusks that were ramrod-straight (the 'straight-tusked elephants'), and some with tusks even bigger than the modern African elephants'.

But, in addition, elephants have shown a remarkable propensity for miniaturisation. The problem is the one we have met both in this chapter and the last: big homoiotherms need an enormous amount of food – enough not simply for individuals but to sustain entire populations. Big mammals cannot survive on small islands in viable numbers and if they are to survive at all then they must produce diminutive races which, with time, may become distinct species. In the last chapter we met the dwarf red deer of Jersey. Cyprus and other islands of the Mediterranean harboured dwarf hippos until well into human times. But dwarf elephants are known from islands worldwide. They have been found on islands off California. Some of the most extreme types came from the Mediterranean: *Elephas falconeri* from Crete, Malta, Sicily and Cyprus was less than a metre high. On Wrangel Island to the north of Siberia dwarf mammoths apparently survived until the time of the Pharaohs. Indeed, a painting in one of the Pharaohs' tombs shows a brown bear and a mysterious elephant which is no bigger than a sheep but has well-developed tusks and so is clearly adult. Its tusks are curled, its head is domed, and the beast is clearly hairy. In a letter to *Nature* (vol. 369, 1994, p. 364) Israeli archaeologist Baruch Rosen suggests that this astonishing beast could well be a dwarf mammoth, taken as a gift to the Egyptian court. There may have been no direct trading links between Egypt and northern Siberia but we can well imagine such an exotic beast being shuffled from one end of Asia to the other like some precious jewel, over the course of its long elephantine lifetime.

We also saw in the last chapter that giant poikilotherms *can* survive on islands in viable numbers, and cited the 'dragon' of Komodo which is the world's largest living lizard. In *Nature* (vol. 326, 1987, p. 832) Jared Diamond of the University of California has suggested that Komodo dragons evolved their huge size specifically to prey upon the dwarf elephants of the small Indonesian islands. Most modern lizards are small enough to bask on an elephant's foot. The fact that lizards once preyed upon elephants shows what astonishing possibilities lie just beneath the surface.

Proboscideans have produced the most striking elephant morphs and we are fortunate that the living types are among the finest and biggest; yet the proboscideans have not had a monopoly

on the elephant ecomorph. At least two orders of the peculiar
South American ungulates the astrapotheres and the pyrotheres
produced big-bodied, short-necked forms which also had trunks
– as is indicated by the position of the nasal opening on their fossilised skulls. In short, the ecomorph of the elephant has been
shaped in large part, as those of all creatures have, by the principles
of engineering. The elephant morph is a logical form to adopt: a
huge and almost invulnerable body with a limb-like nose with
which to manipulate and communicate with the outside world.

Proboscideans have always tended to be elephant-like; the
more tapir-like moeritheres were simply early types. But there are
three ungulate lineages in particular which have been extraordinarily diverse: the rhinos, the tylopods (which is the group that
includes the camels), and the collection of long-gone and little-
known South American creatures collectively known as
meridiungulates.

THE SOUTH AMERICANS: 'MERIDIUNGULATES'

When South America began its long separation as an island it
must have had on board a group of those ancient Cenozoic creatures whose relatives, in other continents, became for example
the perissodactyls and the artiodactyls. On South America they
evolved into at least four quite different orders which are loosely
grouped together as 'meridiungulates'. All are now gone. Some
suffered badly after the Great Interchange, while several survived
until the coming of human beings, about 12,000 years ago.

However, in their day – a 'day' that lasted at least 40 million
years – they radiated to emulate most if not all of the ecomorphs
that other ungulates, and indeed some non-ungulates, explored in
the rest of the world. The meridiungulates are not widely known
and do not feature in most standard texts. But they provide some
of the most extraordinary examples of convergent evolution the
world has seen.

Two of the four main meridiungulate orders – the litopterns
and the notoungulates – were particularly diverse. Thus some
litopterns resembled the three-toed equid hipparion, but
Thoatherium was as one-toed as a modern *Equus*, although it never
had long jaws and high-crowned teeth like a modern horse –

showing that individual features of different animals may converge, while others remain different. But then, high-crowned teeth and long jaws evolve to cope with grass and *Thoatherium* died out in the Miocene, before South American grassland truly came into its own. Contrariwise, *Macrauchenia* was a litoptern with the general form of a camel – a long-necked, long-legged browser, big but not hugely heavy. But the form of its skull shows it also had a proboscis, perhaps like an elephant's. *Macrauchenia* was the last survivor of all the litopterns and died out only in the Pleistocene. There seems no reason why such a well-equipped creature should have died out.

The other main order of meridiungulates, the wonderfully various notoungulates, reached their peak in the Oligocene, when there were nine entire families. We have already met two of them: *Homalodotherium*, shaped like a giant sloth or chalicothere, and the rhino-like *Toxodon* which again, like *Macrauchenia*, lasted until the Pleistocene.

THE ASTONISHINGLY VERSATILE RHINOCEROSES

The Rhinoceratoidea have been the most various superfamily of large mammals of all times. The primitive *Hyrachyus* was a runner the size of a collie dog, while the later *Juxia*, also a runner, was as big as a horse. Many rhinos have been hippo-like: *Teleoceras* was one. Most were hornless, and many were for all the world like their tapir ancestors. Indeed, only the members of the still-surviving Rhinocerotidae ever had horns, and these have often been bizarre. The single horn of *Elasmotherium* was enormous: its base extended over both nose and forehead. Several species, such as *Diacteratherium*, had nose-horns side by side like rifle sights. Some members of the rhino superfamily took the form of a modern giraffe – and achieved this form long before the giraffids did. One of them, as we have seen, was by far the biggest land mammal that ever lived. Between them, early rhinoceratoids dominated ecosystems in every continent except Antarctica, South America, and Australia. Though they are often supposed to be primarily African, they reached Africa only 25 million years ago, which was quite late in their history. In fact the rhino superfamily arose in North America and for a long time the North American rhinos

were extremely important, though they became extinct during
the last great period of late Miocene cooling, around 5 million
years ago. The Panama landbridge that might have enabled them
to live on in South America opened too late for them to take
advantage.

The rhinos descended from ancestral tapirs. (Modern tapirs
have remained resolutely tapir-like since the Eocene.) We might
in fact suggest that the rhinos have been the adventurous arm of
the tapirs – just as we, human beings, may be seen as the adventurous arm of the anthropoid apes.

WHY HORSES ARE HORSES

The perissodactyls as a group are extraordinarily varied – *vide* the
rhinos and the palaeotheres – but the horses, although there have
been hundreds of species that have lived all over the globe (except
Australia), seem simply to have become steadily more horse-like
as the Cenozoic has worn on. The first acknowledged equid
appeared in North America in the early Eocene as a woodland
creature the size of a fox and is officially known as *Hyracotherium*
(because it was at first thought to be a hyrax), though it is popularly and more aptly called 'eohippus', or 'dawn-horse'. It had
four toes on each of its front feet and three on each hind foot.
Then over the following epochs *Hyracotherium*'s many descendants in general grew bigger and bigger, steadily lost their surplus
toes, and tended to develop high-crowned teeth (a condition
known as 'hypsodonty') and the long deep faces that such big
teeth require to accommodate them. In practice this evolutionary
course followed in two distinct lines. One group, known colloquially as 'hipparions' (a general name commandeered from just
one of the many genera), retained three toes on each foot. In the
other line the loss of toes continued until, as in the extant genus
Equus, only the middle toe remained. The last hipparions died
out in Africa in the Pliocene, only about 3 million years ago, and
their footprints are preserved in fossil mud alongside those of
Australopithecus afarensis – one of the earliest known members of
the family Hominidae and possibly, or probably, our own direct
ancestor. The one-toed equids are with us still though sadly
reduced to just seven species, including the zebras and asses,

which are all placed in the genus *Equus*.

This apparently single-minded evolutionary progression enormously impressed Victorian and early twentieth-century zoologists. They saw it as a prime example of orthogenesis – 'straight-line' evolution towards some apparently pre-sighted goal – and even those post-Darwinian biologists who ostensibly stripped theology from their scientific thinking seemed to cling to the notion that horses were somehow 'destined' to become horses, and had stuck rigidly to their script. Such an interpretation, with or without overt theological connotations, can be found in every standard text of evolution. Children are brought up to believe that orthogenesis is real, and indeed is the norm.

Modern zoologists have condemned this orthogenetic interpretation, for they reject the idea of destiny and find the notion that God directed things superfluous. The old-style palaeontologists, say the moderns, suffered from wishful thinking. They misread the horse's fossil record just as they misread that of human beings. They liked to believe that evolution did indeed pursue paths that were inevitable. So they interpreted hominid fossils to show human beings becoming steadily brainier and more like us, and interpreted the fossils of man's chosen companion as if it was the ambition of ancient equids to provide vehicles for us to ride upon. In truth, say the modern biologists, ancient horses were perfectly capable of evolving in a whole host of different directions at any one time, just like every other animal. What about the tiny *Nannippus* of late Miocene North America, which reversed the trend to hugeness and hypsodonty, and went back to the woods?

In fact, the idea of destiny in its theological form should be rejected. Horses did not grow bigger and toothier because they were destined to do so. Yet *Nannippus* remains very much an exception. The general trend, seen in genus after genus among horses, and in hipparions as well as one-toed nags, is to become bigger and toothier. Those facts will not be denied. But we do need a new interpretation.

So here it is. As the Cenozoic wore on the world grew cooler and drier and by the time of the Miocene grassland was taking over from forest. Like many other ungulates, horses over time became better and better adapted to eating grass. This explains their hypsodonty – and one North American hipparion even developed open-rooted teeth: teeth that grow throughout life to compensate for wear. At the same time horses became more and more cursorial, the better to cover the ground. They also became bigger – because grass is poor fodder and suitable only for big animals, which have a lower metabolic rate than small ones.

Yet many other grass-eaters – the deer and the antelope, for instance – did not generally evolve the huge bulk of the horse (although a few have done so). But then deer and antelope are ruminants and, as we have seen, ruminants are more efficient herbivores than horses. When the body size is large, the poorer digestive efficiency makes little difference because food requirements are low relative to body weight. But when the body is smaller and the metabolic rate is higher, the poorer efficiency does make a difference. Hence big horses could compete with big ruminants, but small horses could not compete with small ruminants. The option of becoming small was not really open to horses because they could not out-compete the ruminants once the latter got into their stride. *Nannippus* slipped through the net briefly, but only briefly. The equids may well have 'wanted' to radiate into a wide range of sizes and habitats, as some modern biologists would have us believe they did, but in practice their survival depended on bulk. So their evolution was not 'orthogenic' in the Victorian sense; they were not trying to become anything in particular. They were just out-competed when they contrived to be anything other than big. But the *appearance* of orthogenesis is there nonetheless. It is idle to deny the actual narrowness of horse evolution.

The big-bodied cursorial option has served the horses well, however. Both the three-toed and the one-toed lineages spread out of North America into Eurasia and then into Africa, and eventually into South America when the opportunity arose in the Pliocene. Wherever they finished up they often radiated again, and some of the emergent forms migrated back to where they had come from. Thus there has been much to-ing and fro-ing between Eurasia and North America whenever Beringia has emerged above the waves. Overall the pattern of horse distribution has mirrored one of those superior fireworks which burst to form an array of stars, each of which then bursts again to give another generation of stars, and so on. *Equus* itself evolved in North America about 4 million years ago and migrated to Eurasia and so into Africa.

After the last separation of North America and Eurasia, however, around 8,000 years ago, horses finally disappeared from both Americas. They, too, it seems, fell to the first human colonists.

VARIATIONS ON A THEME OF CAMEL: THE TYLOPODS

Tylopods practise foregut fermentation as the ruminants do, but differently: their stomachs have only three chambers instead of the ruminant four. The only tylopods left to us are the camelids – the camels and llamas and their ilk – but there is a great deal more to the tylopods than that. In fact the group as a whole is thought to have evolved around 40 million years ago (late Eocene) from pig-like ancestors (Suina, in Figure IV.2); and some members of one extremely successful group of tylopods, the merycoidodontids or oreodonts, retained the pig-like mien. Throughout the Oligocene until the end of the Miocene the oreodonts were the dominant herbivores of North America. However, like the passenger pigeon, they show how the mighty can tumble – although the oreodonts' demise, unlike the pigeon's, cannot be laid at the human door for they died out long before the genus *Homo* evolved.

Other tylopods – including some of the oreodonts – took different forms. Some resembled rabbits. But the finest and most significant apart from the oreodonts were the beautiful, strange, deer-like Protoceratidae which diversified in the warm south of North America. They had simple horns on their heads like cattle – but the males also had extra bony horn-like outgrowths on the tops of their muzzles, well in front of their eyes, again like riflesights, and in some species these were long and forked like antlers. Perhaps they were used for sparring and perhaps merely for display. Protoceratids arose in the late Eocene and evidently survived the great North American decline of the late Miocene only to die out in the early Pliocene.

Camels themselves are known for their resistance to drought but their real skill is their ability to starve. After all, camels do need to drink every few days (up to a hundred litres at a time) while many desert antelope have no need to drink at all except for a lick of dew. No – the crucial advantage of camels over ruminants is one that they share with pigs: the ability to convert surplus energy quickly into fat, and to mobilise that fat again if the food runs out. Ruminants cannot do this. They need a constant input of carbohydrate. Overall, then, camelids can endure greater uncertainty and more prolonged privation than ruminants can. Today their last strongholds are in the deserts of the Middle East and central Asia, and – as llamas and vicuñas – in the high Andes of South America.

Ecomorphically, camels are the tylopod answer to the giraffe: the long-necked *Aepycamelus* from the middle and late Miocene of North America was particularly giraffe-like. But they first arose in the late Eocene of North America as short-legged creatures less than a metre high. They peaked in the mid-Miocene around 10 million years ago and did not migrate to Eurasia or Africa until about 5 million years ago. They did not reach South America until the Pliocene interchange. Thus they were most widespread in the early Pleistocene, when they ranged throughout the Americas and much of the Old World – but only a little after that they collapsed almost everywhere. They finally disappeared from their North American land of origin only about 12,000 years ago, not long after the first people arrived. Now, like the horses which disappeared at the same time, camels are again doing well in North America as feral animals, showing that as far as they are concerned there is nothing wrong with the terrain.

So far, the story of the ungulates has been somewhat gloomy. Many wonderful groups have gone, including some that might have been swept aside by our own ancestors. The remaining group, the ruminants, have over time lost at least as many fine representatives as, say, the perissodactyls have done. But in terms of species and range they are flourishing still.

THE TRIUMPH OF THE RUMINANTS

Ever since the Miocene the genre of large herbivory has belonged increasingly to the ruminants. Presumably – no other explanation seems necessary – their supreme ability to digest bulk fodder efficiently has enabled them to dominate both the forest and the ever-spreading grassland over a greater area of the world than any other surviving group. It seems odd, though, that they have never produced any megagiants comparable with the rhinos, elephants, uintatheres, titanotheres or brontotheres of other orders. The giraffes are the biggest ruminants, and the cold Pleistocene produced some huge deer and cattle, but there has been nothing in the proboscidean or rhinoceratoid class. Perhaps this is pre-emptive competition again. Even the ruminants may have been unable to invade niches that were already so competently occupied.

There are six families of ruminants. Two are small and perhaps ancestral: the chevrotains (Tragulidae), which seem to retain the features of the very earliest ruminants, and the musk deer (Moschidae), which perhaps demonstrate the erstwhile link between the giraffes and the deer. Of the other four families, two are much depleted – the pronghorns (Antilocapridae) and the giraffes (Giraffidae) – while two, the deer (Cervidae) and the cattle, antelopes, and sheep (Bovidae) are now the most speciose of all large families of mammals.

The antilocaprids are now down to one species – the pronghorn – but they have had a fine past. They apparently arose in North America during the Miocene and together with the tylopod protoceratids they showed how to live on the plain in cursorial herds without being either a deer or an antelope. They differ from antelope most obviously in their headgear. As in antelopes (and other bovids) the horns of antilocaprids have a body core and a horny sheath (which is made of the hardened protein keratin). In contrast to bovids, however (although with a superficial resemblance to deer), the sheath, but not the bony core, is shed and regrown each year. Antilocaprid headgear can take extraordinary forms. The horns of the modern pronghorn look fairly unremarkable: like those of a chamois (a bovid) though with a single fork (like the antlers of a young roe deer). But some extinct types had several pairs of horns arrayed along their faces like protoceratids, and the horns of others were elaborately branched. Antilocaprids also have the most highly evolved feet of all the artiodactyls for they retain only the functional third and fourth toes, and all trace of side toes has disappeared.

All but one of this fine family disappeared in or by the Pleistocene, though it is not easy to see why. They were and are extremely swift, probably reaching speeds of eighty kilometres per hour. Presumably they once were chased over the plains by the cheetah-like cats of the North American Pliocene which may or may not have been close relatives of the modern *Acinonyx*.

Thus were enacted scenes precisely like those of modern Africa – but in a different continent and with a different cast. Nature is endlessly inventive yet endlessly reinvents.

The deer, Cervidae, first arose in the Oligocene, presumably in Eurasia, and – in stark contrast to the antilocaprids – they remain the only large herbivores to compete in variety and range with the bovids: there are thirty-six living species ranging almost from pole to pole. As a group they are remarkable for their branched and often enormous antlers, which are made of bone but are shed and regrown each year, with each year's contribution being bigger than the previous year's. Antlers grow allometrically, both within a single animal as it ages and between different species – which means that big animals not only have bigger antlers than smaller ones but also have antlers that are bigger in proportion to their bodies. Thus moose, which are the biggest of living deer, have huge, flattened antlers, and some extinct types had even bigger ones. Biggest of all was a relative of the modern fallow deer called *Megaloceros* which is often called the 'Irish elk' since its antlers have been found in such abundance in the Irish bogs. Its body was about the size of a big moose but its antlers could span 3·7 metres and weigh forty kilograms. It has sometimes been argued that the Irish elk 'outgrew its strength' or caught its wonderful antlers in overhanging trees. This must be nonsense. Irish elk were highly successful – not exclusively 'Irish' at all, but flourishing in the late Pleistocene through the Old World as far as China and Siberia. If they were really so damagingly constructed they could hardly have evolved at all. But this was yet another creature to come up against the formidable genus *Homo* – from *H. erectus* to *H. sapiens*. This, rather than any overhanging tree, was probably their undoing.

The Giraffidae probably evolved from deer some time in the Miocene. The only two remaining species live in Africa (the giraffe and okapi) but the family almost certainly arose in Eurasia – zoogeography is mocked again. Most extinct giraffids were very unlike the modern giraffe. *Sivatherium* for example was a huge bull-like creature from the Pliocene and Pleistocene of India whose ossicones were flattened and branched to resemble the antlers of a moose – although they were not made to be shed. Various unrelated lineages, including camels, litopterns, and rhinos, have just as much claim to the giraffe-like ecomorph as the giraffids do.

The Miocene also gave rise to the family that has become the most speciose of all large animals – the Bovidae, which includes the cattle, antelopes, sheep, and goats, and a mixed bag of 'goat antelopes' such as the chamois, takin, saiga, and musk ox. Now there are 120 bovid species in forty-six genera but in the Pleistocene there were at least twice as many. They are now at their most various in Africa and the oldest known types date from the Sahara of about 20 million years ago – yet the bovids may not owe their origins to Africa. They could just as soon have arisen in Europe or Asia. They did not reach North America until the Bering Strait was bridged in the Pleistocene, when bison and the modern forebears of bighorn sheep and mountain goats flooded across into a continent which had already lost many of its native animals to a change in climate.

The plethora of antelopes in Africa accounts for much of the present variety of bovids: they contrive to carve up the vegetation and especially the grass between them, so there is scope for many different specialists. Elisabeth Vrba contends that their variety evolved in waves, with entire suites of species appearing at intervals in Africa since the Miocene, each in response to some global shift in climate. The most recent to unfold has been the gazelle genus *Gazella* which arose about 2·5 million years ago – apparently prompted into being by the same climatic shift that encouraged *Homo* to evolve. In modern gazelles we are privileged to see the process of species formation still in action and for this reason it is often hard to tell one from another: Arabian and Dorcas gazelles are only now being sorted into species, and there may be more types than we are at present aware of. *Gazella* and its almost exact contemporary *Homo* make an intriguing and instructive ecological and evolutionary contrast. *Gazella*, as herbivorous specialists, have formed at least fifteen species but stayed in much the same area; while the hyper-generalist *Homo* is now reduced to one species that is spread all around the world.

Some of the most magnificent cattle lived in the Pleistocene. The cold favoured large body size: *Pelorovis* of Africa had horns that spanned four metres. In Eurasia and North American bison achieved considerable variety as they shifted from continent to continent in vast herds, with several long-horned types in addition to the present more compact forms. The ones that feature in European cave paintings are long-horned. I am sure that in bison we see an evolutionary principle at work that is well recognised among plants but seems to have been little recognised in animals – introgression. That is, creatures separate into subpopulations which then evolve independently to form what for all the world look like new species, but then the apparently different types come together again to form what is effectively a hybrid. If the separation has not proceeded too long and the two parent species 'click' then the 'hybrids' fare very well. The fossil record suggests that this has occurred in bison, and their ecology – their ability to occupy entire continents and to circumnavigate the globe when opportunity presents – makes them admirable candidates for such a process. Most palaeoanthropologists concede that a similar process may well have taken place between subgroups of the equally peripatetic *Homo*.

So that is a lightning tour of the ungulates: creatures which, above all, shaped the ecology of the open plain which our own genus, *Homo*, evolved to inhabit in such sharp contrast to its forest ancestors. We have preyed hard upon the ungulates – and still do. Since long before we came on the scene, however, they have been the prey of specialist mammalian carnivores.

CARNIVORES AND CREODONTS

At the very start of the Cenozoic 65 million years ago there lived a creature now called *Cimolestes* which, at the time, would have been hard to distinguish from dozens of other tree-shrew-like contemporaries. But within a few million years – by the mid-Palaeocene – *Cimolestes* had given rise to two entire mammalian orders that were dedicated to carnivory. First into their stride were the Creodonta, which appeared in the Palaeocene about 60 million years ago, radiated spectacularly until the Oligocene around 30 million years ago, but disappeared entirely from their final stronghold in Pakistan by the late Miocene, 8 million years ago. The second group, the Carnivora, appeared early but put up only a modest showing until the Oligocene, around 35 million years ago, after which they have flourished. Nearly 240 wonderful and often beautiful species are with us still, in 98 genera, from the tiniest weasels the size of a gerbil to walruses and elephant seals, Siberian tigers (the largest of all cats) and Kodiak bears (the largest of all living land carnivores). As always, however, we find that the living cast of creatures is but a fragment of what has gone before; that at many times and places in the past there have been entire roll-calls of major predators where now there are one or two or none at all; and that the extinct forms include entire ways of being and ways of life. And of course in both creodonts and true Carnivora we find the familiar patterns: each order, and each family within each order, often adopting many different styles of life, and each style emulated independently by many unrelated creatures.

Meat-eating is a high-risk strategy. Game theory shows that predators fare best when they catch prey that is roughly their own size – but any prey animal as big as the attacker puts up a fight. Scavenging may look easier but corpses occur patchily and there is fierce rivalry for what there are. But the risk is worth the game. Meat is very high in nutrients compared to plants and carnivorous mammals get by with occasional meals – just a few meals a day for a small meat-eater or a few a week for a large one – while herbivores must spend almost their entire lives in foraging. A wild elephant feeds for seventeen hours a day.

The secret of successful mammalian carnivory lies it seems with the carnassial teeth: cheek teeth modified into scissor-like blades, top and bottom, that shear through skin and flesh. Many Carnivora have in fact abandoned specialist flesh-eating and those that have – including omnivorous but often fruit-eating raccoons and fish-eating seals – have also often abandoned carnassial teeth. But for the committed meat-eaters, both Creodonta and Carnivora, the carnassials are the tool of the trade. Yet it may be that the carnivores in the end surpassed the creodonts because their teeth were *less* committed to meat-eating. The carnassials of carnivores are no less fierce than creodonts' but they occur further forward in the mouth: that is, they are fashioned from the rear premolar and the first molar, leaving molars behind the carnassials for crunching and grinding. The carnassials of creodonts were formed from the rear-most teeth. While carnivores could more easily eat plants if the meat supply failed, as modern dogs (and especially foxes), bears, and badgers are happy to demonstrate, creodonts would have found this difficult. Perhaps this gave the carnivores the edge when the going got really tough. As can hardly be overstated – and as successful creatures from kangaroos to human beings demonstrate – the art of survival is to scrape by in the worst of times and not merely to flourish in the best.

Over time there were forty-five or so genera of creodonts in two families, the short-lived Oxyaenidae, which died out in the Eocene around 40 million years ago, and the much more various Hyaenodontidae, which evolved in the Eocene and ranged through North America and Eurasia. Between them they adopted the forms and presumably the life-styles of bears, dogs, hyaenas, raccoons, cats, weasels, and otters. The bigger ones preyed upon brontotheres, chalicotheres, and rhinos. The hyaena-like *Hyaenodon* of the Miocene, 20 million years ago, was the creodont equivalent of the modern lion, both hunting and scavenging. *Apataelurus* reinvented the sabre tooth. The largest of all creodonts was *Megistotherium* of the early Miocene Sahara, which was heavier than a modern bison.

Thus the creodonts did more or less everything that the true carnivores did. But the true carnivores, we must assume, did it better.

THE DOG GROUP AND THE CAT GROUP: THE 'TRUE' CARNIVORES

The very earliest of the true carnivores were pine-marten-like creatures that lived around 65 to 60 million years ago and were known as miacids. They then gave rise to two separate groups. In the New World there arose the Canoidea ('dog-like') which came to include the Canidae (dogs), Ursidae (bears), Mustelidae (weasels, otters, badgers), and Procyonidae (raccoons and coatis). The modern pinnipeds (marine carnivores) are believed to have arisen from mustelids, and so form a parallel group to the otters, but since they play little part in our own history, I will not dwell on them. In the Old World the miacids gave rise to the Feloidea ('cat-like') which now include the Viverridae (civets), Herpestidae (mongooses), Felidae (cats), and Hyaenidae (hyaenas). But in the Oligocene, 30 million years ago, the Bering land-bridge came into being for the first time and there was some interchange of carnivores between the two land masses, although the canids did not enter the Old World at this time, and in fact made their first appearance in Eurasia only in the late Miocene, around 6 million years ago. A few North American carnivores also managed to raft to South America before the Pliocene convergence, including the raccoon known as *Cyonasua* which evolved into the huge *Chapalmalania*. *Chapalmalania* was like a giant panda: another fine piece of convergence.

Hundreds of species have disappeared from these carnivore families and some entire ecomorphs have gone with them, including all the sabretooths. Three entire Carnivora families have disappeared altogether: the father of them all, the Miacidae; the Amphicyonidae or 'bear-dogs', with bodies like bears and heads like dogs (convergence here of bits of animals), which thrived from 50 million years ago, during the Eocene, to 5 million years ago (the late Miocene); and their almost exact contemporaries the Nimravidae which were for all the world like cats, although they are now generally allotted a separate family of their own.

DOGS, BEARS, AND RELATIVES: THE CANOIDEA

The Canidae themselves are an ancient group, dating from the Eocene around 40 million years ago; although the very earliest were short-legged and mongoose-like, they quickly adopted the dog mode and have not changed much since, except for a considerable enlargement of the brain (and presumably of corresponding intelligence). In the early Oligocene there were only five genera; by the late Miocene, 10 to 6 million years ago, they peaked at forty-two; and nowadays there are between ten and twelve, depending on who is counting. Although the canids have become so significant in Africa and Eurasia – wild dogs, bush dogs, wolves, jackals, and foxes – they remained exclusively American until the late Miocene. They have taken just 6 million years to conquer the Old World.

Most dogs have been dog-like: hunting by running and chasing, often in packs; some scavenging, and with a penchant for omnivory – but some have broken the mould. Some of the earliest kinds were cat-like. But the 'borophagines' such as *Osteoborus* had big, bear-like bodies, short faces, and huge crushing teeth: that is, they filled the bone-crushing role of the modern hyaena. In fact hyaenas, which as cat-relatives evolved in the Old World, made a very poor fist at migrating into American when the

Bering land-bridge opened even though the modern spotted hyaena *Crocuta* is one of the most successful of all modern carnivores. *Crocuta* apparently never reached America but if it had it might have found the bone-crushing dog *Osteoborus* was a formidable rival. For its part, *Osteoborus* remained exclusively American, from the Miocene to the Pleistocene.

One of the most spectacular of all dogs, and resolutely doglike, was the dire wolf *Canis dirus* which lived in Pleistocene California. It was like a modern wolf only much bigger, and was evidently a scavenger. The fossil remains of several thousand individuals have been found in the tar pits of La Brea, Los Angeles. Dire wolves appear to have had some fierce scraps with the massive sabretooth of the day, *Smilodon*. Many bones of each have been found deep-scarred by the teeth of the other.

Although modern studies of body proteins and DNA suggest that bears (Ursidae) diverged from raccoons (Procyonidae) in the Oligocene, 30 million years ago, with the giant panda diverting from the rest of the ursids in the early Miocene, around 20 million years ago, the fossil record reveals no bears until well into the Miocene. In short, they are a comparatively recent group. Most bears have been bear-like – big and versatile omnivores – although the modern polar bear in practice is almost carnivorous, while the sloth bear of Asia is a termite eater and the spectacled bear and giant panda veer towards vegetarianism.

But again, we have lost some glories. The biggest bear these days (and the biggest of all land carnivores) is the Kodiak, a subspecies of the grizzly. But the cave bear, which braved the worst of the Pleistocene ice ages in northern Europe and Russia and survived into recent times, was even bigger. For tens and perhaps hundreds of thousands of years it irritated our predecessors *Homo erectus*, *H. heidelbergensis*, *H. neanderthalensis* and finally *H. sapiens*. Late Palaeolithic *H. sapiens* may well have hastened the cave bear's extinction. But although cave bears are believed to have been vegetarian they must have been formidable opponents. Whether they lived in caves as a matter of course is unknown, but they certainly hibernated in them, apparently in large groups, as the weather became particularly impossible.

Yet other bears have assumed the habit of dogs and become runners. The giant short-faced bear *Arctodus simus* was the biggest true land carnivore that ever lived – almost half as tall again and at least twice as heavy as a modern grizzly. It lived in North America from the early Pleistocene, around 2 million years ago, until recent times – a mere 10,000 years ago. But it had long legs for running (presumably) and short jaws for gripping – in fact it was built and perhaps hunted like a giant Rottweiler. It must at least have terrified the first human beings in America and Dr Valerius Geist of the University of Calgary has speculated that *Arctodus simus* and other bears may even have delayed the human invasion of that continent. Geist points out, after all, that even in recent centuries the less formidable grizzlies of North America have often made life very difficult even for people with modern weapons. Even more of a runner was *Hemicyon* (its name means 'half dog') of Miocene Eurasia and North America, which was as big as a modern brown bear but more lightly built, and may have hunted in packs like a wolf.

CATS, HYAENAS, AND OTHERS: THE FELOIDEA

Also dating from the Miocene – around 15 million years ago – are the Hyaenidae. Now they are specialist bone-crushers: carnivore palaeontologist Alan Turner of Liverpool University comments that the spotted hyaena, *Crocuta*, which is the most successful of the modern types, 'can crush and digest anything it can get into its mouth'. *Crocuta* can make a meal from the skeleton of a zebra after lions have taken all that they possibly can, munching the steeliest of bones like celery, and digesting not only the marrow but also the protein within the bone itself. They excrete stools rich in calcium that fossilise to form 'coproliths'.

But, as Dr Turner has shown, the hyaenas did not adopt this extreme and formidable specialisation until the dogs arrived from the New World in the late Miocene. Before that, they had themselves been more dog-like. *Crocuta* has in recent times been successful not only in Africa, where it still thrives, but all through Asia and Europe as well (there are some in my local Yorkshire caves), yet it failed to trek through Siberia and into Alaska when the Beringian land-bridge opened. The only hyaena that did make the crossing was *Chasmoporthetes* which was obviously a long-legged sprinting hunter rather than a scavenger – the hyaena's answer to the cheetah. But *Chasmoporthetes* fared badly in North

America though it did well throughout Eurasia and Africa.
Meanwhile in North America, as we have noticed, bones were
being crushed by the hyaena-like dog, *Osteoborus.* So hyaenas
have played at being dogs and speedy cats during their comparatively brief sojourn on Earth while dogs have at times emulated
hyaenas. The biggest and most formidable bone-crushing hyaena
of all was *Percrocuta* of middle and late Miocene Africa and
Eurasia. *Percrocuta gigantea* of China was as big as a modern lion.

Two families can claim to be 'cats'. The true cats are the
Felidae, which of course are with us still (with around thirty-six
species). But the felids in their early days were accompanied by
cat-like creatures that now are placed in a separate family, the
Nimravidae. Both groups arose in the Eocene and got into their
stride in the Oligocene, but the nimravids faded and disappeared
by the late Miocene, about 8 million years ago. Both the nimravids and the felids have demonstrated two ways of being a cat:
biting cat and sabretooth. People mistake sabretooths just as they
mistake Irish elks and dinosaurs. They did not die out because
their body form was too extravagant. They were extremely successful animals for tens of millions of years. As already outlined
above, marsupials from at least two different families adopted the
sabretooth form – *Thylacosmilus* and *Thylacoleo.* At least three different lineages within the Felidae have independently adopted the
sabretooth mode. And the nimravids produced *Nimravus* in the
Oligocene and early Miocene of Europe and North America with
its long, low, leopard-sized body – and its sharp sabre teeth. Thus
the mammals as a whole have produced convincing, cat-like
sabretooths at least six times.

In practice the felid sabretooths had teeth of various sizes.
Those of *Megantereon*, which apparently spread from India into
Eurasia, Africa, and North America from the late Miocene to the
early Pleistocene were relatively short (though longer than a biting cat) and cats with this design are called 'dirktooths'.
Homotherium from the Pleistocene of Africa, Eurasia, and North
America had longer teeth than the dirktooths but flatter and more
decurved than the biggest sabretooths: a design known as 'scimi-
tar tooth'. *Homotherium* apparently walked on flat feet like a bear
and died out only 14,000 years ago.

But everyone's idea of a sabretooth was the Pleistocene
Smilodon, with species in each of the Americas. Its teeth were

hugely long and its jaws opened 120° or more to give them full purchase. In cross-section they were flattened from side to side – like the blades of a sabre – and not round, as often wrongly depicted. The backs of each sabre were serrated, like steak knives. Exactly how the sabretooths, scimitartooths, or dirktooths killed their prey is uncertain (how could it be known?) but features which *all* sabretooths have in common, whether felid, nimravid, or marsupial, offer a clue. Thus they all tend to be muscular, particularly in the chest and forelimbs. *Smilodon* is exaggeratedly so, with chest and arms like a wrestler and comparatively short hind legs. In other instances we have seen convergence of individual features – the litoptern with the camel-like body and the elephantine trunk, and the amphicyonids with bearish bodies and dog-like heads – but in sabretooths there is no such mosaicism. No sabretooth ever developed the long running legs of a cheetah, for example.

In short, the constancy of form in sabretooths suggests that, whatever lineage they belonged to, they were built for ambush rather than a chase. Presumably they leapt from beneath at their prey – a brontothere, a rhino, a chalicothere, a mammoth – and held on tight around the neck (as a boxer would say, 'getting inside', or 'closing' with the opponent), away from the victims' slashing horns or claws or tusks. Then presumably they somewhat carefully sliced their sabres into the throat, perhaps severing the carotid or jugular and producing a faint in seconds. The teeth with their flattened cross-section could not have simply been thrust through the skull as is sometimes depicted for they would have broken. Neither, probably, did they simply disembowel their victim and wait for it to die. Severe damage to the unprotected throat, and particularly to the windpipe and the blood vessels to and from the brain, seems the most likely method. Killing a large animal is not easy. Here we see again that huge ecological success attended those creatures – a wide variety of them – that evolved an effective method. Just one trick is all it takes.

The biting cats evidently separated from the sabretooths around 15 million years ago – mid-Miocene – and have by now divided into four commonly recognised genera: the big cats, *Panthera*, and the small cats, *Felis*, are the big groups, while the cheetah is conventionally placed in its own genus *Acinonyx* and the clouded leopard is classed as *Neofelis*. Of the modern cats, *Neofelis* has by far the biggest canine teeth relative to its size – as if it was yet again reinventing the sabretooth line. Molecular evidence now suggests that *Acinonyx* is not so different from the other cats as its anatomy suggests: it may indeed be a close relative of the North American puma. The genus *Felis*, however, may be a mixed bag, with the South American small cats such as ocelot and margay having divided from the other *Felis* in the Miocene, around 12 million years ago.

Whatever the truth of their relationship, most of the cat genera have in their time spread from Eurasia into North America and Africa. North America harboured extremely cheetah-like animals in the Pleistocene – which may indeed have been true cheetahs – and had bona fide lions which entered via Beringia around 35—20,000 years ago. It now seems too that some of the North American lions may in fact have been tigers – so tigers may not be so exclusively Asian as generally supposed. Jaguars, now exclusively American, clearly originated in Eurasia. The cave lion of Pleistocene and recent Europe was a subspecies of the modern lion – *Panthera leo atrox* – but 25 per cent bigger: the biggest felid that ever lived, greater even than a modern Siberian tiger. Archaeological evidence suggests that the last ones died out in the Balkans only at about the time of Christ. Once more the apparently ancient world meets the present day.

Finally, we may note the richness of the carnivore fauna in any one time and place. Even nowadays in some parts of the world several species each of big cats, dogs, bears or hyaenas may divide the prey between them. But in times past the cast was often bigger, and included in particular the sabretooth predators of the megaherbivores and perhaps the fearsome Rottweiler running bears. Carnivores are pertinent to us too because, like us, they are intelligent and sociable, and of course are hunters; in a different way they faced and solved the same problems as our own ancestors. Clearly, too, human beings have had a tremendous impact upon the carnivores, and still do have, for we have brought many to the point of extinction. Equally clearly the carnivores have had a tremendous impact upon us. Perhaps they affected the speed and direction of our migrations around the globe. Beyond doubt they helped to sharpen our wits in our long history on the plains of Africa and Eurasia.

So now it is time to introduce our own group.

THE PRIMATES

From the 1730s to the 1750s the Swedish biologist Carl Linnaeus initiated the methods of taxonomy and systematics by which animals are named and placed into groups. He it was who first formally established the binomial system of naming species that still applies: generic name first, and then specific name, as in *Homo sapiens* and *Panthera leo*.

But Linnaeus cannot be classed as a 'modern'. Most modern biologists seek a system of classification that truly reflects relationships, as discussed earlier. Different members of the genus *Homo* or the genus *Panthera* are thus supposed to be closely related to each other literally – that is, to share a recent common ancestor. But the idea that different species may indeed have shared a common ancestor implies evolution. Lions and tigers, though both placed in *Panthera*, are clearly different, and if they did have a common ancestor then each has altered since that time in its own particular way. Such alteration over time *is* evolution. But serious consideration of evolution did not begin until the late eighteenth century, several decades after Linnaeus, and he did not entertain it. He supposed merely that God had a tidy mind, and had created different creatures in orderly groups. If God chose to provide several variations on a theme of *Panthera* – why not?

With such a Godly background Linnaeus was happy to impose value judgments of a theological nature. Thus he gave the world the term 'Primates', to include human beings, apes, and monkeys and their relatives. The term of course means 'first'. Other mammals and birds he called 'Secundates' and the rest of the animal kingdom were 'Tertiates'. Only the term 'Primate' has stuck, and most people have forgotten its implication of hierarchy. In theory (though not always in practice!) modern biologists prefer to eschew the notion that any group of animals is 'higher' than any other.

Indeed the notion of hierarchy should be eschewed – unless, as I argue in later chapters, we are talking only of 'technical' ability in carefully defined areas. Yet Linnaeus did have a point. The primates are undoubtedly *different*. Oddly, however, what makes them special is their extreme generalness.

THE ADVANTAGE OF BEING GENERAL

Look at any mid-Mesozoic mammal of the kind from which all subsequent mammals have evolved. Biologists commonly compare the general shape of such creatures to that of a modern tree-shew. I have said that tree-shrews are shaped roughly like a mouse, but without too much exaggeration we might compare them to a newt. In other words, the typical Mesozoic mammal has the general form of the tetrapod: that is, of the very first animals that ever came on land. It has four legs to which it gives more or less equal emphasis – no particular bias towards the hind limbs, as in kangaroos or many a dinosaur – and it has five toes on each limb, giving a foot which in a general way provides grip – just enough, for example, to cling to bark or perhaps to slap down on an insect. It stands bent-legged on the permanent qui vive and because it is small it has an enormously high ratio of strength to weight. To cap the design, it has a long tail for balance.

This standard tetrapod ecomorph, as we have seen, serves the bulk of mammal species even today – notably the rodents and the small marsupials and carnivores – and, stretching the point only slightly, we can say it has also served a host of reptiles (including the modern lizards) and the tailed amphibians. It is indeed a good all-purpose form which answers the problems of life on land with the simplest possible principles of engineering: a leg at each corner, everything kept small to avoid problems of weight, a tail to even things up and away you go.

Most mammals that have aspired to be bigger than stoats and rats have modified this basic form, as we have seen. The spring-like legs became stilts and then pillars. The pentadactyl foot has often been reduced to a peg. Tails have often been abandoned. Even limbs have at times been sacrificed – or, in the case of the bats or indeed the birds, fantastically re-created as wings. The carnivores kept their five toes but shortened them, adding claws for weaponry (as in cats) or reducing the foot to a pad (as in dogs, which might just as well be hooved for all the use they make of their feet). In short, most mammals that aspired not to be rats or polecats broke out of the mould by severe modification of the basic tetrapod ecormorph.

The outstanding exception has been the primates. From the beginning, and emphatically, they retained their four-limbedness.

Some types, such as the lemurs and bush-babies, developed exceedingly powerful hind limbs and leap as prodigiously as any kangaroo. Yet their forelimbs remain important to them, both for locomotion and for other purposes: they have not been down-graded like the forelimbs of an ostrich or a *Tyrannosaurus*. Indeed the apes, from the Oligocene onwards, were able to re-exploit the forelimbs as prime agents of locomotion, and invented the hand-over-hand mode of swinging known as brachiation. Then again, some of the committed brachiators have reduced the thumb and turned the remaining fingers into hooks. But on the whole the primates, in sharp contrast to the dogs or horses or whales or bats, have hung on to the basic five fingers of the tetra-pod and turned them to good purposes. They use them as pokers and prodders and in particular have swung the thumb around, and often the big toe as well, so that they oppose the rest and convert a perfunctory grip into a firm grasp.

In short, while other mammals have made a virtue of speciali-sation – transforming the tetrapod endowment of limbs, toes, and tails, and sometimes spurning it altogether – primates have pre-ferred simply to improve on what they were given. Modern primates take many various and extraordinary forms, from human beings to galagos, but the basic general form is always clear to see. This is why, as Linnaeus and all taxonomists since have found, primates are so hard to define. They possess very few features, if any, that are not possessed by other mammals, and particularly by the most primitive; indeed their differentness lies in their extra-ordinary conservatism. But generality leads readily to versatility and the species that has finally prevailed, and in the end has trans-formed the ecology of the whole world, is the one which, more than any other, has exploited this generality most emphatically. We human beings have had such extraordinary success precisely because we have not converted ourselves into horses or bats or lions. As generalists we are able to emulate any and all of them. Thus, as discussed more deeply in Chapter 6, we are the animal equivalent of the Turing machine: the universal device that can be turned to any task.

Natural selection has favoured physical conservatism and hence generality primarily because the primates elected to stay in the trees. As we will see, they are a remarkably ancient group, which got well into their stride during the Cretaceous when the dinosaurs were still supreme: I love the notion of the earliest primates, pointy-nosed like modern tree shrews and vocal as a lemur or a squirrel, scolding the dim heads of *Diplodocus* probing among the canopy for shoots. Thus the rise and radiation of the primates coincides with that of the angiosperms – and indeed they are protegés of the angiosperms, exploiting the novel fruits, the succulent leaves and above all the complex and variable geometry of the new-styled trees.

For trees – and particularly complex and variable trees – are hard task-masters. Of course they encourage the ability to grip – first in a general way and then with the increasingly opposable thumb for good measure – and although many specialist birds do well in the trees with only two legs, and some snakes climb remarkably with none at all, common sense suggests that a versatile limb in each corner is an advantage.

Of outstanding significance is the mobility of the joints. Primates (or some of them at least) have uniquely versatile shoulders. In this respect, contrast human beings with cats. Cats are lissom, elegant, agile – every fine epithet of physicality applies to them. We compare the finest athletes to them, and dancers. Yet cats cannot move as we do. Little old ladies roll their shoulders in the warm-up for aerobics: creakily, perhaps, but they do it nonetheless. If we tried to make a cat do the same it would cry with pain, for we would dislocate its joints. We can spin our arms through almost all the points not simply of the compass but of a sphere. No other creatures can do this. Only the boneless trunk of an elephant or the tentacle of an octopus or the multi-boned neck of an ostrich has such universal mobility. The significance of this hypermobility often goes unremarked yet it can hardly be overstated. For without the mobility of the shoulder – and of the wrist, with the convenient standard elbow in between – we could not make proper use of our hands. If a horse had hands and all the nerves and brain to go with them it still could not thread a needle, because its to-and-fro forelimbs would not allow it to bring those hands into appropriate juxtaposition.

Here again, we see the opportunism of evolution. For our wonderful shoulders are the gift of our apeish ancestors who invented brachiation. We have abandoned the way of life that gave rise to brachiation and have therefore abandoned the skill itself – and yet we have made supreme use of that skill in a new context. Thus in ourselves we can see the supreme conservatism of the primates, and also the way in which each individual feature has been developed: the primitive pentadactyl limb converted first to the gripping hand and then to an organ of unparalleled dexterity; the forelimb first made strong and mobile for the purposes of locomotion and then freed to become the perfect and necessary foil for the extraordinary hand.

Yet physique is only the raw material of action. What the animal *does* is what counts. Here again, the trees played a vital part because, for reasons that are commonsensical, they demanded a commensurate development of the nervous system. Life in the three-dimensional world of trees requires excellent vision. Hearing is particularly useful because the animals are so often hidden from each other, while their enemies hide from them. Scent is at least as useful in the trees as on the ground, and many modern primates make extensive use of pheromones and other olfactory signals. More than this, though, life in the trees demands balance, and hence coordination, in particular of hand and eye. Where the eye prescribes the body must follow precisely, for any failure is severely punished.

In practice – as the modern lemurs demonstrate – marvellous senses and extraordinary coordination do not necessarily lead to all-round intellectual excellence. Lemurs are lovable but those who love them best tend also to acknowledge that they are dim. Nonetheless, a powerful principle in evolution is that of pre-adaptation: a muscle, an appendage, a gland, a set of nerves that has evolved for one purpose (or, as we should say, in response to one set of selective pressures) is often at some later time pressed opportunistically to another. As discussed in the next chapter, human evolution seems to have relied heavily upon the coercion of basic primate qualities that initially evolved for quite different purposes, including the mobile arms. Similarly, it is not fanciful to suggest that the extreme development of the human nervous system builds upon the complexity that the primates in general have evolved to ease their lives in the trees.

So much for generalities. What of the creatures themselves?

THE VARIETY OF PRIMATES

Biologists recognise about 200 species of living primate. They are a speciose group, as might be expected with forest species of modest size. Another 250 species are known from the fossil record. But the oldest known primate fossils are about 65 million years old and same kind of logic which tells us that there must have been at least 200,000 species of mammals in times past also tells us that there must in reality have been at least 6,500 primate species throughout the Cenozoic. So we know only about 3·8 per cent of the primates that lived throughout that time.

From what we know of it, though, the evolutionary tree of the primates seems to be basically Y-shaped. That is, in the beginning there was an ancestral primate stock known as the plesiadapiformes or 'protoprimates': the creatures that in a general way resembled modern tree-shrews. These protoprimates then divided to form two main prosimian lines. One of these is now represented by the lemurs, lorises, and bush-babies; the other line has given rise to the modern tarsiers, which are tiny big-eyed creatures, superficially resembling bush-babies, which now live in Indonesia (although their fossil remains have been found in many places, including London's river Thames). Whether the simians arose from the lemur-like line or the tarsier-like line remains uncertain, though most people favour the tarsier line. The prosimians and the simians are collectively known as 'euprimates' to distinguish them from the protoprimates.

The oldest known primate fossils – that is, protoprimate fossils – date from the Palaeocene, 65 to 56 million years ago. But the protoprimates began to decline in the Eocene and by 35 million years ago they had more or less disappeared except for one species in North America. The first known euprimates appeared in the early Eocene – around 55 million years ago – in Belgium, France, England, and Wyoming. They were mouse-sized or rat-sized prosimians, and included species from both arms of the Y: some lemur-like, and some tarsier-like. Finally, the earliest known simians – effectively Old World monkeys – are from Africa, dating from the boundary of the Eocene and Oligocene, around 36 million years ago. Thus the modern groups all arose some time before the last protoprimates disappeared – which means that the modern types arose from only *some* of the protoprimates, leaving others to carry on as before. It is assumed that the apes arose from Old World monkeys – the New World monkeys having found their way to South America at some early but unknown date by an unknown route and henceforward enjoyed (or not) the company of the meridiungulates, edentates, and marsupials that we met earlier. Both the Old World monkeys and the lemurs produced ground-living types – baboons, gorillas, hominids, and a giant gorilla-like lemur in Madagascar which as we will see in Chapter 8 survived until the time of Charlemagne and the Venerable Bede – but the New World monkeys seemed to have remained stubbornly in the forests.

New World monkeys have therefore lived only where the forest has been, within hailing distance of the Equator. In the form of spider monkeys and some others, however, the New World monkeys have included some of the most fabulous acrobats of the entire animal kingdom.

But if the oldest known primate fossils are only 65 million years old, why do biologists suggest that the primates as a whole are much older than this? Well, it is clear first of all that the protoprimates were already diverse by the time the first fossils appear, which suggests a long period of evolution before that. The same point – plus their wide distribution – applies to the first-known euprimates.

Logic dictates, too, that the oldest known fossils cannot possibly be the oldest representatives of their kind. Fossilisation is a rare event, after all. And when animals first appear they are rare. The earliest fossil bones are therefore likely to date from a time when their erstwhile owners were already common. Logic similarly dictates that if an animal is particularly unlikely to form fossils – as primates seem to be – then palaeontologists are particularly unlikely to find the very earliest types. In fact this logic can be translated into a mathematical formula.* The fewer fossils there are (relative to the calculated number of extinct species) the older the group is liable to be relative to the number of fossils found.

In practice, as we have already noted, only 250 or so extinct primates are known out of a calculated possible 6,500: in other words, we know only about 3·8 per cent of the extinct types. The

*The argument is spelled out by Robert D. Martin in 'Primate Origins: Plugging the Gaps', *Nature*, 20 May 1993, vol. 363 pp. 223–34.

relevant maths then tells us that the oldest known fossils are therefore likely to be about 30 per cent younger than the true age of
the group. Given that the oldest known primate fossil dates from
around 65 million years ago, the probable date of the *actual* oldest primate is probably around 85 million years ago. At that time
– way back in the Cretaceous – the dinosaurs still had 20 million
years to run and several evolutionary flourishes to undergo. The
same kinds of calculations should also be applied to the euprimates, and although the oldest fossils of these date only from the
Eocene they too are then pushed back into the Cretaceous.

In fact we should not stop with this first round of calculation.
For if the oldest primate really does date back to 85 million years
ago then there must have been even more species over time than
the 6,500 that is calculated now. So the percentage known is even
smaller than expected. So the true age has to be pushed back even
further. Palaeontologists seem reluctant to push protoprimate origins much before 85 million years ago, but some suggest that the
first euprimates, lemur-like and tarsier-like, may be as old as 77
million years. So they too may have overlapped the dinosaurs by
an astonishing 12 million years. Thus creatures very like the
lemurs which now can be seen to such advantage in, say, Jersey
Zoo may well have batted the snouts of dinosaurs as the importunate reptiles thrust their heads into the canopies of the
newly-flourishing angiospermous trees.

Similarly, the maths suggests that the first known simians probably emerged not at 36 million years ago, which is the date of the
earliest fossils, but as long ago as 52 million years – at the boundary of the Palaeocene/Eocene. Such an early division does,
however, help to explain how it is that the New World monkeys
have remained so similar to the Old World monkeys in most
essentials, even though the two groups separated so early. It also
explains how monkeys got into South America in the first place:
they probably arose before South America split from Africa to
become an island. In practice, however, the earliest known fossils
of South American monkeys date only from the late Oligocene,
a little over 20 million years ago.

We should ask, of course, whether such calculations should also
be applied to all the other groups we have discussed so far. The
answer in principle must be 'yes', but the results would be far less
dramatic. For example, living on the open plain and in such

numbers, horses have provided us with many thousands of fossils – almost an embarrassment of riches. We probably know a high proportion of the extinct types and the adjustment needed to extrapolate from the earliest known fossil to the origin of the group would be minor, compared to the correction needed for primates. After all, some periods, such as the Oligocene, have yielded very few primates indeed though we know there must have been plenty. There have long been good reasons, too, for supposing that the primates are ancient. The latest revisions of antiquity are dramatic, but not surprising in principle. It seems clear, too, that there were no large mammalian herbivores of any kind in the Cretaceous, so the true ungulates must all be assumed to date from the Palaeocene onwards. Primates and a few other groups of small mammals got under way as early as they did because they did not interfere with the dinosaurs. The emergence of big mammalian herbivores and carnivores was forestalled for as long as the dinosaurs occupied the large animal niches.

That, then, is an outline of the mammals. Yet we should acknowledge that many other animal groups have also done wonderful things throughout the Cenozoic, including of course the fish which have diversified more than any other vertebrates, the insects which have exploited the angiosperms more thoroughly than any other group and today provide most of the species on Earth and a huge proportion of the animal biomass, and the reptiles which prevail in many an environment that is too meagre to support viable groups of mammals – including deserts and islands, and even desert island-continents like Australia. This passing comment is all I can give them, however. But it would be foolish not to give half a dozen paragraphs to the birds.

A WORD ON BIRDS

The more you look at birds the more you realise that the tits and finches that bring such charm to the garden give a misleading impression of their range of form and scope of life. At present there are about 8,600 species of birds – roughly twice as many as there are of mammals – and they divide into about twenty-five orders. About 60 per cent of them – more than 5,000 species – belong to just one of those orders, the Passeriformes or perching

birds. Most passerines are small, like the tits and finches. The
biggest are the crows, and the biggest of all is the raven. Clearly,
the passerines flourish because they fill the niche of small daytime
flier, feeding mainly on insects and seeds, which is not occupied
by the mammals. Indeed the birds as a whole seem to play second
fiddle to the mammals just as the mammals, for such a vast period
of time, played second fiddle to the dinosaurs.

Only when we look at the fossil record as a whole, and turn
our eyes away from the ubiquitous passerines, do we see the true
potential of birds. We see indeed that the passerines were comparative latecomers to the global party. Like the bears, they did
not truly come into their own until the Miocene. Before that, the
role of small day-time fliers was filled mainly by the
Coraciiformes, now represented by kingfishers and bee-eaters.
Taken as a whole, however, the birds may be seen as miniature
dinosaurs which could, if only the niches were again vacated, recreate a world ecology very like that of the Mesozoic: an ecology
which, as then, would be dominated by great terrestrial herds.
Even today on the plains of Kenya the ostriches, bustards, ground
hornbills and secretary birds form a kind of post-Mesozoic sub-
culture. Their chief predator – at least of their young – is another
bird: the giant marshal eagle.

The only flightless member of that Kenyan quartet is the
ostrich, which is the largest of all living birds and belongs to the
ratites: the only major group of birds that have apparently been
flightless from their time of origin in the Palaeocene. The other
ratite survivors are the rheas of South America, the kiwis of New
Zealand, the emus of Australia and the cassowaries of New
Guinea and northern Australia. But the greatest ratites of all were
the moas of New Zealand of which there were about fifteen
species, some smaller than a modern emu but some far taller even
than an ostrich. They survived for just a few centuries after the
Polynesians arrived on New Zealand to become the Maoris,
about a thousand years ago. The moas could dominate New
Zealand because those islands had no native mammals. Yet they
were not free of harassment even before the Maoris arrived. They
were preyed upon by a giant eagle, one of the biggest that has
ever lived, which was short-winged like the modern harpie eagles
that prey upon monkeys in South America, so it could duck
through the trees. But the heaviest ratites of all, and hence the

most massive birds of all time, were not the moas but the elephant birds of Madagascar. The biggest species stood ten feet tall and weighed half a ton.

Many other birds, besides ratites, have re-evolved flightlessness. Flight takes a huge amount of energy and wings need constant upkeep, and the birds seem always to be looking for the easier, terrestrial option. On islands, freed from mammalian predators but at risk from crosswinds, species after species in a great variety of groups have reverted to flightlessness. There are or have been flightless pigeons, such as the dodo of Mauritius and the solitaire of Rodriguez, flightless ibises from Réunion and Hawaii, a flight-less parrot (the kakapo) from New Zealand, flightless cormorants, auks, and of course penguins, and many flightless geese and ducks. The Hawaiian goose (which in fact flies well) is now known to be only one of an entire suite of geese and ducks, some of them flightless, that lived on that island until recent centuries. Some flightless types became truly formidable, for example the carniv-orous diatrymids which flourished briefly from the Palaeocene to the Eocene in Eurasia and North America, and the terrifying phorusrhacids of Patagonia in South America with heads as big as a horse and huge eagle beaks, which flourished from the Eocene right through to the Pleistocene. They must have hunted in packs like wolves – or indeed like some dinosaurs – to bring down a galloping litoptern in full dash. Diatrymids and phorusrhacids were relatives of the modern cranes and rails. The moorhen is a rail. Within its tiny breast is the spirit of *Tyrannosaurus rex*, and within its gene pool is at least some of the potential to release that spirit. It lacks only for opportunity. Perhaps its time will come again.

There, then, are the principal creatures with whom we and our ancestors have shared this planet. They have helped to shape our evolution and our history, and we increasingly shape theirs. It is time to look more closely at ourselves.

The Fifth Column:
How We Became

'The Fifth Column' of this chapter's title is the order of the primates. I see them over 80 million years or more creeping up on other creatures, always a little different from the rest, doing things their own way, rarely being dominant but usually having a presence at least in the tropics, and finally producing a lineage which evolved into human beings who have altered everything. This is a literary metaphor, in the manner described by Misia Landau, but I think it is a helpful one: the heuristic and so legitimate use of myth.

To be sure, primates did not set out to be subversive. It never entered any of their heads that one day one of their number would evolve into us, and that we would then transform the world. I will argue in Chapter 9 that there is more to the notion of 'progress' than most scientists now acknowledge and we have already observed that evolution has an innate tendency to pursue some lines rather than others. But I certainly do not suggest that our own evolution has been driven inexorably from protoprimate to us along some metalled route. If things had gone differently at any stage – if the climate had not changed as it did; if particular gene pools in particular places had not been exposed to particular pressures – then our own particular species or even our entire lineage would not have appeared.

Yet if we look back at our own history we do see a wonderful chain of circumstance. To a degree unique among mammals the creatures that we can reasonably acknowledge as our direct ancestors retained virtually the whole array of basic tetrapod characters, and then over time developed them. Primordial fingers became powerful and dextrous hands and forelimbs expanded into hypermobile arms while the senses and nervous system grew in complexity to provide outstanding balance and coordination. Our ancestors evolved these characters in response to the pressures of their own times – as adaptations to ways of life that were quite different from ours. Yet they provided us nonetheless with the raw material to create an ape that could abandon the trees, and then employ its arboreal inheritance to exploit its new environment in ways that no other animal had ever before attempted. If it was logically and practically possible for an animal to design its own ancestors, then we could hardly have chosen better.

In this chapter I want to ask how the final transformation took place: how one of the forest apes became ourselves.

PONGIDS AND HOMINIDS

'Linnaeus found no difficulty in establishing discriminating characters of the different tribes of apes, but very great in scientific contra-distinctions between the genera man and ape; but it is to be hoped that he had not met with many individuals of either kind that had produced any practical hesitation in determining his judgment.'

Samuel Taylor Coleridge, 'Allegory'

Virtually all details of human evolution have been fiercely fought over at some time and some still are,* but one point at least is universally agreed – that human beings are indeed descended from apes, and that our nearest living relatives are the apes of Africa: the two species of chimpanzees in the genus *Pan*, and the gorillas, *Gorilla*. These ideas were first formally enunciated in 1871 by Charles Darwin in *The Descent of Man and Selection in Relation to Sex* (John Murray and Sons, London). Chimpanzees and gorillas are conventionally classed together with the orangutans, *Pongo*, in the family Pongidae. Humans and their extinct relatives are placed in a separate family, the Hominidae.

At first sight it seems easy enough to distinguish hominids from pongids. At least, as Coleridge commented, it is hard to confuse individuals. We have much bigger brains, both in absolute terms and relative to body size. We walk upright while the apes use their knuckles as forefeet and are essentially quadripedal. Smaller but sometimes sharper anatomical distinctions also help the diagnosis, notably that pongids have big, prominent canine teeth which they use for display while the hominids' canines became more and more

*The principal arguments over the past hundred years or so are excellently described by Roger Lewin in *Bones of Contention* (Penguin, London, 1987).

like incisors as evolution proceeded and are used for eating. Even so, many biologists have complained, as Linnaeus did, that the distinctions are matters of degree and the line is hard to draw. Indeed, modern studies of the kind described in Figure V.1 reveal that the DNA of modern humans is extraordinarily similar to that of modern chimps ('99 per cent overlap' as the biochemists tend to say) and only slightly less similar to gorillas'. This is less than the difference between many pairs of species in some other groups that are virtually considered to be the same animal. Orangs, on the other hand, the Asian wing of the Pongidae, are far more different from chimps and gorillas than the two African genera are from hominids.

For this kind of reason, then, many biologists argue that the present classification makes no sense. A family boundary is drawn between two species that are obviously closely related – chimps and humans – while two that are known to be more distant – chimp and orang – are grouped together. It would surely make more sense to put the humans and all the great apes together in one family, which in practice would be the Hominidae since this name was coined first (by Linnaeus himself in 1758) and by the rules of nomenclature takes precedence. Taxonomy is supposed to represent real relationships, but the pongid/hominid division seems to cut right across the biological realities.

I have great sympathy with this view – I like the idea that human beings and animals form a continuum – and yet feel, on other grounds, that the present taxonomy contains another quite different but at least equally important biological truth: not evolutionary, but ecological.

The classification of living creatures has been guided by two different criteria. The dominant criterion is indeed that of 'phylogenetic' relationship: who is literally related to whom. Thus, as described in Figure IV.1 biologists seek to place living creatures in 'clades' – the members of which are presumed to share a common ancestor, and to be more closely related to each other than to anything else. But biologists also, like it or not, classify animals in a less purist fashion, according to 'grade'. Animals placed in the same grade are broadly speaking related but for various reasons they may not form a true clade. The reptiles – class Reptilia – are a prime example. The Reptilia could be recognised as a clade only if we allowed it to include the birds and the mammals, which both descended from reptiles. Contrariwise, the living reptiles that

Figure V.1: Molecular Phylogeny

Nowadays molecular biologists – or, less grandly, we might simply say 'biochemists' – can throw light on various related issues: how closely are different animals related to each other? Who might be the ancestor of whom? And *when* did two related species first share a common ancestor?

The logic of their approach is simple. Over evolutionary time body proteins alter, and so does the DNA that provides the codes for those proteins – just as gross anatomical features alter. However, there are two distinct differences between proteins and DNA on the one hand, and gross anatomical features on the other. The first is that there are straightforward 'objective' ways of measuring the difference between the proteins or nucleic acids of different animals. For example – and this is a technique first reported as long ago as 1902 – the difference between body proteins from different animals can be judged by the relative strength of their reaction when exposed to particular antibodies. The differences between two samples of DNA can be judged by seeing how tightly they cleave together when given the opportunity to do so, which is a very simple measurement to make. Or, if there is time and opportunity, different protein or DNA samples can be analysed chemically and then compared. Of course, gross anatomical features are also measured, but it is much harder to quantify the differences and similarities of two femurs or molars from different creatures than it is to mix two samples of DNA and measure the subsequent change in viscosity.

Secondly, the gross anatomical features of an animal are exposed to the outside world. These features matter: they determine the survival of the animal. They are, in short, subject to natural selection and can change rapidly (or be pressured by natural selection not to change at all). Thus, two related animals that live different kinds of lives can quickly evolve different features, while unrelated animals living the same lives come to resemble each other through convergence. Often it can be hard to distinguish the homologous features – those that look the same because they evolved from a common ancestor – from those that are merely analagous, where resemblance is due to convergence.

Of course, proteins and nucleic acids also matter, and they too are subject to natural selection. But their molecules contain large sections that seem to do very little and which therefore are not subject to natural selection because small differences in their structure make little difference to their owner's survival. Yet these apparently non-functional regions continue to change, because as time passes so more and more random genetic mutations take place. Mutations in features that affect the animal's function are likely to be eliminated (or very occasionally favoured) by natural selection. But mutations in parts of molecules that do not affect the animal's life simply accumulate. Hence the degree of difference between two animals in the non-functional regions of their proteins or nucleic acids is related directly to the *time* that has elapsed since those animals last shared a common ancestor. Thus mutations within proteins or nucleic acids can provide a 'molecular clock'.

Note, finally, that in practice DNA occurs both in the nucleus and in organelles in the cytoplasm of the cell known as mitochondria. Both nuclear and mitochondrial DNA are used for comparative purposes. Mitochondrial DNA tends in general to mutate more quickly than most nuclear DNA and is good for working out relationships between closely related species or populations within species.

Of course, in addition to DNA and proteins, all living cells also contain RNA which acts as an intermediary between the DNA and the proteins. RNA changes only very slowly over time, but this means that it can provide a molecular clock that operates on a very long time-scale. Hence it is useful for working out relationships between large groups of creatures – classes, phyla, or even kingdoms – whose most recent common ancestors may have lived many hundreds of millions or even billions of years ago.

As noted in the text, studies both of DNA and of various proteins show that chimpanzees and humans are extremely closely related and shared a common ancestor within the past few million years.

are all placed in the same class are not all closely related to each other. Indeed it is clear on various grounds that birds are much closer to crocodiles than crocs are to turtles. The similarities can be seen in detailed anatomy and in the fossils – and even in behaviour. Baby crocs have been seen sitting in the lower branches of trees, chirping for their mother (crocs are excellent mothers) for all the world like sparrows in a suburban hedge. Ecologically, however, crocs are clearly more turtle-like than bird-like. In particular, crocs and turtles are both poikilotherms. So in practice, while acknowledging the phylogenetic relationships of birds and crocs, it is sensible to stick with tradition and leave birds as Aves while keeping crocs with turtles in the pseudo-class Reptilia.

So it is, I suggest, with pongids and hominids. Genetically, the pongid chimp and the hominid *Homo* are extremely close – so close, indeed, that it may be possible to form hybrids between the two. However, we cannot take this for granted because the barriers between species do not in fact depend only upon the overall 'genetic distance' between them but on the possession or non-possession of genes that create specific barriers to successful mating. We can see this principle in action among the tree-snails (in the family Partulidae) of the high volcanic islands of the Pacific. Some pairs that are obviously extremely similar, both in appearance and in their genes, are nonetheless unable to mate successfully, whereas other pairs that are much less closely related can mate to produce hybrids. However, I simply do not know whether hybridisation has ever been attempted between chimps and humans – it would be very easy technically to inseminate a female chimp with human semen but if anyone carried out such an experiment in some far-flung laboratory they would probably keep quiet about it.

But ecologically and morphologically humans and chimps are quite different creatures. Human beings have invented an entirely new ecomorph. And, as discussed further in the following chapters, they have developed a whole new way of life; ecologically, a chimp is hardly more similar to a human than it is to a ground hornbill, which like chimps is sociable and goes hunting in family groups. Indeed it would not be entirely foolish, if classification is to reflect the broad reality of life and not simply the niceties of genes, to place human beings in a new kingdom. In some significant ways they are as different from all other creatures as plants are from bacteria.

But does this not imply disrespect for the chimp? Is it not better to emphasise the chimp's similarity? I would argue precisely the opposite. It is proper for us, indeed it is the only tolerable stance, to respect all other living creatures, and for our respect to be as near absolute as possible. We are powerful, but our power can properly be seen as a 'gift': it was not of our making. And I suggest that power should always acknowledge the principle of *noblesse oblige*. In short, our respect for chimps should not be dependent on their genetic similarity to us. That is merely another form of anthropocentrism. That they are our fellow creatures, and obviously wonderful, is enough. Is it suggested, after all, that we should accord more respect to chimps than to the beautiful, soulful, but more distant orang?

Anyway, we have seen that the pongids – at least the existing ones – comprise *Pan*, *Gorilla*, and *Pongo*. As for the hominids, palaeoanthropologists over the years have classified the copious but still frustrating scattering of fossils in many different ways and spawned a host of generic names. Some of these have been abandoned, including *Pithecanthropus* and *Eanthropus*, which was the name once attached to the spurious 'Piltdown man'. Most specialists today recognise either two genera of hominids, or three. I will follow the latter course.*

THE THREE GENERA OF HOMINID

The three known and recognised hominid genera all arose in Africa. The first to arise was *Australopithecus* which sounds Australian but in fact simply means 'southern ape'. (The scientist who coined this somewhat infelicitous cognomen was himself Australian, though it would be mischievous to suggest that this biased his nomenclature.) These early australopithecines had

---

*In *Nature* (4 May 1995, vol. 375 p. 88), Tim White of the University of California, Berkeley, and his colleagues proposed that the oldest known hominid, which they had previously called *Australopithecus ramidus*, should be renamed *Ardipithecus ramidus*. At the time of writing this footnote – late July 1995 – palaeoanthropologists are not yet universally agreed that *ramidus* is different enough from other members of the *Australopithecus* genus to warrant a new generic name. For present purposes, therefore, I am sticking to the original name of *Australopithecus ramidus*. But if the name *Ardipithecus* does become accepted then all statements in this text concerning the number of accepted hominid genera must of course be increased by one.

thinnish crania and smallish jaws and are said to be 'gracile'. In general they were between a metre and a metre and a half in height, with crania (and hence with brains) that were roughly the same size as a chimp's.

Then, it seems, *Australopithecus* produced two branches, which evolved in very different directions. One branch developed thick-boned skulls and jaws, and are said to be 'robust', and these robusts are commonly placed in their own genus, *Paranthropus*. The other branch remained gracile but developed bigger brains: this branch became the genus *Homo*. Thus the evolutionary tree of the Hominidae is generally seen to be essentially Y-shaped: gracile australopithecines in the stem giving rise to robust paranthropines on the one hand and gracile hominines on the other. (Incidentally, some palaeoanthropologists include the genus *Paranthropus* within the genus *Australopithecus*, and hence recognise only two genera: *Australopithecus* and *Homo*. They argue that the different robust species may have evolved independently of each other, from different australopithecine ancestors, and therefore are not truly related. In this case, *Paranthropus* would not be a 'natural' grouping. I have no views on this. I am following the three-genus grouping, which also has strong supporters, mainly because it seems to me to be tidier.)

The question now – as it has been ever since Darwin – is which of the apes did the hominids derive from? Who was the immediate ancestor of *Australopithecus*?

The answer is that nobody knows, because although we have good fossils of ancient hominids we have no fossils at all from apes that could be candidate ancestors. The chimps – the 'common' chimp and bonobo (formerly known as the 'pygmy chimp') – are our nearest living relatives, but neither is likely to be our ancestor. Both are too specialised: both have clearly developed characteristics of their own *since* the split with the hominids. It is more realistic to suppose that the chimps and the hominids simply shared a common ancestor – and this creature, 'the common ancestor', is the one that everyone now would dearly like to find. The common ancestor is, in short, the modern equivalent of the old-style 'missing link'. But on various grounds it is very reasonable to assume that the common ancestor was much more like an ape than like a modern human. And since chimps, for all their specialisations, are very obvious apes it is reasonable to think of the common ancestor as an essentially chimp-like animal – which might indeed, when it is found, be placed in the genus *Pan*. But for the rest of this account I will simply call the common ancestor 'the common ancestor' or 'the ape ancestor'.

The next essential question is When? When did the hominids arise from the pongids? Or, more specifically, when did *Australopithecus* diverge from *Pan*?

PONGIDS INTO HOMINIDS – WHEN?

The issue of when the hominids arose from apes has exercised biologists ever since Darwin proposed in 1871 that such a transition had in fact taken place. One powerful tradition has maintained that the split took place a very long time ago indeed – in fact that it happened well before the emergence of the modern pongids, which means that the pongids in general and the chimp in particular could not be our ancestors. Beyond doubt, the study of human evolution has been bedevilled by prejudice and we might detect here the desire of some eminent professors to place as much distance between themselves and chimps as possible. To be fair, however, protangonists of the hominids-are-ancient-and-separate tradition tended rather to suggest that an organ as remarkable as the human brain must have needed many millions of years to evolve. More specifically, the excellent palaeontologists Elwyn Simons and David Pilbeam, both formerly at Yale, suggested in the 1960s that the early Miocene ape *Ramapithecus* showed hominid features in its jaw; extrapolations from this suggested that a discrete line leading to hominids might have begun as early as the Oligocene, more than 25 million years ago. Similarities between us and chimps would then be a matter of mere convergence. By no means everyone agreed with such a view but it was certainly influential. A diagram of human evolution in J.Z. Young's *Life of Vertebrates*,★ published by Oxford University Press in 1962, shows just this: the hominids going their

★I cite *Life of Vertebrates* not as a primary source, which in this context it obviously is not, but as a highly influential one. The author, one of the outstanding zoologists of the mid-twentieth century, tried hard to reflect the orthodoxy of his day. Young's espousal of the hominids-are-ancient-and-separate theory thus reveals the *zeitgeist*.

own sweet way even before the Miocene began.

That idea is now dead. Indeed a stake has been driven through its heart. Some palaeontologists, including Elwyn Simons, argue that palaeontology itself killed it off. That is, more Miocene fossils turned up that on the one hand were virtually the same as *Ramapithecus* but on the other hand were obviously related to orangs. So *Ramapithecus* too must be on the orang rather than the gorilla-chimp-hominid lineage. However, the *coup de grâce* to the hominids-are-ancient-and-separate idea was delivered from the 1960s onwards by the newly emerging techniques of 'molecular phylogeny' – by which the relationships and possibly ancestry of animals are determined not by differences in their gross anatomy but by differences in body chemistry.

Specifically, Vincent Sarich and Allan Wilson of the University of California at Berkeley first examined the albumen protein in the blood, and then looked directly at the DNA, of humans, chimps, and other primates (see Figure V.1). The albumens and DNA of humans and chimps proved remarkably similar: so similar, said Sarich and Wilson, that the two must have shared a common ancestor only 4—6 million years ago: not in the Oligocene, but in the very late Miocene or even the Pliocene.

At the time that conclusion was stunning. At first, many palaeontologists simply felt that Sarich and Wilson were wrong. But now they are vindicated: a divergence 4—6 million years ago – call it 5 million years ago – has become the orthodoxy. The ancient *Ramapithecus* is no longer plausible as a human ancestor, and the realisation has grown that huge evolutionary changes, including the growth of the human brain, can take place quickly when the conditions are right. The time since the late Miocene embraces all of our pre-history that is specifically hominid. For us, the Pliocene-Pleistocene is truly 'the day before yesterday'.

So the next obvious question is 'How?'. How did the chimp-like common ancestor evolve into us?

HOW THE FIRST HOMINIDS BECAME

The three principal species of australopithecine have been discovered in reverse order of antiquity. The youngest is *Australopithecus africanus*, found in a lime-pit in South Africa and

named by Raymond Dart in the 1920s. Older than africanus, and
apparently the species that lasted the longest, is *A. afarensis*, discovered by Don Johanson and his colleagues on a hillside at Afar
in Ethiopia in 1972. The oldest of all is *A. ramidus*, found in 1992,
again at Afar (in a place called Aramis), and reported in *Nature* in
September 1994 by Tim White at the University of California,
Berkeley, and his colleagues.*

In date, *Australopithecus ramidus* is tantalisingly close to the supposed age of the common ancestor. Fragments of seventeen
individuals were found lying on fossilised volcanic ash ('tuff')
which is dated at 4·4 million years. Furthermore, ramidus has precisely the combination of characters that palaeontologists were
hoping to find and were indeed expecting: more ape-like than *A.
afarensis*, less apish than a chimp, but with qualities of both.
'Ramidus' comes from the Afar word 'ramid' meaning 'root': a
pleasing piece of nomenclature.

Between them, the different ramidus fragments provided a
complete set of teeth – including one deciduous or 'milk' tooth
– plus the bases of two skulls and, most unusually, pieces of all
three bones from a left arm. There is plenty here to go on even
though there are some frustrating omissions.

Thus the teeth reveal an animal that really does seem to be
halfway between an ape and the later, more human-like afarensis.
The canines are still prominent but compared to a chimp's, say
White and his colleagues, they appear 'low and blunt'. The bottom canines are also worn as if they were used for eating rather
than display. The enamel of the canines and other teeth is thin
like a chimp's, not thick like a human's. It is not as thick even as
afarensis's. The milk tooth was a first, lower, milk molar – a tooth
which has always proved particularly instructive in deciding who
among the apes and hominids is related to whom. In ramidus this
tooth is narrow like a chimp's, not wide like a human's: according to Tim White and his colleagues it is 'far closer to that of a
chimpanzee than to any known hominid'.

The arm bones are broken so it is impossible to say whether in
life they would have been long like a chimp's or shorter like the
known hominids. But the bits that do remain show a 'mosaic' of

* '*Australopithecus ramidus*, a new species of early hominid from Aramis, Ethiopia', T.D.
White *et al*, *Nature*, 22 September 1994, pp. 306–12).

chimpish and hominid details.

But the key quality of the hominids is their bipedalism. The crucial issue therefore is whether *Australopithecus ramidus* walked upright and, if so, whether it did so confidently and with all the appropriate anatomy and reflexes. But the bones that could really tell us – in particular the pelvis and the feet – are missing. There is a clue, though, in the base of the cranium. For in animals that walk on four legs, the place on the skull where the neck-bones join – the foramen magnum – is far back, so when the animal walks its horizontal head is thrust out in front of the horizontal backbone. But in humans and the other australopithecines the foramen magnum is further forward, so that the head balances on top of a vertebral column that is held vertically. The pieces of *A. ramidus* skull show a foramen magnum that is significantly further forward than in a chimp. The inference is that this indeed was an upright animal.

The next species in order of age, *Australopithecus afarensis*, leaves us with far fewer doubts. The first afarensis that was found by Don Johanson and his colleagues included almost half the skeleton. This was the famous 'Lucy' named after the Beatles record, 'Lucy in the Sky with Diamonds', which at that time resounded through the Johanson camp. Afarensis remains have now been found throughout east Africa, from Ethiopia, Tanzania, and Kenya, and they range in age from more than 4 million years to less than 2·5. Lucy herself is around 3 million years old.

If any creature can properly be called a 'typical' australopithecine, it is afarensis. Its brain, at 400—500 millilitres, is not conspicuously larger than a chimp's but afarensis does have a somewhat less protruding face, and its canine teeth are more prominent than ours but far less so than those of any ape or of ramidus. The arms are relatively longer than a human's, but far shorter than a chimp's. Most excitingly, though, we can answer the crucial question which for ramidus remains uncertain. We know how afarensis walked.

For one thing, Lucy's skeleton does include much of the pelvis and some bones of the legs which are proportionally longer than a chimp's and apparently more stilt-like, like a human's. Uprightness is suggested. What clinches the matter, though, is the wonderfully felicitous find by Mary Leakey in the late 1970s, some six years after Johanson's initial discovery. She came across footprints that were made by three *A. afarensis* as they strode across volcanic ash at Laetoli, Tanzania – ash that fell 3·6 million years ago, and is now fossilised. The prints show very clearly what the anatomists hitherto had been able only to guess: that afarensis could walk happily on two legs, effectively in the heel-and-toe fashion of true human beings. Incidentally, those fossil prints were criss-crossed by the tiny hoof-prints of a three-toed hipparion. There are scenes from history I would love to have witnessed. The Sermon on the Mount would be one. The little band of afarensis and the three-toed ponies on the Pliocene mud of Tanzania would be another.

The discovery of Lucy and the footprints of her fellows finally answered a question that had taxed palaeoanthropologists ever since Darwin: whether the first hominids became bipedal before they became big-brained, or whether they acquired their big brains first. For reasons that in retrospect seem largely mythological, leading scientists of the early twentieth century favoured the latter view: that human evolution had been 'brain-led'. It was largely for this reason that they fell so easily for the hoax of Piltdown, in which, in 1912, parts of a modern human skull and the slightly doctored jaw of an orang-utan were stained to make them look old and buried side by side in a gravel pit in Sussex.*

---

*Although some palaeoanthropologists were never taken in by Piltdown, the ones who were included some of the most distinguished and expert of their time – Sir Arthur Keith, Sir Grafton Elliot Smith, and Sir Arthur Smith Woodward in Britain, and Henry Fairfield Osborn in the United States. Who planted the spurious bones is one of the great whodunnits of the twentieth century although the leading candidate is their discoverer, the lawyer and amateur bone-seeker Charles Dawson. Eminent professionals should not have been fooled by the mock-up, but it precisely met their preconceptions: Arthur Keith's belief that the hominid line was ancient and separate from the pongid, and Elliot Smith's firm-held belief that hominid evolution had been 'brain-led'.

These preconceptions sadly affected their response to the first report of *A. africanus* in 1924 – which was the first australopithecine to be found and in some ways was therefore the palaeoanthropological discovery of the century. Their failure to acknowledge the importance of africanus in turn confused the entire field of palaeoanthropology for the following three decades. In fact it was left to the Australian anatomist, Raymond Dart – who also gave the australopithecines their somewhat cumbersome appellation – to report and describe africanus in February 1925. Arthur Keith, Elliot Smith, and Arthur Smith Woodward denied that *A. africanus* was any kind of human ancestor, partly because they were already wedded to Piltdown and partly because both *A. africanus* and Raymond Dart were colonials, and therefore not pukka, whereas they (and Piltdown) were true Englishmen (or in Keith's case a Scotsman, which is the next best thing). This sounds bizarre, but is generally considered to be the case.

This was what they were looking for: a creature with apish features in which the brain had clearly developed first. That Piltdown was a hoax was finally revealed by chemical tests at the British Museum in 1953. As we have seen, the actual facts of the case did not become clear until Lucy *et al* appeared in the 1970s: that our australopithecine ancestors were slim and upright, broadly similar to small humans though with relatively longer but far from ape-like arms, and with a face that was somewhat flatter than an ape's but topped with a small apish cranium. The big brain was imposed later on to this quasi-human form.

Finally, the youngest of the gracile australopithecines, *A. africanus*, is South African rather than east African, as afarensis and ramidus were. In general africanus looks more human than afarensis, with a less prominent face and more incisor-like canines. Africanus seems to have appeared about 3 million years ago, and died out some time after 2·5 million years ago. It was not as long-lived as *A. afarensis*.

Then there were the 'robusts' whom some prefer to call *Paranthropus*, which is the convention I follow here. They were not in fact conspicuous bruisers: at less than a metre and a half they were no taller than the graciles. But they had heavier skulls that in some were crested for muscle attachment, and huge jaws with millstone teeth, presumably for grinding coarse vegetation; as Elisabeth Vrba has commented, 'They tried to chew their way out of trouble.' Conservative classification recognises two species from East Africa – the earlier *P. aethiopicus* from about 2·6 million years ago and the later *P. boisei* who presumably descended from aethiopicus and lived from about 2·3 to 1·2 million years ago. In Southern Africa lived *P. robustus*, from around 2·0 to around 1·0 million years ago – the most recent australopithecine (defined broadly) to survive.

Finally, the hominines (members of the genus *Homo*) first appeared around 2·2 million years ago in the form of *Homo habilis*. Events after that occupy most of the rest of this book. First it is pertinent to ask how these various hominids were related to each other: who really gave rise to whom.

RELATIONSHIPS

Exactly how the three gracile australopithecines are related to each other, and to the later paranthropines and hominines, is unknown. Ramidus may be the first true hominid, or there may be other distinct species between ramidus and the missing common ancestor. It seems highly likely, however, that ramidus gave rise to afarensis, and that afarensis gave rise to africanus.

Beyond that, there are several theoretical possibilities. Perhaps africanus gave rise to *Homo*, leaving afarensis to produce the paranthropines. Perhaps africanus gave rise to the paranthropines, while the hominines derived directly from afarensis. Perhaps afarensis generated africanus *and* the paranthropines *and* the hominines – in which case africanus, like the paranthropines, was simply a dead end. Perhaps afarensis themselves, despite their variability and ubiquity, are off the main line. We just do not know. But it does seem reasonable to assume that afarensis is probably the ancestor both of the paranthropines and of the hominines – although for the time being africanus will have to be left floating, perhaps as a human ancestor, perhaps as a paranthropine ancestor, and perhaps as an evolutionary twig that blossomed for a time in the south and then faded.

So now we should ask the biggest question. 'Why?'. I suggested in Chapter 3 that big evolutionary changes generally take place only when the ecosystem is given a kick, and the various lineages – those that have the genetic wherewithal to do so – are forced to change. So what did the kicking in this case?

WHY DID THE AUSTRALOPITHECINES BECOME?

The broad answer to the question 'Why?' surely lies in the global changes discussed in Chapter 2: the cooling of the Earth that took place throughout the Cenozoic as the Himalayas rose and leached the insulating carbon dioxide from the atmosphere. The cooling did not occur smoothly, for that is not the way the world works, but in jerks, and in the late Miocene came a sudden fall in temperature and with it increasing aridity, for coolness and dryness go together. The habitat changes when this happens, and animals that cannot simply move out die (there was a huge die-off of native mammals in the late Miocene of North America). Forests retreat when the world cools and dries, for trees above all need water. In the Miocene almost worldwide it was the grasses that stepped opportunistically into the breach. They had played only minor roles since the warm, wet Eocene, but now they came truly into their own.

At first in late Miocene Africa the margins of the great central forest turned into more modest woodland. These woods were closed at first – the canopy meeting overhead – but they became increasingly open as the cooling continued. Then, at around 2·5 million years ago as the Pliocene neared its end, came another burst of cooling and drying and much of the woodland gave way finally to the kind of savannah that we see today: wooded in parts, but much of it merely dotted with scattered acacias.

The 'common ancestral ape' that lived in the late Miocene forest of Africa evidently produced scions for all occasions. One lineage became the chimps, which adapted more and more to the dwindling but still vast forest. The other lineage became the hominids, who adapted first to the more open woodland, and then, when the time came, to the newly expanding savannah. In general, the gracile australopithecines were creatures of the woods – although afarensis finally adapted to a wide range of territory, both wooded and more open – while the genus *Homo* truly rose to the challenge of open country and became a creature of grassland. Indeed, *Homo* appeared right on cue, soon after the global cooling of 2·5 million years ago.

We have direct evidence that *A. ramidus*, the creature closest to the common ancestor, was a creature of woodland. A marvellous assemblage of plant and animal remains from the immediate surroundings shows that this was the case.★ Thus there were thousands of seeds of *Canthium*, a plant commonly found in African woods and forests. Primates were the commonest large vertebrates, including baboons and colobus monkeys – the latter accounting for 30 per cent of all the fauna. The most frequent bovid by far was a medium-sized kudu, another woodland creature.

★These accompanying fossils are recorded in a separate paper: 'Ecological and Temporal Placement of Early Pliocene Hominids at Aramis, Ethiopia', Giday Woldegabriel *et al*, *Nature*, 22 September 1994, vol. 371, pp. 330–3.

Then there was a pygmy hippo, *Hexaprotodon*, an extinct genus: another woodland creature, like the modern pygmy hippo of west Africa. It seems that the pygmy hippos declined as the woodland bovids rose to prominence, while the common hippo, *Hippopotamus*, escaped bovid competition by staying in the water. There were pigs alongside ramidus, too, plus a three-toed horse, *Hipparion*, and *Ceratotherium praecox,* the early form of the modern African white rhino. There were two giraffe species, both very like the modern giraffes. Then, too, there was a marvellous assemblage of proboscideans — not a lot of them, but they were there. There were members of the modern family, Elephantidae. There was a straight-tusked gomphothere, *Anancus.* And there were some of the amazing deinotheres, *Deinotherium*, with their lower-jawed, downward-pointing tusks. At the other end of the size-scale there was a small squirrel, plus two species of bush-rats and a mole-rat.

The carnivores were equally impressive, and clearly geared to the complete range of herbivores. At the small end was the dwarf mongoose *Helogale*, and there were otters, civets, canids, cats, and hyaenids. Then at the top of the predatory size-range was the puma-sized sabretooth *Megantereon*, the ancestor of *Smilodon*. And finally, to cap them all, there was the first-ever bear to be found in east Africa, of the genus *Agriotherium*. The African woods and forests have been sadly deprived of bears ever since. We tend from our northern vantage point to think of grizzlies and polar bears in temperate habitats but bears are just as at home in tropical forests and may still be found in the forests of India (sloth bear), South America (spectacled bear), Asia (Asiatic black bear), and south-east Asia (sun bear and giant panda). Why Africa has had no bears in living memory south of the Sahara is a mystery.

Finally, for good measure, the ramidus fossils were accompanied by those of bats, birds, tortoises and crocodiles. For *Australopithecus ramidus*, some of these creatures would have been food, some competitors, and some mortal enemies. But if ramidus had had the wit or the leisure to be naturalists they would surely have been in heaven. The fauna they lived among was truly fabulous.

That the first australopithecines lived in such woodland was crucial to their evolution, and hence to ours. If they had remained in dense forest then it is hard to see how they could have evolved at all, for dense forest seems to demand the ecomorph of the chimp. If they had been forced to transpose in one swoop from forest to grassland then surely they would have failed, dying not least by the jaws of lions and hyaenas.

But woodland is perfect country to promote the kind of evolutionary changes that turned the common ancestor, a forest ape, into a hominid. Such woodland is of the kind that in mediaeval England was known as 'forest' – clumps of closed woodland with bushy clearings – and in Africa this habitat expanded as the Pliocene wore on. England's existing New Forest shows the form exactly. Sherwood Forest, home of the legendary Robin Hood, was also of that type. Indeed, such forest covered vast swathes of mediaeval England and huge numbers of people made their living from it: cutting and coppicing trees (lopping them to the ground, and then harvesting the long, thin branches that spring from the stumps), burning charcoal, hunting game, grazing cattle and herding pigs. These people were collectively known as 'foresters': a very different *métier* from that of present-day graduates in forestry who cultivate trees for woodpulp and timber. So important were such forests to the mediaeval economy that half the laws of England were concerned with them: who could graze what, where, and when, and the dire punishments that would befall transgressors. Magna Carta is largely concerned with forestry, in that traditional sense. In short, the 'foresters' of the English Middle Ages demonstrated by their number, variety, and overall economic importance that woodland is rich and varied territory offering many opportunities to the imaginative incumbent. The imagination of the australopithecine was closer to that of an ape than that of a human being but the stimulus was there nonetheless.

For example, and most significantly, the woodland existence of the australopithecines explains how they evolved their bipedalism. For if they had gone straight into grassland we would have to ask how they could have survived before they learned to walk and run so well on two legs. But if they had stayed in the forest then it is hard to see how they would have become bipedal at all. Chimps are not bipedal, after all, and neither are monkeys. Why should an ape that is still living in dense forest become bipedal?

But in their African woodland, their mediaeval 'forest', we can envisage them living a double life, half in the trees and half out of them. They may well have continued to sleep in the trees, on platforms, as chimps and gorillas do. They probably took to the trees at the first sign of danger – which in large part explains their survival in the face of lions and hyaenas. They would also have used the trees as vantage points. In similar fashion, cheetahs sit at the tops of termite mounds to watch for prey and meerkats climb to the tops of bushes to scan the sky for hawks. But increasingly the early australopithecines fed on the ground. Increasingly, they dashed across the clearings both to escape the many dangers and in pursuit of prey. This way of life – retreating to a safe place and dashing out to feed with a weather eye on predators – is common in nature. We see it in virtually all desert rodents which live in holes, in the small carnivores which prey upon them but keep their eyes open for bigger carnivores, and in rock hyraxes which sally forth to forage but must dodge the desert eagles as they go. Thus we may envisage Lucy and her tribe, standing upright in the boughs at the edge of the copse, holding for balance to a branch above, in a good, safe, all-seeing position – highly reminiscent of a watchful meerkat. Lucy was found on a barren hillside, right enough. But when she and her kind lived there in the mid-Pliocene, it was a much friendlier place.

But did the early australopithecines really dash after prey? Did they eat meat, and how much of it? This is a crucial issue, and has been a highly contentious one. I am quite sure that they did, and that meat-eating has played a key part in human evolution.

AUSTRALOPITHECINES AS PREDATORS

The way that animals live, how they spend their days and the extent to which they socialise, is largely determined by what they eat. Committed herbivores need to eat more or less all day (or all night) if they are to fuel themselves sufficiently, while big predators eat only occasionally and spend most of their time dozing or frankly comatose. Some creatures *need* to be sociable in order to feed efficiently, for example most vultures, which rely upon each other to seek out cadavers. Other animals, such as Sumatran rhinos, need to be more or less solitary if they are to find enough to eat. Clearly, too, diet determines ecological impact: predators stand higher on the food chain than herbivores do, but in general are less numerous than herbivores. What australopithecines ate, then, and how they found their food, is a crucial matter. It largely determines what kind of creatures they actually were, how many they were and what effect they had on all about them.

To a great extent diet can be inferred from anatomy, but there are drawbacks. We know, for example, that the fearsome predatory jaw power of the giant panda is expended (even squandered) on bamboo. More to the point, primates tend to be generalists, and tend to lack the dental extremes of the most specialist feeders. Patterns of dental wear offer clues to diet, but the deep scars left by the coarsest foods, for example the skins of wild fruits, tend to blot out the milder abrasions of softer fare. But the softer fare – including meat – may have a far greater influence on the animal's welfare and way of life.

Thus there is scope for honest doubt about the diets of early australopithecines. But a lot of argument, too, has been based merely on preconception. Thus in *African Genesis* in the 1960s the journalist Robert Ardrey contended that the australopithecines were ravening carnivores. He also argued that carnivory is a prime source of aggression in animals, and further suggested that modern humans are innately aggressive because they are the scions of carnivores. Other writers, particularly in the gentler 1970s, depicted australopithecines as the world's first flower-children, whiling away the African millennia in vegetarian communes. You pays your money, it seems, and you takes your choice.

If we apply common sense, ecological principles, and knowledge of other animals and people that face some of the same problems as the australopithecines, then we must conclude that Ardrey was more right than wrong, although not in the way that he argued. The unsurprising reality, probably, is that the first australopithecines were omnivores, eating everything. In fact versatility was the key to their immediate success and to their later evolution – including the evolution of the large brain. They may indeed have eaten only small amounts of meat – perhaps not much more than 10 per cent of total calories. On the other hand, even such a small commitment to meat can have a profound effect on a creature's ecological success, on its effect upon other animals and – as Ardrey suggested, though not quite accurately – on its personality.

First, I suggest that the notion that the first australopithecines did not eat significant amounts of meat is belied in part by their teeth. Admittedly, although their front teeth are small, the first known australopithecines had big wide molars and premolars, clearly designed for grinding vegetation – relatively bigger than a modern human's or indeed a chimp's. But were they big and millstone-like enough to enable their owners to subsist exclusively on the coarser vegetation they would find outside the lush tropical forest? Wouldn't active creatures with such teeth and guts have needed meat to carry them through?

On evolutionary grounds, too, it would be surprising if they were not meat-eaters. After all we know that we eat meat, and that our immediate stone-age ancestors did, and that some of our number today – such as the Eskimos and South American gauchos – eat meat almost exclusively. We also know, thanks to Jane Goodall, that chimpanzees not only eat meat but are formidable hunters. It would be odd indeed if the lineage that runs from chimp-like common ancestor to australopithecine to *Homo* had switched away from meat and then switched back again.

Furthermore, I am sure that the way in which chimps obtain meat is highly instructive in a way that is reminiscent of Ardrey's ideas though not quite the same. Thus Ardrey argued that *because* australopithecines were meat-eaters this *per se* made them particularly aggressive. Such a broad generalisation surely has to be rejected, because in practice the modern committed predators that we know about simply are *not* more aggressive than many specialist herbivores. I would feel happier in the presence of a wolf than a zebra stallion, while a wild bull Asian elephant effectively means instant death.

What is true, however, is that specialist predators employ 'aggression' as a tactic or indeed as an essential weapon for procuring food. A lion that contrives to bring down a zebra, or a sabretooth that leaps at a mammoth, runs a tremendous risk. The flailing hooves and the clubbing trunk can be lethal. The predator must do as the boxer does: slip the opponent's guard, and 'get inside'. But that takes nerve, and 'nerve' requires hype. The necessary heightening of mood is achieved by mental preparation and surges of adrenalin. Without it the predator would be ineffectual and would also endanger its own life. Every rugby player or boxer knows that the easiest way to get hurt is to be half-hearted. Only the rapid and committed strike can succeed.

In short, aggression is not gratuitous viciousness. It is a tactic: a device for raising the physiological tempo and focusing the mind in times of extreme physical exertion. Of course it is risky to invoke a state of mind in which caution is thrown to the winds. But of all the options available to the hunter it is the *least* risky. It is riskier by far to hold back. To avoid the fight altogether is simply not an option – not, that is, if the predator is ever to eat. Shakespeare's Henry V made the general point as well as it can be made at the siege of Harfleur (Act III Scene 1):

> In peace there's nothing so becomes a man
> As modest stillness and humility:
> But when the blast or war blows in our ears,
> Then imitate the action of the tiger;
> Stiffen the sinews, summon up the blood,
> Disguise fair nature with hard-favour'd rage;
> Then lend the eye a terrible aspect;
> Let it pry through the portage of the head
> Like the brass cannon; let the brow o'erwhelm it
> As fearfully as doth a galled rock
> O'erhang and jutty its confounded base ...

Heroic rhetoric, shameless hype – but also sound advice. Wolves indulge in similar exhortation as they leap and 'yip' before the hunt, egging each other to action. Domestic dogs respond in this wolfish way to the universal cry of 'walkies!', which for them has little to do with exercise but is a symbolic adventure. Jane Goodall observed the rituals of hype in chimpanzees. In fact, as has now been captured on film, the hunting technique of chimpanzees is quite horrible. For hours a sinister mood seems to overtake them, a conspiratorial silence. Then the mood becomes frenzied, and together – and cooperatively – they encircle and close in upon some hapless monkey. Yelling, screaming, and shaking branches, they induce stark terror which, in turn, causes the prey to make mistakes. When the monkey is finally caught it is torn, literally, limb from limb in an orgy of excitement. Horrendous. But perhaps from a survival point of view such apparent excess is necessary. The hype increases the vigour of the hunters and confuses the prey. Chimpanzees do not have the appearance or more conventional predators, and until Jane

Goodall began her studies many biologists assumed they were vegetarians. But their massive strength, their cooperativeness, their intelligence, and their controlled use of 'aggression' make them very proficient indeed. Chimpanzee hunts seem usually to succeed while co-operative lions are content to make one kill in every four attempts, and the solitary tiger one in ten.

I find it easy to envisage the first australopithecines in their semi-tropical Mio–Pliocene Sherwood employing very chimpish techniques: hurling themselves *en masse* from the trees in an orchestrated frenzy, armed with sticks, and beating a monkey, a pangolin, a small antelope or a pig insensible before it had time to gather its wits. And such creatures, noisy, cooperative and frenetic, would in practice have had little to fear even from the mega-predators such as leopards and hyaenas. Such predators tend to be specialists. They do what they do. These hyperactive hordes would have been outside their ken: too unpredictable; too weird. The early australopithecines, one might suppose, would have been creatures to leave alone. Better stick to antelope.

Thus Ardrey's original thesis is not quite right. The early australopithecines were not in a general way 'aggressive', any more than a lion or a domestic cat is especially aggressive. But like lions and pussy-cats they were able to deploy aggression as a necessary technique for obtaining food. However, unlike lions and other cats which go about their work in appropriately professional silence, the method of the australopithecines was that of the chimpanzee: the creation of mayhem and confusion; the method of gang warfare. Professor Bernard Wood of Liverpool University has pointed out that the names given to early species of *Homo* are often designed to suggest that our ancestors were serious-minded people, perhaps with their eye on their glorious future. Thus they are called *H. habilis*, 'handy man', or *H. ergaster*, 'working man'. But, Bernard and I agreed, *Australopithecus hooliganensis* might have been nearer the mark. Our first hominid ancestors succeeded, probably, by being at times extremely unpleasant – to a degree which, among other animals, only modern chimpanzees achieve. Controlled bursts of temper are one of the keys to our success. This is a chilling and salutary thought. It shows how naive it is to suppose that what comes naturally to us is *ipso facto* morally right.

To return to our thread, how much meat would the early

australopithecines have obtained in this way? Would it have made a significant contribution to their diet?

Rob Foley of Cambridge University argues on ecological grounds that the first hominids to make a truly significant switch to meat were members of the genus *Homo*, and notably *H. erectus*. They might have obtained 20 per cent or more of their calories from meat, while the australopithecines – like modern chimps – perhaps obtained only 10 per cent.

But for three reasons I feel that this putative 10 per cent could have been highly significant. First, modern nutritionists generally agree that human beings do not need to eat large quantities of meat. We are perfectly able (and indeed are advised) to obtain the bulk both of calories and of protein from plants. But very few modern nutritionists advocate a vegan diet, with no meat at all. For the protein in plants, though often sufficient in gross amount, tends to be of dubious quality. It often lacks particular essential amino acids. Meat protein, by contrast, is 'first class'. It contains all the essential amino acids in appropriate ratios. Meat (including offals) also provides minerals such as zinc and vitamins such as B12 which can be difficult to obtain adequately from plants. So meat, for humans, is valuable not as a bulk food but as a guarantor of quality. A little goes a little way – but that little is very advisable. It will convert a marginal or frankly poor diet into one that is more than adequate. Thus I suggest that australopithecines who ate modest amounts of meat would thereby have increased their ecological range and their survivability out of all proportion to the apparent quantity.

A second aspect to this is pointed out by Rob Foley. In the tropical rainy season there are plenty of plants to eat but the animals are hard to catch because they spread themselves far and wide to reap the bounty. In the dry season vegetation is hard to come by but animals are easier to catch because they gather in the least awful places, for example around the shrinking water holes. As marsupials and camels demonstrate in their different ways, and as will become clear later in the context of game theory, one of the principal arts of survival is to get through the bad times. Meat-eating would have carried the australopithecines through the dry seasons. Again, this would have increased their range and survivability enormously.

Thirdly, diet influences social life. Some hunters are solitary

killers, for instance tigers and leopards, but some decidedly are not
– including dogs of all kinds, lions, and ground hornbills. Primate
hunters – chimps and hominids – are definitely of the social kind.
As loners they would probably be fairly hopeless unless they were
well armed. Cooperative hunting requires mutual trust, and in
general the fruits of hunting are exploited most efficiently when
they are shared because a good kill provides far more food than
any one individual can consume, and a little for everyone goes a
long way. Thus hunting, even on a modest scale, would have consolidated social bonds, which in any case are strong and intricate
in many primates. It would also, probably, have encouraged division of labour among the sexes. We cannot be sure that
australopithecine males would have done most of the hunting but
that is certainly the case among modern hunter-gatherers and as a
tactic it makes sense. Hunting is always dangerous and men, who
are not needed to bear or suckle children but who can supply
sperm in more than adequate amounts, are more expendable.

However, there is an odd sense in which the apparently small
dependency on meat is *worse* for prey species than is total commitment. For the population of a specialist predator must dwindle
if it overhunts its prey. The classic example is the northern lynx,
whose population rises and falls with that of its principal prey, the
snowshoe hare. But a non-specialist predator – one that can eat
many different kinds of animal, or eats both meat and plants
omnivorously – is not dependent on any one prey species. When
the favoured prey is reduced, it simply changes diet. But if the
favoured prey is truly preferred, then the predator may pick it off
in passing even after it has become rare. Thus do sea-otters make
very short work of sea-urchins, which they love; they subsist on
clams when the sea-urchins decline but nonetheless continue to
zap their favourite food in passing. Thus are feral pussy-cats in
Australia picking off the small marsupials one by one. Thus could
modern whaling ships drive blue whales to extinction if they
were not constrained by law – because the steady supply of per-
mitted minke whales provides enough to keep them at sea, and
they can simply take the blues *en passant*. In general, animals like
us – which eat meat opportunistically, and simply shift diet when
the favoured prey becomes rare – are able to break the ecological
law which says that predators are bound to be rare relative to their
prey.

The overwhelming point, though, is not that australopithecines were hunters, significant though it is. The key point is the one I stressed in Chapter 3: that natural selection will produce significantly new creatures only under the right conditions. Here in the benign Miocene version of Sherwood forest was everything that was needed. The woodland setting provided endless variety – and endless reward for creatures that could fully exploit that variety. Versatile animals could make their living virtually in an infinity of ways and therefore could hang on even in the bad years, while the more specialist species were subject to the vagaries of weather. The australopithecines responded to that variety. The genes were right: they could partake of fragments of the central gene pool of apes, the common ancestors, which may well have been vast and must have been extremely various just as the modern chimpanzees are various. The population sizes were right (or some of them were) – not too big and not too small, and isolated or semi-isolated at the forest edge in precisely the way that was needed to encourage speciation.

And, perhaps most significantly of all, the ecomorph was right. Here were creatures with hands that had been honed to grip, and arms that were designed to whirl through all the points of a sphere and hence provided the perfect foil for those hands. These features had been evolved for arboreal purposes – but now, more and more, they were freed from the chore of locomotion as the australopithecines increasingly cultivated the arts of bipedalism. In all these faculties, the hominines picked up where the australopithecines left off.

Before we move on to the hominines, however, there is one theoretical matter that deserves attention if we are really to understand what happened. So far I have mentioned six different species of australopithecine – three graciles, and three robust paranthropines. But is that all there were?

HOW MANY AUSTRALOPITHECINES WERE THERE REALLY?

The australopithecines we know about seem to include about half a dozen species, spanning the period between 4·4 million years ago (ramidus) to something under 1 million years ago (the age of the latest paranthropines). For various reasons, however, we cannot be confident that we know all of them. For a start, there is space, in time and in body form, to fit in at least one more species between ramidus and the common ancestor. More generally, we know that the primate fossil is extremely 'spotty' – and indeed that we probably know only about 3·5 per cent of all extinct primate species. In particular, there are virtually no anthropoid fossils from late Miocene Africa, when the australopithecines apparently split from the apes, and the later fossils, from the Pliocene and Pleistocene, are geographically patchy. A great deal (may) have gone on of which we know nothing.

In fact broad, arm-waving generalisations suggest that entire suites of species may be missing. For the retreat of the African Miocene forest would have provided exactly the conditions needed for the creation of new species. The wooded margins of the central Miocene forest would have covered a huge area with hundreds of isolated or semi-isolated pockets able to hold many different, self-contained viable populations of middle-sized animals such as apes, all of which could be constantly and repeatedly seeded from the vast central gene pool of ancestral apes.

In short, many different subpopulations of ancestral ape around the wooded margins of the central forest might have taken to the ground in the same way as the australopithecines did. Those different types would not be 'true' australopithecines, although they would have been related through their common ancestry, and perhaps resembled the australopithecines through convergent or parallel evolution. Other populations of ancestral apes might have become ground-living quadrupeds – the ape equivalents of baboons. If they did, they have disappeared without a trace – although the gorilla is essentially a ground-living quadruped which has stayed in the forest (or perhaps it was driven back in by the emerging hominids). The australopithecines themselves have spread to new areas and speciated – perhaps to form a suite of ground-living apes comparable with the array of forest-living monkeys of South America. Semi-isolated around the forest edge they would have had a much greater opportunity to speciate than the ancestral apes, which would have remained in touch with each other in their more-or-less continuous central forest – although, in truth, the modern 'common' chimps are now clearly divided into several (some would say many) different subspecies.

Finally we may note that, if there was such speciation, the australopithecines we know about may not actually be our direct ancestors. They may merely be aunts. Our true ancestors – and a good many more besides – may have disappeared without trace. But we can draw comfort: if the australopithecines we know about were not our true ancestors, they must surely have been very similar to the creatures who were.

There are two main objections to such speculations about undiscovered australopithecines. First there is no direct evidence to back it up – although this is less important than it may seem because we only began the speculation in the first place because we needed to fill in the obvious gaps in the fossil evidence. The second and larger objection is theoretical. We know that evolution is chancy, so although the central pool of ancestral apes may have had the opportunity to produce many different ground-living descendants only a small proportion of those opportunities are likely to have been taken. In fact it is very possible that only one of the many theoretical opportunities was seized. Perhaps, after all, ramidus and afarensis represent the only lineage there has been.

Rob Foley has imposed some order on speculation by applying ecological principles based on direct knowledge of other animals. Thus he has found – perhaps unsurprisingly, but you cannot take anything for granted – that the number of species in a genus of animals of any given body size is related to the total area that that genus is known to cover. The area covered by the australopithecines is not known for sure, but it can be estimated. They do not seem to have left Africa – or at least, all claims to have found them in Eurasia are generally considered mistaken. They probably lived at the forest edge, and because the central African forest was huge its margins were commensurately extensive. In theory such an area might have supported twenty or thirty species of australopithecine. But Rob Foley has found that such areas actually tend to support only about five species of mammals of roughly equal size that are related to each other.

In practice, ramidus and afarensis represent the only australopithecine lineage that we know about between the late Miocene and about 3 million years ago. But after that various others start to come on line (including africanus and aethiopicus), and from then on, as we will soon see, the fossil record does sometimes show about five hominid species coexisting at any one time – australopithecines alone or australopithecines-plus-hominines. Thus at around 2·5 million years ago africanus coexisted with the last of afarensis, plus *P. aethiopicus*, and *Homo habilis* is known to have appeared soon after. So perhaps, from the mid–Pliocene onwards, we do know most of the australopithecine types there are to know. But early Pliocene and late Miocene types remain enigmatic. It still seems somewhat unlikely that australopithecines were the *only* chimpish apes to take to the ground, and that *A. afarensis* was the only one of its kind to exploit the benign Pliocene woodland.

One further point, of course, is that each of the known australopithecines may represent more than one species. Thus some say that the widespread and highly variable afarensis fossils come from more than one species. Some suggest that there are two kinds of africanus. Others divide *Paranthropus robustus* into two: *P. robustus* from the site at Kromdraai, and *P. crassidens* from Swartkrans.

Here, I am following the ideas of Bernard Wood. As he points out, it is not at all easy to decide how many species are represented by the various fossils. To begin with, hominid fossils are usually fragmented, they come from widely different areas, and those from the same area often represent several or many individuals. If corresponding fragments seem to come from creatures that are very similar to each other, then it seems reasonable to conclude that they do indeed come from the same species. But if they are different, then they *may* come from the same species, or they *may* come from a single species that is highly variable. For we know from observation of living animals that some species are extremely variable. Those that live in different regions may differ in size and to some extent in shape – though they may still be perfectly capable of mating successfully if brought together, and so would generally qualify as the same species. We may also expect that long-lasting species would vary over time.

We know, too, that males may be very different from females – usually, in mammals, larger and more bulky. This is 'sexual dimorphism'. Confusingly, some primates are extremely dimorphic (including gorillas and baboons) and others hardly at all (for example gibbons and marmosets). This dichotomy has enormous social significance. When the males are much bigger than the females, as in gorillas or elephant seals, we can generally assume polygyny: each alpha male has many wives. When the sexes are much of a muchness, simple pairs are more likely. But when a pile of fossils seems to fall into two size groups, does this imply two coexistent species, or a marked difference between the sexes? This can be an extremely hard nut to crack.

To sort the fragmented and scattered hominid fossils into distinct types – which may or may not in the fulness of time be accorded the status of 'species' – Bernard Wood has applied two lines of thought. First, like many other modern anatomists, he applies the general methods of analysis formulated by the German biologist Willi Hennig in the 1960s: those of cladistics. The basic notion is to decide rigorously which characters that are shared by the various fossils are truly 'homologous' – that is, were inherited from a common ancestor – and which are merely 'analagous', and have become similar through convergent evolution. Next the 'cladist' (the analyst employing cladistic methods) must decide whether the homologous features, or characters, truly reflect a close relationship or not. For example, modern chimps and humans have hands which are very similar in detail, which suggests both that they are indeed homologous and that the common ancestor of modern chimps and humans also had such a hand. But the mere fact that chimps and humans have five fingers on each hand (a 'pentadactyl limb') is not enough. *All* four-legged land vertebrates (terrestrial tetrapods) have pentadactyl limbs unless, like horses, they happen to have shed a few. Mere pentadactyly is simply a 'primitive' feature which tells you nothing about special relationships. Primates in general hang on to many primitive features and often seem to reinvent them – in the way that neanderthals reinvented ridges over the eyes (brow-ridges). In general, it is far from easy to tell whether shared features are truly homologous and, if they are, whether they are not merely primitive.

Secondly, however, Bernard Wood has drawn a distinction between features that you might expect to vary and those you would not expect to vary. You might expect, for example, that mere size might vary quite a lot. After all, modern humans are all shapes and sizes. But there are certain features in which you would not expect much innate variation, for example the width of the nose. So mere variation in general body size would not in general prompt Bernard to suppose that a given pile of fossils represented more than one species. But marked variation in nasal width might well suggest this.

By such means Bernard Wood has concluded that the present fossils of *A. afarensis* probably represent only one species, although it is highly varied. The known africanus, too, he believes are one species (though there are specimens which others say are different which at the time of writing he has not yet been able to study). He suggests that the South African robust *Paranthropus* is really only one species, *P. robustus*, and that the proposed *P. crassidens* from Swartkrans is just a variation. He does acknowledge, however, that the east African robust australopithecines really do represent two species: the more ancient *P. aethiopicus* and the more recent *P. boisei*.

Overall, therefore, Bernard Wood concludes that the known types of australopithecine and paranthropine represent five species while others believe there are at least seven, with *A. africanus* and *P. robustus* each divided into two. More fossils might resolve the issue. We must also, of course, add on at least one and probably several that preceded, and for a while perhaps accompanied, *A. afarensis*.

But however many australopithecines there were, it does seem that one of them, some time after 2·5 million years ago, gave rise to the genus *Homo*. Again we should ask how and why.

HOW *HOMO* BECAME, AND WHY

I have suggested that the australopithecines arose from a lineage of chimpish apes in the late Miocene as worldwide cooling, probably exacerbated in east Africa by a tectonic rise in altitude, produced a broad band of woodland around the tropical forest. *Homo* evidently arose from a lineage of australopithecines as a second burst of cooling, around 2·5 million years ago, began to transform those woods into harsher territory more like the grassy savannah of modern Africa. Scions of the chimp-like common ancestor probably could not have adjusted to open grassland all in one go. But australopithecines, already moving easily on two legs, were equipped for the adjustment. We may legitimately doubt whether the forest-bound common ancestors would have made the transition to the ground if the climate and the terrain had not altered, and we may just as legitimately ask whether the australopithecines would have abandoned their semi-arboreal mode unless a second, further burst of aridity had finally taken most of their trees away from them.

The oldest accepted member of the genus *Homo* was described by Louis Leakey, John Napier, and Phillip Tobias in 1964. The first discovered fossils came from Olduvai Gorge in Tanzania and are dated at 1·8 million years. Leakey, Napier, and Tobias called their find *Homo habilis* – 'handy man'. Others have been found since, and the oldest now known, from Malawi, dates from 2·5 million years ago.

To be sure, some palaeoanthropologists doubted at first whether *H. habilis* was different enough from *Australopithecus* to be placed in the *Homo* genus while others doubted whether he differed sufficiently from the later *H. erectus* to be placed in a different species. But *H. habilis* has a significantly larger brain than the australopithecines – at around 600–750 millilitres. For this reason almost everyone accepts both that *H. habilis* is a true *Homo*, distinct from *Australopithecus*, and that he is indeed significantly different from *H. erectus,* whose brains, at 800–900 millilitres, are significantly bigger still. Furthermore, as discussed later, Bernard Wood now suggests that the various *H. habilis* fossils that have now been found through Tanzania, Kenya, Ethiopia, Malawi, and possibly from southern Africa in fact represent at least two species, *H. habilis* and *H. rudolfensis*. Let us just assume for the time being, however, that the first true hominines (members of the genus *Homo*) did indeed appear at about 2·5 million years ago.

Homo habilis, too, rather than any australopithecine, is considered the probable author of the recognisable stone tools that were found in his vicinity. The australopithecines who were there earlier must also have used tools, as chimps do; indeed they must have *made* tools, for Jane Goodall showed that modern chimps make tools (for example shaping twigs to fish termites from their nests) and it is inconceivable that the australopithecines actually lost such skill. But australopithecines either stuck to wooden tools as befits a woodland animal or, if they used stones as tools, they clearly did not fashion them in a recognisable way. That is, they might have used pebbles for clubbing prey or for pulverising and hence tenderising the flesh – the hamburger may be as old as the steak in the hominid diet – but apparently they did not chip them into blades. Without such chipping, it is impossible to see whether an australopithecine stone was a tool or not. But *Homo habilis* was a definite chipper. So he was not a mere maker of tools: he was an artificer of stone. This was a very significant shift.

The varied lifestyle offered to the australopithecines in their pleasantly open forest encouraged the handiness that they had so felicitously inherited from their arboreal ancestors. In *Homo habilis* we see the final fruition of that hardiness. But then we see something more: the interaction and mutual stimulation of hand and brain to create an evolutionary feedback loop in which both were developed to a new and unprecedented degree. Again, everything had to be right for this loop to become established: the gene pool, the ecomorph, the population size, and the right degree of selective pressure (not so mild as to induce no change, and not so harsh as to obliterate). The late australopithecines that became hominines, faced with the new pressures of expanding grassland, provided precisely the combination needed for brains to expand.

We tend to take for granted that brains and intelligence are a good thing, and hence assume in a general way that they ought to be favoured by natural selection. But natural selection, as we have seen, is concerned only with the short term — and under what circumstances could it specifically favour a big thinking brain? After all, the brain is an expensive organ whose maintenance requires more than its fair share of the body's energy. Big-brained animals weight-for-weight need more food, and more food means more effort and more risk. Natural selection cannot favour such extravagance unless the brain provides a commensurate pay-off. And it seems to me that under most natural circumstances *a big, contemplative brain is totally useless*. What for example would a codfish do with the brain of Jane Austen? How would it express its genius? On what would it inscribe its novels? Who would read them? The literary fish would of course quickly fall to one with sharper teeth. In short, a large brain can be favoured by natural selection *only* if its cerebrations can be translated rapidly into useful action, where 'useful' must be interpreted in the crude terms of survival. But a dextrous hand can provide precisely the interpretation needed: the ability to turn stones into tools with which the rest of the environment can be adjusted to the animal's needs. Thus in a truly 'handy' man in a conducive environment natural selection could indeed enhance brain power — and did.

By the same token, a superbly dextrous hand is pointless unless instructed by a sympathetic brain. Fit a duck-billed platypus with the hands of Alfred Brendel, come back in a million years, and you would find them re-evolved into paddles. What use has a platypus for such refinements? But *Homo habilis* was developing the brain that could tell its dextrous hands what to do.

So the two enhanced each other. The more agile the hands became, the greater was the challenge presented to the brain, and the greater were the rewards if natural selection could rise to that challenge – and the more imaginative the brain became, the more dexterity was favoured. To put the matter formally: each organ provided conditions in which natural selection would favour the further development of the other. We see such 'positive feedback loops' throughout nature, notably when two species are locked together in a burst of co-evolution. Thus a particular orchid may become more and more closely adapted to the whims of some particular pollinating moth, which in turn becomes more and more closely geared to the orchid. Each eggs the other on: each provides circumstances in which natural selection favours particular adaptations in the other. In the development of the hominine brain and hand we see the co-evolution of two organs within the same creature. We also see the most significant natural feedback loop that has occurred in the entire Cenozoic, and perhaps throughout the lifetime of the entire planet.

The fossil record suggests, too, that the resulting loop produced results quite rapidly: the hominid brain developed from the size of an ape's to the size of habilis's in a few hundred thousand years at most, and probably in far less – and from habilis to us in another 2 million. On the geological scale such a burst could reasonably be seen as a 'punctuation'. Certainly the human brain has not been expanding in an uninterrupted haul since the Oligocene, as many earlier palaeoanthropologists supposed must be the case.

More generally, and perhaps more mundanely, we can see how *Homo* adjusted to increasingly open and grassy country, just as we envisaged the adaptation of *Australopithecus* to its woodland. In that open ground *Homo* would have been more exposed and vulnerable to predators than *Australopithecus* in the woods, with less cover and no instant, vertical escape route. The prey, too, would have been more agile: more cursorial antelopes and fewer bush-rats.

On both counts we can assume a premium on increased cooperativeness, both for defence and for hunting, and with cooperativeness a premium on social intricacy and intelligence. The need for tools – meaning weapons – also increases in these more vulnerable creatures, again for both defence and offence.

In creatures of open country, too, natural selection must surely favour increased mobility. First, animals of the plain need speed over the ground, again both for escape and attack. Then, in addition, animals that succeed in a grassy environment need to be able to cover the space. Good grazing occurs patchily, and you need to move from area to area whether you are a herbivore seeking fodder or a carnivore following the herbivores. Woodland is in general more concentrated. The first *Homo* inherited efficient bipedality and on the open plain they perfected this skill to become both sprinters and, perhaps, long–distance travellers. Indeed they may have become the first primate nomads (if 'nomad' is defined broadly).

The original uprightness of the australopithecines was, I have suggested, an adaptation to life in low trees. But on the plain it served some quite new purposes – yet another example of nature's fortuitousness. For on the open plain there is no leafy canopy to shield against the Sun. But recent studies have shown that upright creatures suffer far less from the heat than animals that carry their bodies horizontally, in the manner of most mammals. The reason is a common sense one: that an upright body exposes a smaller area to the Sun when it is overhead and at its hottest. Modern studies have also shown that the breeze is significantly faster and more cooling at a metre and a half or more above the ground than at ground level. Thus a five-foot creature standing upright keeps a cool head – and, of all the organs of the body, the ever-demanding brain is among the most distressed by overheating. (Heat-seeking reptiles, by contrast, make use of the warm microclimate closer to the ground.)

Thus, because of their inherited uprightness the first hominines were well protected against overheating. This in turn would have given them a unique advantage. For most predators far prefer to hunt at night or in the cool of the morning or the evening. We may reasonably doubt whether any hominids, who rely so heavily on sight, would ever have relished night-time hunting. But they may well have had the wherewithal to be daytime hunters,

even on the burning plains. This would have given them a dual
advantage: they could attack at a time when prey animals preferred to stay still and seek what shade there is, and they could
avoid the direct rivalry of lions and hyaenas. Presumably in those
early days on the open plain the first true hominines acquired
those additional features which are so peculiarly human: first the
pattern of hair, sparse over most of the body (particularly in people from tropical countries) but retained on the head, where it
clearly provided extra protection from the noon-day Sun; second,
our extreme sweatiness, which is a highly efficient device for
cooling, albeit a device that makes prodigal use of water and raises
the constant spectre of death by dehydration. (Incidentally, I have
never favoured the sometime popular notion that human beings
acquired their pattern of hair and sweating during a hypothetical
phase as semi-aquatic animals. The idea is ingenious but gratuitous. The scenario suggested by the fossils – creatures adapting to
open country many miles from the sea – seems to say all that is
needed.)

Most significant of all though, perhaps, is that the transition
from woodland to grassy plain finally released the arms and hands
from all commitment to locomotion. They were no longer
needed even for balancing in the low boughs. They were freed
forever for the thousand and one tasks to which human beings
have subsequently put them. They enabled quasi-nomadic *Homo
habilis*, if such they were, to travel *en famille*, carrying their infants
as they marched. This in turn allowed the youngsters to prolong
their childhood and the period of learning and brain maturation
that childhood allows. Hand and arm together became the agents
of tool-making, and this in turn had two further implications of
tremendous significance: first in providing the feedback loop with
the brain, and second in enabling the hominines to *throw* with
increasing force and accuracy. Thus we became the first specialist
daytime tropical hunters and also – crucially – the first big terrestrial predators that were able to kill at a distance. Before we
developed our skill as throwers of spears and rocks only a few
minor creatures, such as archer fish and spitting cobras, had even
begun to exploit the arts of ballistics. As discussed further in
Chapter 6, the significance of the spear and bolas and later of the
arrow can hardly be overestimated.

Overall, by perfecting bipedality *and* developing the arms and hands the hominines created a new ecomorph, and one of immense versatility and power. For other big, cursorial bipedal animals have generally abandoned the forelimb altogether. The ostrich does not use its wings for propulsion yet it does precious little else with them either – it employs then merely for balance during its headlong sprints or for sexual display. The forelimbs of *Tyrannosaurus rex* were shrivelled to a vestige. In both creatures and virtually all other true bipeds the mouth and neck serve as a third limb. But hominids can keep their heads and senses out of the action while they fight and even when they feed. A few animals habitually use their forelimbs for purposes other than locomotion, including bears, cats, squirrels, chalicotheres, pangolins, giant sloths, aardvarks, and chimpanzees. But all of them move quadrupedally. Their 'hands' must also be feet.

The human being, able to move as well on two legs as most other animals move on four, and employing the liberated forelimbs for all manner of other purposes, is effectively two creatures in one: a kind of centaur, though without the superfluous bodily bulk of the horse. As if that were not enough, the forelimbs are immensely mobile and tipped with dextrous hands – thanks to the many years of development in the trees. Those early arboreal primates were not rehearsing to be us – emphatically not – but they might as well have been. Anatomically, in short, the hominids and particularly *Homo* represent a new form of creature, distinct from all other animals including the apes. Even without alluding to the brain, it is not species-ist to remark, as Hamlet did, 'What a piece of work is a man!'.

This, then, was the first *Homo*. As already mentioned, the first widely acknowledged species was *H. habilis*, although the known early fossils may represent two distinct species, *H. habilis* and *H. rudolfensis*. Leaving that aside for the time being, one of those two – almost certainly *Homo habilis* – evolved further to produce *Homo erectus*. For the human lineage, as Rob Foley says, *Homo erectus* was the 'watershed'.

HOMO ERECTUS

Some people doubted the provenance of at least some *H. habilis* for they had an australopithecine *mien*. But although the initial dis-

coverer of *Homo erectus* called him *Pithecanthropus* – 'ape-man' –
there can be no doubts at all about his humanity. Here was a tall
and upright creature fully justifying the adjectival 'erectus'. The
brain was not as big a modern human's – only about 900 millilitres
whereas ours are either side of 1,500 millilitres – but it was twice as
big as a chimp's of comparable body size. An erectus male would
not quite have passed muster in a modern bus queue, for his eyes
peered and doubtless sometimes glared beneath lowering ridges of
bone across the brows – truly, as Henry V put the matter, 'like the
brass cannon'. And since his cranium lacked the capacity of the
modern skull it also wanted the modern globosity. The head sloped
away behind the eyes, without the ballooning bulge above the ears.
But here in erectus was a human nonetheless.

However, the reasons that Rob Foley regards *H. erectus* as a
'watershed' are ecological rather than anatomical. In particular, he
infers on ecological grounds that erectus must have eaten a great
deal more meat than the australopithecines – perhaps 20 per cent
of total calories rather than the calculated 10 per cent of the australopithecines. As I have suggested, even 10 per cent had far
greater significance than the figure immediately suggests. Twenty
per cent or more is very significant indeed. As a hunter erectus
must surely have been abetted both by his growing intelligence
and by his increasing skill with missiles.

More immediately obvious than this, however, and at least as
important, is that *H. erectus* was the first hominid traveller: *the first
to leave Africa.* Thus, the oldest known erectus are from Kenya, by
Lake Turkana, and date from around 1·8 million years ago. But
the first erectus to be discovered was by Eugene Dubois in 1891,
and is less than 1 million years old. For decades it has been supposed that the first *H. erectus* left Africa just over 1 million years
ago, but recent *H. erectus* finds in Java seem to date from as long
ago as 1·6 million years, which suggests a much earlier departure.
The earlier date would not be surprising. As we saw abundantly
in Chapter 4, animals can spread from one continent's end to
another in a few hundred years simply by expanding by a few
kilometres per year. But erectus did not spread beyond south-east
Asia, to Australia and the Pacific. He was a landlubber. Sailors
came later.

However, we need not assume that erectus merely spread passively out of Africa through the growth of population. I am sure

they were a grassland specialist, and like other grassland specialists they must have employed strategies for quartering the ground, and seeking pastures new. Arabian oryx, for example, discover new grassland simply by sniffing the wind. But they also remember where they have been before. So when they are placed in new territory they build mental maps within a few years and know exactly where they are within apparently featureless areas of thousands of square kilometres. This has been closely observed in recent years as captive-bred Arabian oryx have been reintroduced to the wild in Oman. Modern-day Australian aborigines apparently have much the same ability. Indeed such mental map-making seems to be usual among animals – a common skill, but one in which most modern humans seem to have become particularly feeble.

In addition, there may also have been true adventurers among the ranks of erectus who risked their own lives in exploration. Perhaps indeed there were erectus Marco Polos. This is a romantic notion, but not mere whimsy. We know after all that most animals have some spirit of adventure – it is a necessary survival tactic in an ever-changing world – and that some are more adventurous than others. Propensity for major exploration is a high-risk strategy, but *in extremis* (for example when the immediate habitat is already overpopulated) the only alternative to high-risk emigration may be to sit tight and die. As we have seen in the context of aggression, high-risk strategies are sometimes the best options. We know too that many young animals, for example, young foxes, are banished from the parent territory to seek their fortunes elsewhere.

Even more intriguingly, the insights of Professor Bill Hamilton of Oxford University tell us that straightforward neodarwinian natural selection favours creatures which benefit their own kin as well as those which are merely selfish. After all, the kin contain copies of the genes of the 'altruists' and since natural selection seems to work most powerfully at the level of the gene, genes for altruism are favoured (provided the altruist can tell kin from non-kin). Human beings are family animals and at least some erectus – probably, as ever, the young dispensable males – might have ventured forth as a matter of policy. Worker bees do this, after all, in search of fresh flowers. Then they return to tell the rest what they have found. Perhaps the adventurous *H. erectus* were more like worker bees than Marco Polo for I doubt if the young adventurers would have put an entire continent between themselves and their kin – and, unlike Polo, they would have travelled more in hope than expectation for there was no established trade route for them to follow. But the underlying biological principle would have been the same. The adventurer benefits himself by aiding the society – the extended family – of which he is a part.

Indeed, many palaeoanthropologists have asked why *Homo* took so long to extend out of Africa. Successful species do spread, after all. If erectus really did not leave Africa until nearly a million years ago, then he must have hung about in Africa for more than half a million years – and habilis before him for several hundreds of thousands. Contrast this stay-at-home policy with that of, say, lions, which seem to have raced around the world, tracking the herbivores which followed the shifting grasslands or fled from advancing ice.

The answer surely lies largely in the continuity of habitat. Many modern hunter-gathering people live in rainforests – in south-east Asia, South America, and central Africa – and yet we have seen that human beings initially arose by rejecting the habitat of their pongid ancestors. Modern rainforest people have re-adopted a *modus vivendi* that does not come easily – just as, on a much longer time-scale, whales have returned to the sea from which all vertebrates emerged. Ecologically-speaking the modern people of the rainforest have been pushed to the margins. The Australian aborigines, who had a vast land mass to themselves for at least 40,000 years, never seriously penetrated the huge and apparently rich rainforest that now is in Queensland but which, during the total span of the aborigines, has shifted over much of the continent. Without pressure to move into the forest, they remained as denizens of open space.

Australian aborigines are of course modern people; much more flexible than *H. erectus*. If they prefer to avoid the forest (given that they have the choice), it seems doubly likely that erectus would also have done so. Neither would erectus have known how to cross big rivers, or felt at home on mountains or in desert. Thus to reach from Africa to Java he needed a continuity of grassland. There may never have been an uninterrupted route from Africa to south-east Asia – not at any one time, that is – so the Maco Polo scenario should not be taken too literally. But if appropriate stretches of land came into place intermittently, each reaching further east than before, then over time he would get to what then would have seemed the edge of the Earth.

Finally, *H. erectus* was apparently the first hominid, which means the first animal of any kind, to harness fire. He did not have to create it. Fires occur spontaneously in nature and many ecosystems – notably grassland – depend upon it. The significance of fire is hard to overestimate. Fire applied to grassland or to scrub creates more grassland. By using fire hominids can make more land suitable for themselves. Many animals do this up to a point. Fruit bats, birds, and orang-utans disperse the seeds of the forest trees on which they feed and hence increase their own food supply. Sheep maintain grassland by grazing it, and spread the grass over bare patches by manuring them and carrying seed. But the only non-human animal I can think of that creates its own habitat on a massive scale is the beaver which, by flooding the land, makes more good beaver territory. Such a positive feedback loop rapidly creates huge populations – indeed the beavers grew so numerous that the Hudson Bay Company was launched on the bounty of their pelts. We can imagine humans creating grassland which encouraged more humans, and so on. Indeed the very act of setting fire is a precursor of farming.

In practice, the hominids known broadly as *Homo erectus* may have embraced more than one distinct species. Bernard Wood recognises two: *H. erectus*, who extended from Africa to south-east Asia as described, and *H. ergaster*, who apparently remained in Africa. As we will see, this possible division could be of great significance. But whether or not *H. erectus* is taken to include *H. ergaster*, erectus was a highly significant creature. He survived from nearly 2 million years ago to as recently as 100,000 years ago in outposts of south-east Asia. Thus he occupied the world for most of the time that hominines have existed and if any species deserves to be acknowledged as the archetypal human it is not us but erectus. He should also be acknowledged as a tremendously successful species in his own right. He was not merely a rehearsal for *H. sapiens*.

Nevertheless erectus was the forerunner of *H. sapiens*. And, in general, whatever *H. erectus* did *H. sapiens* did more efficiently, on a larger scale, and with more ecological impact.

From about 400,000 years ago the fossil record of Africa, Asia, Europe and – especially important – the Middle East, reveals creatures that have decidedly bigger brains than *Homo erectus* (around 1,100 millilitres and more) and yet are not as brainy or as melon-skulled as 'fully modern' human beings and in general have somewhat erectus-like faces. In particular, they tend to have brow-ridges of varying degrees of prominence, and their faces tend to protrude.

When you look more closely, however, you see that these post-erectus but pre-modern people vary greatly from place to place and from period to period. Indeed many biologists over the years have placed the variants in different species. Others, however, have concluded that they did not know enough about those ancient peoples or how they were related, and have simply lumped them all together in a rough-and-ready way as 'archaic *Homo sapiens*'. One confusing feature is that some of the more 'primitive'-looking types – for example with bigger brow-ridges and/or smaller brains – are sometimes shown by modern dating methods to have lived more recently than more modern-looking types, with flatter faces and bigger brains.

The big-brained hominines – those with brains about the same size as ours – are of two main types. The ones who genuinely are like us – the 'fully moderns' – first appeared in the fossil record, again in Africa, around 120,000 years ago.

But there is also a joker in the hominine pack: the neanderthals. They had a very ancient-looking face with brow-ridges which in males in particular were huge, but also brains which if anything were slightly larger on average than those of the moderns. They reached their most extreme or 'classic' form in fairly recent times – after 75,000 years ago – but died about 35,000 years ago. Thus between 120,000 and 35,000 years ago the world contained two types of big-brained hominines – although, as we will see, they occupied the same area for only a part of that time.

Overall, we can conclude in a general way that erectus (or ergaster) gave rise to 'archaic sapiens' who then gave rise both to true moderns and to neanderthals. But within this broad picture three kinds of question remain. The first is the matter of relationships: *which* erectus-grade people gave rise to archaics, and *which* archaics produced moderns. Secondly, we should explain how erectus, archaic sapiens, and modern sapiens all managed to spread themselves through Africa, the Middle East, Europe, and Asia. Thirdly – who were the peculiar neanderthals? Who were their ancestors, do they have living descendants and if so who are they, and if in fact they all died out then why did they do so? The story seems to work out most tidily if we deal with the neanderthals first.

THE NEANDERTHALS

The first neanderthal remains to be discovered – of a child – turned up in Belgium in 1829. The next – a woman and child – were found in Gibraltar in 1848. But the first to attract special attention were the top of a man's skull and pieces of his arm, thigh, and pelvis which were dug from the banks of the Neander Valley near Düsseldorf in Germany in 1856. This was the first acknowledged 'Neanderthal Man'.

But this extremely significant character did not immediately impress the palaeontologists. Indeed they queued up to insult him. Between them they wrote him off as a diseased, freakish, Cossack soldier who had abandoned his uniform and hidden naked in a cave while deserting from some unpromising battle (as one would, of course). In the end, however, an Irish anatomist called William King identified him correctly as a distinct type of human whom he called *Homo neanderthalensis*. Many neanderthal remains have since turned up in Germany, Belgium, France, Croatia, Italy, Israel, Iraq, and Uzbekistan – so now we know that the neanderthals were basically Middle Eastern and European, with the most extreme types, the heaviest and most beetle-browed, coming from northern Europe.

Dating is now more certain, too, and shows that the most distinctive or 'classic' neanderthals lived surprisingly recently. They did not reach their climactic form until about 75,000 years ago and lasted another 40,000 years before their apparently rather sudden demise. Since fully modern people first appeared around 120,000 years ago the two were contemporaries for many thousands of years and remains of moderns and neanderthals have been found side by side in the Middle East, dating from around 90,000 years ago. Fully modern people were living in northern Europe around 40,000 years ago, and beginning to work stone and make other tools in the delicate and precise fashion that characterises the 'Upper Palaeolithic'. So these effectively modern people lived alongside the neanderthals in Europe for at least 5,000 years.

Classic neanderthal features clearly took a long time to evolve. People with vaguely neanderthal-like characters were living from around 400,000 years ago – remains include skulls from Petralona in Greece and Arago in France – and by 280,000 to 130,000 years ago many had become more neanderthal-like, as in Swanscombe, England, and Steinheim, Germany.

So what is a 'classic' neanderthal? To the untutored eye, he simply seems to re-invent or re-indulge the features that we popularly associate with primitive human beings. He is very heavy-boned ('robust'), so that his femur bones are extremely thick-walled compared to those of people today and his joints are larger. His limb bones are somewhat bowed and by today's standards the forearms and shins are short relative to the upper arms and thighs. The joints are big and so are the regions of muscular attachment. Neanderthals were stocky and muscular.

Their heads, though, are the most distinctive. Their skulls were as big as a modern's, or even bigger, but they were not globose as ours are. They were low-crowned and flat, with a sloping forehead, and were capacious because they were long from front to back. The jaws were long too, leaving plenty of room for three molars at the back, and for a space behind them – not like us, in whom the third and rearmost molar sometimes fails to erupt at all and when it does is crowded and forms an often troublesome 'wisdom tooth'. The neanderthal chin is receding but the front teeth are strong, suggesting to some that the mouth acted as a third limb, a kind of vice. The nose is protruding and wide. The brow-ridges are heavy. Neanderthals left artefacts, too, including well-made stone tools, though not as well made, delicate, or varied as the ones left by modern people from 40,000 years ago onwards. The positions of some of the neanderthal remains strongly suggest that they buried their dead, and the presence of pollen from many different plants around some of the bodies has suggested to some that their funerals were floral ceremonies.

Finally, cartoonists and scientific illustrators alike commonly depict male neanderthals with three days' growth of designer stubble, presumably to emphasise their receding chins. But in fact their Mousterian tool-kits did not include safety razors and it is reasonable to suppose – indeed unreasonable to suppose anything else – that the males had huge bushy beards, which evolved emphatically as secondary sex characteristics. Neanderthals are also traditionally drawn with black hair; but it seems likely to me that such northern creatures would have been blond or ginger. With their great manes of red or yellow hair and their huge red beards their heads would have glowed like sunflowers in the slanting northern sun, their faces as round as an orang-utan's, though shaped by hair rather than by flesh. It is a fanciful vision but it has more thinking biology behind it than the standard image of the male neanderthal as a kind of down-and-out.

But what can we really conclude about their lives? Different commentators argue in very different ways. Some writers have presented neanderthals as mystics: beneath the louring and hugely-muscled exterior lurked gentle if somewhat bewildered moon-worshippers. Some, too, construe the enormous strength of the neanderthals as a virtue and argue that because of it they did not need to make so many or such varied tools as the puta-tively more feeble moderns of the same period. But others are less charitable, even derisory. They point out that big bones and big muscles require more food to maintain – which is a theoretical disadvantage – and suggest that the neanderthals needed their enormous strength to make up for their lack of dexterity: Most commentators agree that their general stockiness is an adaptation to the late Pleistocene cold: the same shortening of extremities is seen, for example, in modern Eskimos or in Arctic foxes and hares, and the most extreme neanderthals come from the more northerly latitudes.

However, there are disagreements of detail and there are puz-zles. It is suggested that the extremely large nose of the neanderthal acted as a heat exchange system to warm the freezing air of the Pleistocene north Europe before it entered the lungs. Fair enough. Saiga antelope, which still thrive on the steppes of central Asia, seem to have adopted the same mechanism. Yet this broad wide nose is seen apparently evolving in pre-neanderthal people – well before the 'classic' phase after 75,000 years ago – who were living in a presumably modest climate in the Middle East. We can overdo the 'cold-adapted' scenario since neanderthals obviously lived in sunny times as well.

The scowling and conspicuous brow-ridges, so reminiscent of primitive erectus and his predecessors, turn out to be structurally quite different. Erectus ridges are solid: here was a hard-head indeed. Those of neanderthals are puffed out with air spaces. I feel that the ridges – like the huge if hypothetical beards – were for decoration: that they were secondary sex characteristics selected because they attracted mates, like the antlers of the stag or the tail of the peacock. Such an explanation fits modern thinking very well. For biologists have pondered the evolution of the peacock's tail (or the stag's antlers) ever since Darwin. To be sure, antlers are useful for tackling rivals but the peacock's tail seems a disaster: it requires huge inputs of energy to produce, yet it is an obvious encumbrance. Latest thinking, however, says that this is precisely the point. The tail is *intended* to be a handicap. It says to the female and to rival males, 'Look at this enormous extravagance! Yes, it does indeed take enormous energy to grow it. Yes, it is a terrible weight. But *despite* this, I can survive, and this proves that I am better than all the other peacocks!'.

This kind of explanation – 'the handicap principle' – sounds absurd at first hearing, but the more that biologists have looked at it, both in the field and with the aid of mathematical models, the more it seems to make sense. Males in particular do indeed advertise their hidden reserves of strength and fitness with anatomical and behavioural extravagances that are pure bravura. Herein, indeed, seems to lie the secret of the pongid's big canine teeth. They are not used for eating and seem to play little or no part in fighting but they are *signals*. They just say, 'Look at these!' – like Shelley's Ozymandias: 'Look on my works, ye Mighty, and despair!'.

Herein, too, perhaps lies the reason why the hominids over time lost the big pongid canines. Some other signal must have taken over from them. Primates are great communicators by eye: some, for instance woolly monkeys and gorillas, prefer to avoid each other's gaze except in moments of specific aggression; others, including male baboons, flutter coloured eyelids to attract attention. The brow-ridge exaggerates the stare: again the eye is caused to 'pry through the portage of the head'. The big hollowed brow of the neanderthal, perhaps, took the principle to extremes. It made the stare impressive indeed. It also said, like the

peacock's tail. 'See what energy I can afford to waste on this gratuitous architrave of bone!'. Perhaps, too, the *lack* of a brow-ridge
in the fully modern hominid was the obverse of this particular
handicap. Perhaps moderns were saying to their potential mates,
'See, I can survive *even though* I lack the brutish strength of those
other fellows!'. Perhaps indeed modern men emerged first as
campus intellectuals. And perhaps such speculation can be taken
too far.

Then again, where some see evidence of ritual in neanderthal
graves – in the arrangement of bones and the variations of pollen
– others see accident. As a flood recedes from a cave it may leave
a circle of flotsam as neat as any banquet. A variety of pollen in a
grave may simply reveal that the dead person or his burial party
had been wandering in the fields.

So much for neanderthal culture. Of crucial importance too is
the impact of neanderthals on other creatures. They were obviously formidable hunters. Their tools suggest this, and it is
difficult to see how they could have survived through the northern ice except by eating meat, as Eskimos and Lapps do today.
The rough vegetation of the tundra is strictly for specialist herbivores, with their huge guts and millstone teeth. Yet the
herbivores of the north may have made easy hunting as they gathered in great herds wherever there was grazing. Then again,
however, because the grazing was rough and the climate was cold
the predominant herbivores were big – mammoths, rhinos, bison,
horses – and the predators had to have appropriate technique.

But I am sure that Clive Gamble of Southampton University is
right to suggest in *In Search of the Neanderthals* (Christopher
Stringer and Clive Gamble, Thames and Hudson, London, 1993)
that the neanderthals did not have what I am inclined to call the
logistic skills of the fully modern people who shared the continent with them for so many thousand years. Neanderthals,
Gamble suggests, hunted in an opportunistic way, killing what
was there to be killed capably enough, but not anticipating very
astutely from year to year which animals were likely to be where,
or seeking to influence their movements. By contrast, he says,
their late Palaeolithic modern contemporaries knew how the animals moved and where they were to be found, almost in the
manner of a modern whaling captain. And different modern populations in different places increasingly traded with each other,

both goods and information, until in effect they quartered the entire continent in a cooperative network that was quite different logistically from anything that any previous animal had devised. Indeed I will argue in the next chapter that the palaeolithic people whom we loosely classify as 'hunter-gatherers' might rather be seen as wildlife managers – which perhaps is how the *modus operandi* of modern Australian aborigines should be interpreted.

In short, the crucial difference between neanderthals and moderns does not lie in the shape of their heads or the muscularity of their bodies. It lies in things that do not directly fossilise, suggestive though the fossils and artefacts may be. It lies in their culture and above all in the logistics of their lives: in what the people actually *did*, and the effect of their actions on the world about them. Logistics are not easily measured, as a bone or a stone tool can be measured. But they can be quantified, as I will discuss in the next chapter.

Such, then, were the neanderthals. Whether we decide that they really belong in their own species, *Homo neanderthalensis*, or are simply a subspecies of *Homo sapiens*, namely *H. sapiens neanderthalensis*, they clearly were a discrete group who evolved from some 'archaic' stock and developed along their own distinctive lines. Perhaps we might suggest that the neanderthals are the hominine equivalent of the australopithecine *Paranthropus*. Perhaps we should see the evolution of *Paranthropus* away from the graciles as the first great bifurcation in the hominid lineage – and note that the ones who muscled their way out of trouble were the ones that died out. Perhaps we might see the offshoot of the neanderthals as the second great bifurcation of the hominid lineage which, as things have turned out, was similarly doomed. Perhaps the neanderthals did better than they otherwise might have done, and reached the physical extremes that they did, *because* of the Pleistocene ice ages: their general stockiness equipped them for the cold, and their muscularity no doubt helped them to take on the big herbivores of the northern plains. Perhaps the first fully modern humans killed them off, as William Golding argued in *The Inheritors*. Or perhaps our own ancestors simply adapted more quickly and adroitly to putative changes of climate as the last ice age built up, and won out in the end by the drip, drip, drip of competition.

And perhaps there are too many 'perhapses'. It is time to move to a theoretically more tractable problem, though one still shot with disagreement. Who, among the plethora of ancient hominines, was related to whom? Who gave rise to whom, and when and where?

RELATIONSHIPS

The arm-waving picture is that erectus (defined broadly) begat 'archaic *Homo sapiens*' who begat neanderthals on the one hand and 'fully modern' people on the other. No one disagrees with that broadbrush statement. Disagreement begins when we ask for details, and start to look closely at the fossil evidence. In particular we need to explain how all three broad categories of *Homo* each became spread through Africa, the Middle East, Europe, and Asia, and how types that are more primitive in appearance sometimes prove to be more recent than those who look more modern.

  Basically, there are two broad kinds of explanation which for reasons that will become apparent are called the 'Candelabra hypothesis' and the 'Out of Africa' hypothesis. Just to anticipate, my own feeling (in common with most practising palaeoanthropologists) is that the Candelabra hypothesis is deeply flawed – in general it is unbiological – but I also feel that it contains an element of truth which should be taken seriously. On the other hand, I feel that the Out of Africa hypothesis is often stated in too simple a way and that it needs elaboration before it really works. But let us take these two main kinds of idea one by one.

CANDELABRA

The Candelabra hypothesis is championed mainly by Milford Wolpoff of the University of Michigan, who presents a view of human evolution from erectus onwards that seems unimprovably simple. He begins by arguing as almost all palaeoanthropologists now do that *Homo erectus* arose in Africa, and then became the first-ever hominid to migrate out of Africa, through the Middle East, and down to the furthest reaches of the Asian mainland – a mainland which at times in the past million years or so has embraced the present-day islands of Sumatra and Java. No one disagrees so far.

But Wolpoff then argues that all the different groups of erectus, wherever they happened to be all around the world, evolved into the various kinds of archaic, so that by about 400,000 years ago all the erectus groups everywhere in the populated world had turned into, and hence been replaced by, groups of archaic sapiens. Then, he says, all these different archaic groups, dotted around the populated world, continued to evolve until by about 100,000 years ago and onwards they had each evolved into fully modern sapiens. He claims, in fact, that all the modern races of human beings have arisen *in situ* from the archaics who lived before them in the same region, and that those archaics in their turn had previously evolved *in situ* from the erectus who were there before them.

In this scenario the neanderthals were just one particular race who happened to develop from erectus people in western Eurasia. Modern people arose from a different band of erectus. But, says Wolpoff, the moderns did not wipe out the neanderthals. They simply interbred with them. Thus, he says, modern Europeans and Middle Easterners contain genes that are specifically neanderthal. After all, there are plenty of stocky people around nowadays with big noses. Wolpoff obviously does not regard neanderthals as a separate species, *Homo neanderthalensis*. At most he sees them only as a sub-set or subspecies of ourselves: *Homo sapiens neanderthalensis*.

Wolpoff supports his idea by reference to the fossils. For, he says, within the archaic fossils now found in Asia he can see characters which resemble those of modern Asian people. The same is true, he says, of African or European archaics. In other words, he sees modern racial features welling up in the archaic lineages hundreds of thousands of years ago, and becoming more like the typical features of modern races as time passes. Other palaeoanthropologists say they can see no such proto-racial features either in archaic sapiens or in erectus. I would not presume to comment. This is one of those technical discussions that really has to be left to the people who look at bones for a living.

There are broader objections to the Wolpoff scenario, however. For if it is really the case that different erectus populations in different parts of the world each evolved first into archaic sapiens and then into moderns, this would imply a truly extraordinary degree of parallel evolution. Parallel evolution is really a special, and therefore rarer, form of convergence. That is, two or more lineages are said to converge when they start out differently (or at some point become different) but then begin to resemble each other more and more, like the horses and some of the litopterns. But parallelism implies that two or more lineages continue to evolve along similar lines so that at any one point in their evolution they remain in step with one another. Parallelism certainly happens, for the reasons discussed in Chapter 3: that natural selection is far more constrained than many modern biologists have liked to suppose, and different lineages of animals do tend to produce similar solutions in response to comparable selective pressures. So in theory, yes, the erectus people of China could have turned into modern Chinese over tens of thousands of years while the erectus people of Scandinavia transformed into modern Swedes. But such a degree of parallelism over such a time really does begin to stretch credulity. Furthermore, we know that although modern Chinese people do look very different from extreme, blond Swedes, we also know that the genetic differences between the two are minute. If the Chinese and the Swedes really had arisen *in situ* from the archaics and the erectus that were in south Asia or in Scandinavia before them, then we would expect to see a much greater genetic difference between the modern people than in fact is the case.

Wolpoff does answer such objections, however. For he argues that although the different erectus, and then archaic, populations evolved separately in different parts of the world, nonetheless they were all in touch with their neighbours. Since they were in touch, they exchanged genes through miscegenous matings. In fact, he says, there was enough gene flow between neighbouring groups to ensure that they all evolved along broadly similar lines – and enough, too, to ensure the near-homogeneity of the entire modern human species – but not enough to override the local effects of natural selection in each region, which shaped each racial type and went on shaping them over tens or hundreds of thousands of years.

Thus, Wolpoff and his supporters see the human family tree shaped like a candelabra. The stem is formed by *H. erectus*, which divides to form a series of parallel candle-holders, each with an archaic at its base and a modern sapiens at its tip. Hence the nick-name of Wolpoff's hypothesis.

In common with many other biologists, I find that scenario broadly implausible. Evolution does not seem to work this way. The refinement – the flow of genes between the lineages that would keep them in step – would not work unless the degree of flow was exactly right: enough to ensure broad similarity, but not enough to obliterate local difference. Yet I do believe that Wolpoff is correct to emphasise the importance of gene flow between populations – again this phenomenon of introgression. I am sure that introgression plays a far greater part in animal evo-lution than most zoologists admit (although botanists are generally happy to acknowledge its importance in plants).

More of this later. It is appropriate first to discuss the alterna-tive picture.

THE 'OUT OF AFRICA' HYPOTHESIS

The Candelabra hypothesis has an element of 'Out of Africa'. It acknowledges, after all, that erectus probably arose in Africa and then spread outwards. But Candelabra envisages only one dias-pora – that of erectus. The hypothesis that is properly called Out of Africa, championed not least by Dr Chris Stringer at London's Natural History Museum, requires more than one.

However, different people seem to describe the Out of Africa hypothesis in slightly different ways. Some seem content with only two emigrations, but some prefer three. Let us look at each in turn.

OUT OF AFRICA I: THE TWO-MIGRATION VERSION

The two-migration version of Out of Africa supposes conven-tionally enough that *H. erectus* was the first to emigrate, at least a million years ago and perhaps a lot more. Then, effectively as in the Candelabra story, different erectus populations in different parts of the world continued to evolve – and in particular most of them developed larger brains. Hence, more or less independently, different erectus populations evolved into a variety of 'archaic

Homo sapiens', one of which developed into the neanderthals. Thus this version of Out of Africa sees the archaics as updated versions of erectus, arising in different parts of the world from whichever erectus people happened to be there. So far, then, this version of Out of Africa resembles Candelabra.

But, unlike Candelabra, this scenario supposes that most of the archaic *Homo sapiens* which arose locally from *H. erectus* were dead-ends. They did not progress to become 'fully modern sapiens'. They simply died out.

For modern sapiens himself, this version has it, emerged only once, from a particular group of archaics evolved from erectus-grade hominids who had stayed in Africa. These unique, fully modern sapiens first appeared in Africa around 120,000 years ago, and some time afterwards they also migrated out of Africa and into Eurasia. The earliest fully modern sapiens bones outside Africa have been found in the Middle East, dating from around 90,000 years ago.

As these new people spread out they must have encountered populations or archaics who were already ensconced. Some of the archaic populations who had occupied the route in earlier times may well have disappeared by the time the new modern sapiens arrived – perhaps killed off by the fluctuating climate of the Pleistocene. We simply do not know how many archaic groups the newcomers encountered. But we do know of one group, in the Middle East and Europe, who were firmly established and waiting to greet the new emigrants from Africa. For we do know (since any other suggestion is inconceivable) that the new, modern sapiens must have encountered the neanderthals. Indeed 90,000-year-old modern skeletons from the Middle East were found side by side with neanderthals. We also know that the moderns had reached Europe by 40,000 years ago and at that time the neanderthals still had another 5,000 years to run. The prolonged coexistence of the two groups is undeniable. Whether they lived amicably together, or in a state of cold war, or on different sides of the hill, or as colonials and subjects, we are all free to speculate. There are certainly many countries nowadays – indeed, this is the rule rather than the exception – where different groups of people who do not have much in common, or like each other, at least manage to occupy the same space over time, effectively by living in parallel psychological universes. Perhaps some similar social interaction took place between the first modern Europeans and the neanderthals. It is however abundantly clear that the moderns came storming through this long relationship and have multiplied to occupy the entire Earth as no other creature has ever done before, while the neanderthals have faded away. Whether or to what extent there was intermarriage between the moderns and the neanderthals before the latter disappeared again is a matter for speculation. It is almost inconceivable that there was none at all. It does seem likely, then, that specifically neanderthal genes are with us still, just as Milford Wolpoff suggests.

So this version of Out of Africa admits only two emigrations: first of erectus, who spread themselves around and then evolved further into various kinds of archaic, and then of the fully modern sapiens people who evolved in Africa from one particular group of archaic stay-at-homes. However, this version seems open to the same kind of objections that are levelled at Candelabra. It suggests that different erectus populations in different places all evolved along similar lines so that they finally produced a roughly similar suite of 'archaic sapiens'. In response, again, we may simply acknowledge that natural selection is subject to restraints, and that different lineages often do tend to evolve along similar lines. Even so, the objection holds. It is at least worth looking for an alternative hypothesis.

The most obvious alternative is to suggest that more than two groups of hominines emigrated from Africa.

OUT OF AFRICA II: THE MULTI-MIGRATION VERSION

As I feel that the multi-migration model is the most convincing so far I would like to describe it in full, beginning at the beginning with the ancient *Homo habilis* in Africa.

According to Bernard Wood, as you may recall, *H. habilis* is really two species: *H. habilis* 'proper', and *H. rudolfensis*. The latter came to nothing, but *H. habilis* evolved into *H. erectus*. But, again according to Bernard Wood, *H. erectus* is also two species. The one that most people call *H. erectus* is the one that migrated out of Africa, and indeed was discovered by Eugene Dubois in south-east Asia. The other one was *H. ergaster*, who stayed in Africa.

According to the multi-migration model, *H. ergaster*, the stay-at-home in Africa, is the true ancestor of modern *H. sapiens*, not the migratory *H. erectus*. For according to this model *H. erectus*, having migrated, did not evolve further in any significant or particularly observable way. They simply lingered on – albeit for a very long time indeed in some places, including south-east Asia where, as mentioned, they may have survived until 100,000 years ago. It was *H. ergaster*, and only *H. ergaster*, still in Africa, who evolved to produce a creature who should be acknowledged as an 'archaic *Homo sapiens*'.

So then (this multi-migration model has it), some of the new archaics emigrated from Africa – again leaving some at home. These archaics then spread through Eurasia, pushing aside the erectus populations they happened to find *in situ*. These archaics then adapted to whichever locality they found themselves in. Those in northern Europe adapted to the extreme cold and became the classic neanderthals.

But, according to this scenario, the archaics who had moved out of Africa did not evolve further, or at least not in ways that are revealed in the fossil record. But further evolution to a significant and observable degree did take place in the archaics who had remained in Africa. For these African archaics gave rise to people who could pass muster as, and indeed *were*, the first fully modern *Homo sapiens*.

These new, modern sapiens then did exactly the same thing as the archaics and the erectus people had done before them. Some stayed at home to become modern Africans. Some migrated into Eurasia and pushed aside the archaics who had got there before them – including the neanderthals – or perhaps mated with them, just as the two-migration version supposes.

Just to cap the point, there is empirical evidence to support the overall notion of Out of Africa, in either version: modern studies of mitochondrial DNA from different races of modern humans suggest that they all shared a common ancestor who lived around 200,000 years ago in Africa. Thus the molecular studies coincide at least roughly with the fossil picture: the first modern humans arose from an African archaic, and they arose as a single entity.

However, some may argue that the three-wave (or 'multi-wave') version of Out of Africa is too *ad hoc*; that it is a bad thing in science simply to add complexity gratuitously, and that we have added too many diaspora. But I would take the fight to such opposition and argue that the traditional models – Candelabra and the two-wave version of Out of Africa – are far too conservative – indeed, I would even argue that the stripped-down three-wave model which I have just described is also too conservative. In philosophical vein, I would argue that the scientists' predilection for the simplest possible explanations – which manifests in a desire for conservatism – can lead us all astray. For in practice whenever we are able to observe nature directly we see that the reality is almost invariably more complex than it seems, so explanations that are irreducibly simple (like Candelabra or the two-wave Out of Africa model) are (I would say) innately likely to be wrong.

But there is a more subtle point, which is that simplicity should be sought not at the level of observation (what actually happens) but at the level of principle (what causes things to happen). We have seen after all with reference to climate that very simple forces often – indeed generally – produce extremely complex effects. The mathematics of chaos explains how it is that simple effects can have such enormously complex consequences.

Spurred by such thoughts, and acutely aware of my own presumptuousness. I would like to offer a fourth kind of account.

THE RECIPROCAL CASCADE MODEL

I am supremely unqualified to pass detailed judgment on any particular fossil, hominid or otherwise. If an expert tells me that such-and-such a bone belonged to a neanderthal or an *A. afarensis*, I take his or her word for it. It is ludicrous for the non-specialist to do otherwise and science is a collective pursuit in which we have to trust each other (although it will always remain true that outsiders are free to select their own experts). The account that follows, then, is a mind-game. For I do feel qualified to play mind-games, and suggest that in some fields at least they are not played enough. The essence of such games is to define and to lay out possibilities – and it is logically possible to lay out *all* of them, especially if you include a category entitled 'Possibilities we haven't thought of yet'.

The fossil record and the archaeological evidence from stone age times is poor. Of course there are a great many fossils and artefacts and they are studied by some excellent scientists who glean truly astonishing amounts of information from them. But the fossils and artefacts are sparse nonetheless relative to the number and variety of peoples from whom they derive, and the intricacies of their lives. It is entirely possible that pivotal events and populations have disappeared without any trace, and that we will never have direct knowledge of them. We can only pick up scraps. So there is room for speculation – in fact speculation is necessary if we are to make any headway at all. By the same token, it is absurd to become too wedded to any particular line of speculation. Always we must face the question, 'Who knows?'.

I would like modestly to suggest that if the human fossil record is too sparse to tell us what we want to know, then we might reasonably see what we can learn from the records of other creatures. The one that leaps to mind is that of horses. Of course they are not quite like us, for they are strict herbivores and we are not, and diet affects the way that animals move around the world, and the kinds of social groups they form, and so on. But we and they do have interesting similarities. We are both creatures of open space; we are both big and mobile; we are both able to traverse a continent in a few decades if the conditions are favourable; we are both slow breeding (although they have a much shorter generation interval than we do); and we have both been extremely successful.

Horses originated in North America, just as hominids and hominines almost certainly originated in Africa. They then spread themselves around the world just as humans did. The question is, what was their pattern of spread? Did they move out of America in one wave, or two, or many? Was their evolution subsequent to 'eohippus' more reminiscent of Candelabra or Out of Africa I or II?

Well it seems to be like none of them, although it has elements of all three. In fact we see horses radiating in North America and sending out various waves in various directions – to Eurasia and then to Africa when the opportunities arose; to South America in and after the Pliocene. Then we see the new groups settling down in new habitats, and radiating in their turn, sending out new offshoots in all directions including the places from whence they had come in the first place. We cannot directly observe introgression. Yet I maintain – albeit primarily as a matter of faith, backed by other people's studies of modern frogs and ducks – that introgression must have taken place: that new horses heading back to where they had come from must at times have encountered others that were still on their way out, and that there were at least occasional matings. To be sure, we do not see such matings between the different species of zebra that now inhabit Africa. But then the three modern species of zebra have drifted far apart behaviourally, and animals that live very different lives will not come together in the wild. If there were many more types of African horse, forced closer together ecologically and geographically, it is at least reasonable to suggest that we might see genetic interchange more often. Overall, as I commented in Chapter 4, the pattern of equid spread was like that of a superior firework: a cascade that produced a further cascade and then a third and so on. In fact, since the sparks often go back to where they began, we might call this a 'reciprocal cascade'. It is a high-falutin expression but it does have a kind of a ring to it.

Horse evolution has been enacted over 50 million years, while hominine history has lasted a mere 2 million. But I do not see that this makes a great difference. Two million years is plenty of time – thousands of times longer than is needed for a flourishing group of creatures to spread from one continent's end to the other.

Taking the parallel with horses, then, I do not see why we need suppose that a conservative view of hominine history is necessarily to be preferred. Instead of asking, 'Did human beings migrate from Africa once, twice, or three times?', why not admit that the hominine stew-pot in Africa might have thrown out dozens of migratory waves? Why not admit – as in horses – that any one those waves, once settled in some far-flung haven, might then have thrown out scions of its own, perhaps spreading back into Africa? Or that the ones that had returned could again move out (in a way specifically reminiscent of elephant history)?

Why not? It is not good philosophy simply to argue that there is no direct evidence for such a mêlée. There is no *direct* evidence for any of the more conservative hypotheses, either. Neither is it good philosophy (although many scientists would probably argue that it is) simply to suggest that conservative explanations are innately preferable because they are more 'parsimonious'. Parsimony is a good principle in science – meaning that explanations should not be made gratuitously complex, with conditional

clauses added *ad hoc* to explain away the untidy bits. But this 'reciprocal cascade' explanation of hominine diaspora is not
inherently complex. *In principle* it is extremely simple. It says that
successful animals are more mobile and more likely to radiate
than is generally supposed and in fact that they could spread over
a continent and back again many times in the kinds of periods in
which palaeontologists customarily trade – especially, one might
add, if they were spurred on their way by the advancing and
retreating ice fields of Pleistocene Europe. It also posits the reality of introgression.

To be sure, this simple principle produces an extremely complicated scenario: we must envisage bands of creatures racing
hither and thither in a quite bewildering fashion, continent-hop-
ping as they go (between Africa and Eurasia and back) and
perhaps swapping genes through rape or tryst and all known
forms of miscegenation. Horses did this throughout the Cenozoic
and modern human tribes in Europe are known to have milled
about in comparable fashion in the long and largely mysterious
millennia between the end of the last ice age and the rise of the
great literate civilisations that began what is conventionally
admitted to be 'history'. I really do not see why the hominines,
whose history is intermediate in time-scale between those of the
Equidae and of the pre-Roman tribes of Europe, should not have
operated in much the same manner as both of them.

This reciprocal cascade view of human diaspora would, of
course, be totally hopeless for explaining how a particular archaic
skull came to be in a particular place. One might as well try to
describe in fine detail how a particular umbrella came to be left at
a particular railway station by a person or persons unknown who
travelled a hundred years ago from a town that no longer exists
on a line whose destination is now obscure. Since the cascade idea
is so broadbrushed and therefore 'vague', it could be thrown out
on the grounds that it has no predictive value: it suggests no
hypotheses that could be directly tested. That criticism might well
be just. On the other hand, the cascade idea might well be true.

However, because the reciprocal cascade notion is novel (I
believe) and has not been subjected to learned criticism, I will
leave it there. The rest of this chapter discusses only the standard
models, Candelabra and the different versions of Out of Africa.
Both raise an interesting issue. How many species of *Homo* have

there been? Indeed, how many species of hominid?

AN INVENTORY OF HOMINIDS

Candelabra supposes that each of the different groups of archaic gave rise to a modern race of modern *Homo sapiens*, and that all the different races of *H. sapiens* demonstrably belong to the same species. No one suggests that even the most distinctive modern peoples, the Australian aborigines, are anything but *Homo sapiens*. If all the different modern sapiens all belong to one species then, logically, all the different races of archaic who gave rise to them must be one species as well. Indeed effectively, in the Candelabra scenario, every *Homo* that came after erectus and ergaster should be placed in the species *Homo sapiens*, although the older types might be acknowledged to be 'archaic'. Even the highly distinctive neanderthals would qualify only for subspecific status.

But no such logic restrains followers of the Out of Africa hypothesis, in either version. This idea does *not* envisage that the different archaic groups reconvened to form the modern sapiens. Instead, all the archaics except one are seen as twigs on the hominine family tree: twigs which came to nothing and, more to the point, *twigs which remained separate from each other.* For people with a penchant for taxonomy, then, it becomes perfectly legitimate to give each of the dead-end archaics a different species name.

Thus some biologists (including Bernard Wood) give the first archaic that evolved in Africa from ergaster the name of *H. heidelbergensis*. (It has a German name because a specimen that is indistinguishable from the basic African type had already turned up in Germany, and been given its German name.) So it was heidelbergensis who spread out of Africa in the second wave of emigration. The various races that heidelbergensis gave rise to in different locations throughout Africa and Eurasia can also be regarded as separate species: *H. daliensis* in China, *H. javanensis* in Java, *H. rhodesiensis* in what is now Zimbabwe, and *H. neanderthalensis* in Europe. In this arrangement, only fully modern people should be called *H. sapiens*. And overall, in this treatment, we recognise no fewer than six species of *Homo*.

But then, before the various archaics and modern sapiens came into being there were *H. erectus* and *H. ergaster*, and before that came *H. habilis* and *H. rudolfensis*. So the total in the genus *Homo* now rises to ten.

Before the genus *Homo* there were *Australopithecus* and *Paranthropus*. Some recognise four paranthropines but Wood, at least, acknowledges only three: *P. robustus, P. aethiopicus,* and *P. boisei*. The known specimens of *A. africanus* may well represent two species. *A. afarensis* may be only one but there must have been others before afarensis. Now, too, we know *A. ramidus*. Conservatively, then, we might reasonably acknowledge seven australopithecines (including paranthropines), which brings the total known hominid family up to seventeen.

Clearly, through most of the past 5 million years – in fact until the death of the neanderthals – there have been several species of hominid on this planet at any one time. Around 2 million years ago there were at least one and possibly two hominines, *H. habilis* and *H. rudolfensis*, and probably at least two robust australopithecines, *P. robustus* and *P. boisei*. About 100,000 years ago there may have been five contemporaneous members of the genus *Homo*, including various 'archaics', the first of the true sapiens, and even perhaps the very last erectus, still holding out in south-east Asia. As with cats, horses, and elephants, our family was much more varied in the past.

I like this approach to human classification. At least it expresses the spirit of the thing: the fact that our own family tree has been as bushy as that of any other successful lineage. It was not a cordon, focused on one central stem that led inexorably and orthogenically to us. To suppose that there was such a cordon is merely to reinvoke *Genesis* in a more expanded form.

Yet the multi-species approach needs qualification. I have suggested that from the Candelabra idea the concept of introgression deserves to be salvaged: the notion that the different emerging lineages of *Homo* swapped genes as they evolved. I have been inspired in this thought by recent involvement with attempts to conserve modern endangered animals by captive breeding in zoos. Here there are two contrasting considerations. On the one hand the different subspecies need to be kept apart, to conserve their 'purity' – so at present, for example, Siberian and Sumatran tigers are kept in separate breeding populations. On the other hand, it is essential to ensure that no one population of zoo animals becomes too isolated, or each group will become too inbred.

Thus Siberian tigers from zoos in mainland Europe should from time to time be brought over to mate with Britain's Siberian tigers, and vice versa.

The point is, though, that such breeding plans have given rise to a large body of genetics theory – and this theory shows that the British and European populations of Siberian tigers would effectively be genetically continuous *even if the flow of genes between them was remarkably small*. In other words, if just one European tiger per generation was brought to Britain – or indeed just one in several generations – this would achieve all the mixing required.

Translate this into the experience of early hominids, from erectus onwards: highly mobile, often adventurous, and marauding throughout Africa and Eurasia. It seems inconceivable to me that newly arriving groups would not have mated at least from time to time with the peoples they met along the way. Sometimes the contacts would have been friendly, sometimes forced. But such things must surely have occurred, and if they did then there would indeed have been gene flow between the many groups, precisely in the way that Milford Wolpoff emphasises. I still think the candelabra hypothesis is wrong. But I also feel that we can reasonably impose considerable gene flow on to the Out of Africa scenario. So in important details Wolpoff would certainly be right. Modern human beings would indeed contain neanderthal genes.

This of course would make the fossil record even harder to interpret than it is already. Introgression can sometimes be observed directly in modern animals: for example, DNA studies of fish from different rivers in the south-western desert of the United States reveal that from time to time in the past – during periods of flood – different populations have come together and exchanged genes. Such studies can even show how often such exchanges have taken place. But no such research can be done on ancient fossils which contain no DNA at all, or far too little to allow such interpretation. Introgression among past hominines, if it did occur, would have to be inferred from the fossil evidence, and such inferences would always be uncertain.

But if there *was* such gene flow between ancient hominines then many biologists would doubt whether it is legitimate to treat the different populations as different species. After all, a species is commonly defined as a group of organisms that can breed together successfully but which cannot breed successfully with others. If neanderthals could indeed mate with modern sapiens then by that strict definition they must both be placed in the same species.

However, the more that modern biologists explore animals (and plants) in the field, the less realistic that traditional definition seems. Clearly, hybridisation in the wild is common. Sometimes the hybrids are simply not fertile, in which case the traditional definition of species holds good (because the mating between the two groups is not wholly successful). Sometimes the hybrids are fertile but are clearly at a disadvantage, and fail to make an ecological impact. This is true of the wild hybrids of yellow-bellied toads and fire-bellied toads. These hybrids occur in a narrow band across the Caucasus where the two populations overlap. But they do not spread out of that band – which suggests that they do not compete successfully with either of the pure-breds on either side. But some hybrids are perfectly viable and healthy. Thus it is that ruddy ducks from the USA are currently interbreeding with the native white-headed ducks of Spain – and the resultant hybrids are threatening to oust the white-headeds altogether. By the traditional definition ruddy ducks and white-headeds should be placed in the same species. But since they look so different and they normally live in separate continents and even behave slightly differently, common sense says that they are separate species. So many modern biologists are content simply to argue that a species is a group of organisms that is evolving as one discrete unit. Neanderthals and modern sapiens probably had very little to do with each other, and were certainly pursuing different evolutionary paths. Thus they can legitimately be placed in separate species – *H. neanderthalensis* and *H. sapiens* – even though they probably swapped genes from time to time, and even though the modest gene flow between them may have had a significant impact on their respective gene pools.

All this, however, is partly speculative, and partly a matter of opinion – opinion for example on what we ought to mean by 'species'. What seems to be more or less certain is that by about 35,000 years ago the hominine genus was reduced to just one species, *Homo sapiens*. Certain, too, is that *Homo sapiens* continued the migratory tradition that was begun by *H. erectus*.

★

THE TRAVELS OF SAPIENS

H. erectus stopped at the coast of south-east Asia, but *H. sapiens*, arriving much later in those parts, pressed on further. Modern humans reached Australia at least 40,000 years ago – that is, at a time when there were still neanderthals in Europe – and may indeed have arrived there tens of thousands of years before that, perhaps as long as 80,000 years ago. Those first Australians must have arrived by boat, for although there is not much open sea between Australia and south-east Asia (since it is loosely straddled by a chain of islands) the two big land masses have never been in direct contact. South-east Asia and its archipelago of islands are Laurasian while Australia and New Guinea are Gondwanan and the sea between them has always been deep. It has certainly been possible from time to time to walk from the Asian mainland to what are now the Indonesian islands, and also from New Guinea to Australia, but not from Indonesia to New Guinea.

We know, too, that within a few more millennia the people of south-east Asia became truly fabulous sailors, for at least by 30,000 years ago they were pressing on into the islands of the Pacific. These early Pacific people may well have included some of the world's first horticulturalists.

Migration out of Eurasia into the Americas had to wait. The first crossing was made not by boat but on foot, across the huge land-bridge of Beringia which appeared conveniently in the late Pleistocene. Most of the most conspicuous animals of modern North America made the crossing at that time, including the bison, wapiti, and moose, and so the megafauna of modern North America is essentially Eurasian. Human beings followed about 13,000 years ago and then spread steadily south to enter South America about 11,000 years ago.

So by the time we reach the end of the Pleistocene, about 10,000 years ago, human beings had colonised or at least set foot on most of the world's great land masses. Indeed only two large areas remained: Madagascar, which surprisingly escaped serious colonisation until after the time of Christ and perhaps even as late as the fifth century AD, and New Zealand, which somehow escaped the first wave of Pacific exploration and did not receive its first human beings until the ninth or tenth century after Christ.

What these modern human beings did as they travelled, and

the impact they had on their fellow creatures, I will discuss in Chapter 8. For now I want merely to observe the obvious fact that the hominines as a whole have been a very successful group during some very trying times. They were direct descendants of tropical, arboreal apes who, extraordinarily, went on to endure the tundra of the Pleistocene and some of the harshest episodes of climate that the Earth has experienced, and have become the dominant life form in every land they have entered. In the next chapter I want to ask how they did it. In brief: 'What's so good about us?'.

What's So Special About Us?

It is impossible to discuss what makes us successful without entering tricky philosophical territory, in which many modern biologists lie waiting to pounce. There are notions that have become extremely unfashionable, which the unwary enunciate at their peril. One such notion is that when one animal survives and multiplies while another goes to the wall then the survivor is in some way 'superior'. By contrast, the fashionable interpretation is (a) that survival is almost entirely a matter of chance and (b) that all talk of 'superiority' is tainted both by theological muddle-headedness and by vicious politics and is therefore out of order. In short, the moderns say, it is better to be minimalist: we are entitled to observe only that at time T animal A and animal B existed side by side, while at time T + 1 animal A was waxing fat and animal B had disappeared. The reasons for this reversal should invariably be ascribed to the environment. Thus we are allowed to infer that animal A was better adapted to the prevailing conditions, but not that it was in any worthwhile sense 'better'. For example, if A was aquatic and B was not and the land flooded then A would thrive while B drowned. But that does not make A superior. Merely 'fitter': more apt.

There is much to be said for this purist approach. We might, for example, assert that an oak tree is superior to a moss and at first sight that seems self-evident. Oak trees are huge and complex while mosses are small and apparently simple. Oaks may dominate the landscapes of entire countries while mosses cling to damp corners. On the other hand, mosses grow in more places than oak trees do and if and when the next asteroid strikes most biologists would put their money on mosses to survive it rather than oak trees.

Then again, the concept of 'superiority' has been used for centuries, and probably for millennia, to justify injustice. Human beings in general have not only subjugated other animals but have been frankly cruel to them, and we have justified this by our own 'superiority'. Tribes have enslaved and murdered tribes, races have murdered and enslaved other races, with the same excuse.

Imperialism in general employs this reasoning: the conquering group feels it has a right to conquer because it is better. Charles Darwin was at pains to distance himself from such nonsense, yet his ideas have been pressed into the service both of imperialism and of racism. Europeans of the late nineteenth century and white Americans through much of the twentieth century have used the idea that they are 'biologically superior', or are 'further evolved', to justify the maltreatments they had already been handing out to non-Caucasians for several centuries. Stephen Jay Gould excellently describes the many misuses of such notions in *The Mismeasure of Man*.

But still I want to invoke the notion of biological 'superiority'. We must of course begin by defining exactly what we mean by it and what we do not. As I will discuss presently, the notion can legitimately be applied only to entities or phenomena that are measurable. It is inadmissable to apply value judgments and to suggest, for example, that if one animal runs faster than another – which is an objective statement – that it is therefore 'better' in some general way. In particular, to suggest that the creature which is measurably superior in any particular respect is *ipso facto* morally superior is bad science (since it is not in the brief of science to make such judgments) and also bad moral philosophy (since this is merely a variation on the deeply suspect theme of 'might is right'). In short, if people festoon the idea of biological superiority with value judgments and moral justifications then they deserve to be attacked precisely in the way that Stephen Gould has so ably done.

But if we avoid such solecisms, as Darwin did and I hope to do, then it seems to me that the idea of biological superiority is not only useful but necessary. It is true, as the moderns assert, that chance plays a large part in determining which creature flourishes in any one circumstance. It is also true that when circumstances change then the baseline statement must simply be that when the survivors are the ones that are most apt – just as a moss may survive when an oak tree does not. Yet it remains the case that there are measurable differences between organisms, and these measurable qualities are at least pertinent to survival.

So, despite the caveats, let us look again at the notion of biological superiority. In practice, I suggest, the expression has two acceptable and useful meanings. One refers to qualities that might be called 'technical', and the other is 'logistic'.

TECHNICAL SUPERIORITY

The idea that animals are simply machines as René Descartes suggested in the seventeenth century is one I find deeply repellent and indeed plain wrong. Certainly they behave in ways that are quite different from any machine; in fact the only machine an animal can fairly be compared to is another animal. Yet animals are machines of a kind. They have mechanical parts, and they convert energy into action, just as a machine does. The components of a machine are measurable and, more to the point, the overall *performance* is measurable. Clearly, some machines perform better than others, and to that extent they are superior.

Of course, we have to judge like against like. We might objectively observe that a BMW is faster than a combine-harvester but we cannot say that it is 'superior'. Clearly, they are not designed to do the same job. But if we take two vehicles that are designed to do the same job then we can make objective comparisons. We might, for example, prefer to own a vintage Bentley than a BMW, because the Bentley is so beautiful. But an engineer who was asked purely to judge objectively would declare that in virtually all measurable respects the BMW is superior. For one thing, at any given speed, the BMW uses considerably less than half as much fuel as the Bentley; in short, it is measurably more efficient, and dissipates less of the available energy in the form of heat. Importantly, if your life depended on fast transport, then you should choose the BMW.

Animals and plants have thousands of characters whose function is obvious and whose performance is measurable just as the performance of a car is measurable. It is clear, for example, that a key function of the protein-lipid membrane that surrounds all living cells is to keep the inside of the cell in a state of chemical equilibrium. The membrane allows some things to pass through it, and not others. Some it positively repels. It is also clear that a double membrane – two protein and two lipid layers – can carry out this task with greater certainty than a single membrane could. We can therefore assert (it seems to me) that double layers are technically superior to single layers. On a larger scale, I suggested in Chapter 4 that rumination is in general more efficient than hind-gut digestion. The ruminant derives more useful energy per kilo of leaf digested than the hind-gut digester does. That is objectively measurable.

The important question, of course, is whether the creatures with the measurable technical advantages survive better. If not, then we must simply say, 'So what?'. Well, to revert to our first example, it seems extremely likely that single-membrane cells evolved before double layers did; yet the only creatures that still retain single-layered cell membranes are bacteria-like microbes living an extremely marginal existence. It does rather look as if the demonstrable superiority of the double-membraned cell has won the day. Similarly, it really does seem hard to deny that the technically superior ruminants have come into their own since the Miocene, when high-cellulose grass began to prevail; that it is the case that the ruminant bovids, rather than the equids, diversified (and in some cases continue to diversify) since the Pliocene; and that the equids cannot apparently compete in the middle-range of body size where difference in digestive efficiency is likely to become significant. *Nannippus* was an exception and the modern Shetland pony is a quasi-domestic artefact.

The issue is not simple. For one thing, technical ability does not always correlate straightforwardly with technical complexity. The homoiothermy of mammals requires greater physiological complexity than the poikilothermy of reptiles – but poikilotherms often win through precisely because they require less food and are therefore intrinsically more efficient. Mammals have to justify their complexity by working harder. Nevertheless, when you compare like with like, you do find that equivalent creatures do the same things with measurably greater or lesser effectiveness, and that in general the more effective ones win out. In short, I submit that 'technical superiority' is a worthwhile concept, and that it does indeed correlate positively, though obviously not invariably, with survival.

LOGISTICAL SUPERIORITY

In recent years ecologists have begun more and more to speak of survival 'strategy'. Effectively it means, 'What is the creature trying to do, and how do its actions contribute to its survival?'.*

What truly makes such thinking worthwhile - and has placed the science of ecology on a quite new footing - is that these strategies for survival can also be quantified. The key to quantification lies in the system of maths that was developed in particular by the Hungarian-American mathematician John von Neumann in the middle decades of this century: 'game theory'.

The basic idea is to assess the likelihood of success of any conceivable move in any conceivable game and hence to *quantify* the chances of winning in any particular line of attack. But this general approach can also be applied to the things that animals do in the wild. For example, ecologists such as John Krebs of Oxford University have looked in particular at the attempts of animals to find food - their 'foraging strategy'. It is possible to demonstrate mathematically what the animals would need to do in order to obtain the best quality or the maximum amount of food with the least effort (or risk). Such thinking has revealed, for example, the point we have made earlier: that in general it is best for predators to attack prey of their own size which are big enough to be worthwhile but not so big as to be risky (unless they cooperate like lions and hominids, when they can take on bigger prey). Indeed it is possible to define objectively any particular animal's *optimum foraging strategy*. From this we can objectively decide how good a particular animal is at doing what it ought to be doing - just as we can objectively judge how efficiently a given herbivore digests a kilo of grass. We have to be careful, of course, and in particular to concede that the animal probably knows its own business better than we do, and that some of the perceived inefficiencies may be manoeuvres to avoid problems that we do not appreciate (for example a detour to avoid a particular predator).

By and large, though, the point applies. We can objectively assess how well animals carry out the things they ought to be doing. By the same token, we can assert that one creature may be carrying out the allotted tasks more efficiently than another - in short, that it is *logistically* superior.

The genus *Homo* had a sister genus, *Paranthropus* ('sister' implying

---

*'Trying' in this context need not imply any act of will. Many biologists happily speak of grass or trees 'trying' to do particular things. The language conveys the meaning colourfully but obviously is not meant to imply that the plants are consciously working to a plan.

that we both descended at roughly the same time from the ancestral *Australopithecus*). *Homo* now dominates the world. *Paranthropus*, in the words of Professor Bob Brain, former director of the National Museum of South Africa, had the ecological impact of a baboon and then died out. Never have two sisters pursued such different paths. The notions outlined above, of technical superiority and more importantly of logistic superiority, explain how the discrepancy came about, not simply between human beings and paranthropines but between us and all the rest of creation.

WHAT DO WE DO THAT IS DIFFERENT?

If we are truly to get to the essence of what we do that is different, then we need to consider our abilities at three levels. First there are our physical attributes: in particular the hand and brain, and the special brain development, repositioned larynx and extraordinary muscularity of the tongue and face that underpin language and rapid speech. Then there are the practical abilities to which such assets have given rise - such as hurling missiles, deployment of fire, farming, and verbal communication. But finally, to grasp what we really do, we should analyse our own abilities in logistic terms, which in principle can be quantified by game theory.

In the tour of our abilities that occupies the rest of this chapter, two points are particularly striking. One is that the difference between what we do and what other animals do often seems very small in technical terms. Consciousness is clearly not unique to us. Our kind of language, projected by speech, probably is unique, but even so the qualitative advance can be analysed into components most of which are not so different in kind from the attributes of other animals. In other words, human beings do not seem to have invented the ability of speech *ab ovo* but to have combined attributes that are already present in other animals. Darwin was keen to emphasise that there is continuity between human beings and the rest - that the differences are primarily matters of degree even when they appear to be absolute - and Darwin has usually turned out to be right.

But the second striking feature is that *very small technical developments may translate into huge logistic advantage.* When you boil it down, the 'new life form' that we have created rests on only a very few extra techniques. Indeed I often feel that we have beaten our fellow creatures out of sight in the same kind of way that a fencing master will invariably overwhelm a tyro. The master may not actually be particularly brilliant (and may well be old and arthritic to boot) but he knows a few things that the novice does not – and a few crucial tricks is all it takes to turn an even contest into a rout. The abilities that have made us supreme could similarly be classed as 'tricks'. If natural selection could be said to work to a plan, then that plan would simply be to produce creatures that can survive for the next generation.

But sometimes the *ad hoc* devices that favour such short-term survival have huge sequelae; new qualities emerge as 'epiphenomena', and whole new vistas open up. This is what has happened to us.

In the rest of this chapter I will look at our various abilities in turn. But in each case I will explore them at three levels: the physical underpinning, the practicalities, and the logistic advantage.

MENTAL TRICKS: THE POWER TO ANALYSE

It is absolutely not true to suggest, as René Descartes suggested in the seventeenth century, that animals do not think. It is undoubtedly the case, however, that human beings think more deeply and broadly than other animals. Brains emphatically do not work in the same way as computers but they do have things in common with them and one such thing is that the capacity to take in and process data is to some extent a function of size and complexity. Our brains are clearly much bigger than those of other animals (relative to body size), and we can also presume that they are more complex: they contain more neurones, which are connected to each other in more intricate ways.

Our superior thinking power has several connotations. First it implies that when we look at the world about us we perceive many more factors than other animals do. We take more into account.

Then, secondly, there is the matter of hard-wiring versus software. Thus many creatures have *ad hoc* mental abilities that go well beyond anything we can do. A nuthatch can hide 100,000 separate seeds for the winter and find every one of them when it needs to. Some of us find it hard to remember where we left our keys. But the ability of the nuthatch is like that of a pocket calculator: wonderful, but inflexible. Move one of the nuthatch's seeds six inches to the left and it is thrown into confusion. We should not *blame* the nuthatch for this. To waste time looking for seeds that are not where expected would be a very poor foraging strategy indeed. But the point remains: the nuthatch does what it does, and cannot deviate. Many other animals (and indeed nuthatches themselves, in other contexts) have to *learn* what to do in any one situation and then are able to respond in a variety of ways: in other words, they *decide* what to do. Thus their responses are not hard-wired. One of the many surprises sprung by field biologists in recent years is that many wild animals are far less hard-wired than old-fashioned behaviourists liked to believe: for example, young cats need to learn how to hunt, monkeys must learn to climb trees, most animals have to learn social skills and the arts of bringing up offspring, and most creatures can respond in a far greater variety of ways to any one situation than tidy-minded biologists of the recent past liked to believe. The fact remains nonetheless that although much of our own behaviour is hard-wired (more than we like to admit, probably), the proportion that is hard-wired is small compared to what is not. And in those areas where we do indeed make decisions, we are able in general to choose between many more possible options than most other animals. In short, to combine the first two points, we take more factors into account and we are able to respond to any one of the factors in a greater variety of ways.

Thirdly – largely perhaps as a consequence of these first two abilities – we do not simply take the world at its face value. We have (it seems) an innate tendency to observe the patterns that underlie the behaviour of the things around us, and to infer the rules that produce those patterns. Of course in form this search for order has culminated in the notion that the whole Universe operates according to universal laws; science being way of searching systematically for those laws. But long before our species hit on that formal method of inquiry our ancestors perceived, for example, that prey-animals moved to particular places at particular times, that they congregated where the grass was green, and so on. Of course other predators do this too. But it seems reasonable to suggest that we - at least *Homo sapiens* - developed such an ability to an advanced degree. Here is one of the points at which a quantitative difference gave rise to a qualitative advance, for once a creature begins to understand the *rules* by which other creatures operate then its power over them increases by leaps and bounds. Once the rules are grasped, then anticipation can lead on to manipulation.

So the first of our mental tricks is a great power simply to analyse - what psychologists call 'cognitive ability'. But it is the next refinement - really a set of linked refinements - that has really made the difference.

MORE TRICKS: THOUGHT AND CONSCIOUSNESS, LANGUAGE AND SPEECH

Descartes suggested that animals could not think because, he said, thought is dependent upon verbal language. Animals do not use words. *Ergo*, they do not think. Descartes was renowned for his logic.

The science of behaviourism which dominated animal psychology from early in this century practically until the 1980s was rooted to some extent in this Cartesian notion. Its other roots belong in positivism: the notion that nothing is worth thinking about except what can be directly observed and measured. Hence the behaviourists regarded animals simply as machines which do not think but merely behave, and regarded the notion that they do think as a piece of muddle-headedness generated by sentimentality.

In fact, biologists have studied animals more and more closely as the century has worn on - far more closely than ever in the past (one of the more pleasing aspects of our times) - and the more they have looked the more it has become obvious that the behaviour of animals cannot be explained simply by assuming they are machines. At least, if they are machines they are incomparably more complex than any machine that any human being has ever devised. They are machines, in fact, only in the sense that we could say for purposes of discussion that human beings are machines. In practice, more and more biologists have come to conclude that it is impossible to explain what animals do *unless* we suppose that they think. As Professor Herbert Terrace of Columbia University suggested at the Royal Society's symposium on animal intelligence in 1984, the task before us now is to explain how animals think even though they lack verbal language.

So what going on? Is it the case that human beings do think verbally (as Descartes supposed) and that animals think in some other way, or is there more to it than that?

There is indeed more to it. The relationship between thought and verbal language has for the most part been misconstrued. But once we construe it correctly we can see what it is that humans do that animals do not. And although the ability of animals goes far beyond anything that they were generally credited with in the past (except, of course, by 'animal lovers' who never lost faith in their abilities), we can see too that the extra verbal tricks of human beings give us a supreme advantage.

Point one is that human thought is clearly not dependent upon words. A key example has been offered by the American geneticist Barbara McClintock, who was awarded a Nobel Prize in 1983 for her discovery of 'jumping genes' (the ability of some genes literally to shift from one part of the genome to another). Dr McClintock describes how this extraordinary notion came to her effectively 'in a flash'. She then related it to her colleagues in the no-frills language of a specialist talking to specialists and it took her two hours to state the idea.★ How is two hours' worth of concentrated verbiage compressed into a 'flash'? Yet we have all, in lesser contexts, had many such experiences. How else does repartee operate? Witticism follows witticism instantly. The joke is conceived long before its verbal manifestation has time to vibrate the airways.

Words, in short, are *not* the necessary raw materials of thought, as Descartes supposed. They trail behind the thoughts. The thoughts themselves flow in us like some dark river in the caverns of the brain (a very Coleridgean kind of notion), just as they must do in animals. Words merely *describe* those ideas. They are labels that we attach to ideas. Or, as Ludwig Wittgenstein said, words *point* at ideas.

★This episode is described in *A Feeling for the Organism, The Life and Work of Barbara McClintock* by Evelyn Fox Keller (W.H. Freeman, San Francisco, 1983).

But to describe ideas in words, to point at them, is not a trivial thing to do. In the language of computers or of librarians this ability enables the thinker to *access* his or her own thoughts. More: it enables us to monitor them, and to direct them. Thus, in the process of thinking, words are not the frontline troops they have seemed to be. But they are the rapporteurs, and they can be the commanding officers. In short, words give us a degree of control over our thoughts which is beyond that of all other creatures.

Why, though, does it *feel* to us (as it clearly did to Descartes) that we think in words? Why do we need to be reminded, as Barbara McClintock's experience reminds us, of the central absurdity of such a notion?

The answer surely lies in the phenomenon of consciousness, and in the circularity of arguments that inevitably surround consciousness.

Many have sought to describe consciousness, and to discuss its evolution. But in the end it is difficult to improve on the notion that seems intuitively obvious: that through consciousness we *know* that we think. Consciousness is the means by which we observe the dark rivers of thought, and direct them. *Inter alia* it offers, as psychologists tend to say, a way of directing the attention of the thoughts to matters that are most important.

But I seem to have said much the same thing just now about words. Is it the case, then, that words and consciousness are the same thing? Well of course the answer must be 'no', for various reasons, one of which is that scholars of animal psychology are also increasingly of the opinion that animals are conscious, contrary to the wisdom of past decades, and perhaps we might adapt the comment of Herb Terrace and suggest that a further task is to explain how animals manage to be *conscious* even though they lack verbal language. It is true, too, that all of us think to some extent in pictures. The image of a blank and accusatory screen flashing across the mind may remind us that the television is on the blink. But once the image is established the words tend to take over: 'Damn! Must get the television fixed!'.

Thus, although we may deny that thought in general is linked ineluctably (or even particularly closely) to verbal language, there does seem to be a strong relationship between *consciousness* and verbal language. Through consciousness we know that we are thinking. Through verbal language we tell ourselves that this is the case. So although it seems proper to admit that other animals are conscious (and impossible to deny that this is the case) we must nonetheless admit that our possession of verbal language makes us *more* conscious than other animals. We might indeed envisage another feedback loop: consciousness employs verbal language in the way that the brain in general employs the dextrous hand, and verbal language enhances the quality of consciousness just as the dextrous hand enhances the brain. Because words are labels attached to ideas, because indeed they point at ideas, we can survey the words as if they were the ideas themselves, laying them out for inspection like fish on a slab.

This is where the circularity comes in, and the illusion that led so many people (including Descartes and the behaviourists) to misconstrue the relationship between verbal language and thought. For the only thoughts of which we are conscious - obviously - are the conscious ones. These do not represent the bulk of our cogitations. They do however provide the means by which we access our cogitations, and hence the means by which we recognise and 'bring to mind' those cogitations. Furthermore, our conscious thoughts for the most part *are* verbal. So the thoughts of which we are conscious - or at least the ones over which we exercise the most control - are verbal thoughts. It generally seems to us, then, that the only thoughts we have *of any kind* are verbal thoughts. It is indeed beyond our imagining - how could it be otherwise? - that we *can* think seriously without words (even though it is obvious that we must), for how can we think about anything consciously - including about thinking itself - without putting the thought into words? And if we do not put it into words, how do we know we are thinking about it? Among the many wise things that Marvin Minksy says in his excellent book *The Society of Mind* (Simon & Schuster, New York, 1985) is that our brains are evolved organs which have been selected to observe and cope with the outside world and which emphatically have *not* been selected for the purpose of self-examination. In short we are innately bad at introspection. Our failure to perceive the nature of our own thinking, or the nature of the consciousness that gives access to that thinking, or of the words that give order to that consciousness, are surely a manifestation of this ineptitude.

So what is verbal language, and how did we come by it?

WORDS, WORDS, WORDS

Biologists have discussed at length whether other animals have language, and of course they do. What is language after all but the ability to convey ideas (some fact about the outside world or about one's inner emotional state) by means of symbols that the receiver understands? And of course animals produce such symbols constantly: sights, sounds, odours, all signalling to the recipient, 'Here is food!', 'Watch out - danger!', and so on. Such language is not merely strictly 'functional'. It often has a conversational mien: squirrel monkeys feeding in the trees chirrup from time to time just to let the others know where they are - and sheep do the same thing on the hillside. Neither are the sounds random utterances. Monkeys such as vervets demonstrably make a range of warning sounds - a true vocabulary - one meaning 'snake', one meaning 'hawk', one meaning 'leopard', and so on, and each suggests a different form of evasive action. Perhaps, unlike us, animals do tend to refer only to what is immediate, rather than to abstract thoughts. But perhaps we have not looked at their utterances closely enough to justify such generalisations. Probably they are less able to convey subtleties - subjunctives and conditionals. But they clearly *think* conditionally - 'If this then this; and if that, then that'. In short it can be difficult to pin down the absolute difference between animal communication and human language. We seem to have incomparably more vocabulary than other animals do. We clearly have a greater capacity for abstraction than they do. But it seems cavalier in the extreme simply to suggest that we have language and they do not. And if - as is the case - they make different sounds to suit different circumstances, then it seems difficult to sustain the idea that we use words and they do not.

Yet there are clear distinctions. For a start we might simply observe that our language, besides being verbal, is open-ended. Animals make particular sounds - 'words' - to pick out items on the central registry of notions peculiar to their species. We do much more than this. We can invent sentences that have never been coined before, and can in principle express notions that have never been expressed before. Furthermore, we can do this effortlessly. Even babies do it. They are wonderful inventors of new thoughts, and coiners of new expressions. One difference is thus

our literally endless ability to devise new words to fit any circumstance - at least in principle, for we do have difficulty in
finding words to express ideas that are quite beyond our experience (as theologians have found both to their cost and to their
advantage).

But a larger distinction was pinned down in particular by
Noam Chomsky. What our language has, and that of other animals apparently does not, is syntax. Underpinning our languages
are a few basic rules which enable us to manipulate the sounds -
the words - in an infinity of ways; by applying the rules of syntax
we can convey an infinity of meanings and infer the right meaning when another speaks. The fine rules of syntax differ from
language to language - from German to Chinese and Chinese to
Finnish - yet there seems also to be a *deep* syntax that is common
to us all. By applying the syntactical rules we not only convey
meaning by word order or word endings (or both) but also are
able to stack subsidiary clause upon subsidiary clause without getting lost. And again I stress we do this effortlessly, and so do
babies.

Words are not necessarily spoken. Obviously, they can be written. But written language is clearly a secondary skill: a way of
conveying visually, and permanently, symbols that are by their
nature sound-bites. In principle, presumably, human beings could
have developed an olfactory language or a visual language. Many
animals, including many insects, are able to convey extremely
precise and detailed information by chemical signals. For example, the 'parasitoid' ichneumon wasps which lay their eggs in the
bodies of aphids are able to tell from chemical signals precisely
how many eggs have already been deposited by other ichneu-
mons, and the sex of those eggs; aphids themselves employ a wide
range of chemical signals including 'alarm pheromones' which
warn others of danger; and so on. But primates have in general
moved from smell to vision since their prosimian days. Vision
offered an obvious route, and of course primates communicate a
great deal by vision, from the blue base of the blue-based baboon
to the hundreds of flickering expressions on the human face. But
sound has its own advantages. In particular, it travels by night and
around corners. Through sound, animals can communicate with
other individuals which are not looking directly at them. That
offers a huge logistic advantage which almost all land vertebrates

(and many aquatic ones) exploit.

Syntax is a way of manipulating words, and since words in practice begin as spoken sounds it is in essence a way of manipulating sounds. The point is important if only because sounds for the purposes of speech (as opposed to those of orchestration) are issued in a linear series, one after the other. But ideas are rarely linear. This is the problem that beleaguers all writers of books: how to present ideas in a linear sequence even though the ideas themselves branch out or go around in circles (for the beginning generally cannot be understood until you get to the end). Ideas can be presented visually in flow diagrams and the rest, but if we commit ourselves to a verbal presentation then we must begin at the beginning – the beginning being almost invariably arbitrary – and work along a single narrow path. This is 'narrative'. Syntax enables us to create an order in this inveterately linear sequence which preserves meaning, allowing us to insert subsidiary clauses and parentheses and emphases and all the other tricks that we take for granted but which, if analysed, are truly miraculous. Perhaps most miraculous of all is that we do take these abilities for granted. We must study the syntactical details of other languages but syntax itself is innate. People robbed of language – slaves, for example, plucked from their own countries and effectively prevented from conversing with their new masters in their new countries – spontaneously invent languages known as 'creoles' which are odd in vocabulary but are perfectly and complexly syntactical. Pidgin languages represent creoles in embryonic form, the first attempt of people to synthesise a new language by imposing syntactical rules on half-grasped fragments of other languages. Pidgins may sound odd to outsiders, but they are truly heroic inventions, a tribute to the human proclivity to create true language in the most unpromising circumstance. Babies have no problems with syntax. They effectively invent their own, and then modify their invention in accord with the special rules of their particular society.

Syntax is innately geared to the spoken word and yet it is possessed by people who have never heard words spoken. The sign language employed by people who are born deaf is perfectly syntactical although, interestingly, the details of the signing syntax may differ somewhat from those of the prevailing spoken language. Perhaps the details of the syntax are modified for visual purposes. But whatever the explanation, the fact remains that syntax is innate, and in practice our syntactical ability - at least in the form it takes now - surely could not have evolved except in association with a spoken language. We can imagine a feedback loop between articulacy on the one hand and syntactical subtlety on the other. Hence deaf people in their signing partake of a syntactical ability that could not have evolved if their ancestors had themselves been deaf. But now that syntax has evolved, it has a life of its own.

From what, though, did this syntactical skill evolve? Chomsky simply asserts that there is nothing else like it in nature; that it is nonsense to speak of its evolution; that it simply arose. But that seems a terribly non-biological idea. We might rather point out that the essence of syntax is the ability to place things in categories and hierarchies. The 'things' in this case are words, the categories are the parts of speech - nouns, verbs, adjectives - and the hierarchies are the clauses and conditional clauses. Other animals cannot apparently order sound-signals in this way, so they cannot convert their vocabularies of sounds into anything that resembles a human language. But they can and do order other things in comparable ways. Even pigeons can learn quite rapidly to tap symbols into a machine (in expectation of reward) in an order that in logical structure resembles that of words arranged according to the rules of syntax. Syntax undeniably represents another qualitative leap for humankind. But again we can at least find parallels in the mental abilities of other creatures. We need not assume that natural selection has conjured our ability out of the air for the express benefit of our lineage. Once more we can see the opportunism of natural selection: adapting an ability to impose order *in general* on to the special case of words. Sometimes opportunism is serendipitous in the extreme.

What of our articulacy - our ability to frame such a variety of words so rapidly? This is no mean thing. No other animal can deliver such a rat-tat-tat of varied sounds so rapidly and so precisely. It requires tremendous wiring not only at the deep level in the ability to formulate the thoughts into words but also in the delivery of the words, the finely coordinated movement of tongue and lips. Again we can find some precedents, although we have to let the imagination run a little. It has been suggested, for instance, that our marvellous ability with tongue and lips is comparable to that of some monkeys, which can peel fruit, swal-low, and spit out the pips simultaneously and at breakneck speed – an ability certainly favoured by natural selection when the food is limited and the competition is fierce and the pips are toxic.

Most intriguing of all, however, and peculiar to ourselves, is the position of the larynx. In most animals it sits high in the throat and serves as a valve. As the animal drinks, the larynx forms a continuous tube with the space at the back of the nose. Thus the air-way – trachea to nose – forms a continuous hose which runs up *through* the stream of fluid that is flowing down the throat into the oesophagus. In other words the animal can drink and breathe at the same time.

But the larynx of the human being has been repositioned half-way down the throat, as is conspicuous in the adult male as the Adam's apple. So human beings cannot breathe and drink at the same time. Any attempt to pull such a stunt results in choking. That seems like an enormous disadvantage – except that the descent of the larynx leaves an enormous space above it, at the back of the nose and top of the throat. The space acts as a sound chamber, like the ceiling of a concert hall. It gives our voices a resonance that other species do not have – or at least, if they do, then they must have resorted to other extraordinary means to achieve it, such as the throat-pouches of the orang-utan or the howler monkey. This resonance, combined with the extreme pli-ability of tongue and lips, gives us a verbal dexterity that is indeed comparable with and as wonderful as our manual dexterity, and it is again uniquely human. Incidentally, there has been much debate of late about the position of the neanderthal larynx. Was it high in the throat as in all other mammals, or low-slung like ours? If high, then their voices must have had a nasal quality: a disappointing quack in such impressive creatures. If low, then their voices may indeed have matched their physiques, and res-onated as one feels they should have across the steppes and the glacier edge and along the Neander Valley.

When our lineage acquired verbal language remains controver-sial. Beyond doubt this ability depends in large part upon the presence of unique regions of the brain known as Wernicke's area and Broca's area. Phillip Tobias, one of the discoverers of *Homo habilis*, claims to have found an indentation in the cranium of *H. habilis* which corresponds to Broca's area. So perhaps speech is as

old as our genus. Others suggest that according to the archaeological record the huge take-off in human culture occurred only
30,000 years ago. So perhaps speech began then. My own guess
veers more towards Professor Tobias than towards such lateness,
though we surely have to envisage a long period of what we
might call 'protolanguages'. All existing languages are emphatically modern, with not a whisker to choose between any
aboriginal language and the most high-falutin German in the subtlety of their syntax. A great deal must have gone on between the
first stirrings in *H. habilis*, if he it was, and the first pontificating
sapiens.

That, then, in broad terms, is the mechanics and the acquisi-
tion of language. What really counts, though, as always, is the
logistic advantage it confers. Here there are two aspects, both of
supreme significance.

HUMAN LANGUAGE AND COLLECTIVE INTELLIGENCE

With our kind of language, unique among Earthly creatures, we
can in principle convey any thought of whatever degree of detail,
however abstract or concrete, from one individual to another.
Obviously with the medium of writing to help us we can pass ideas
from generation to generation *en masse* through indefinite time.
But even without the aids of writing (and the modern elaborations
of sound recording and film) huge amounts of information can pass
from parents to children over vast sweeps of time. We know that
some of the folk memories of modern Australian aborigines are at
least 8,000 years old: they tell of once familiar landmarks that were
submerged after the last ice age and have now been rediscovered
by modern divers, just as the native Australians described them.
Their memories of mythical beasts - bunyips and the rest - may
well allude to diprotodonts and their ilk.

In Western cultures too we have folk memories that are just as
ancient. All of us can draw after a fashion. This ability is not in
our genes. We all learnt to do it as children from our parents; they
learnt it from their parents; and so on, back through tens of thousands of years at least, with early examples still to be seen in high
accomplishment on caves and rocks in all five inhabited continents. What of the needle and the button, the adze and the

plough, weaving and the firing of pottery? They were all invented long before the invention of writing. They are all part of our collective knowledge. They have all been passed on through the generations partly by demonstration but also by word of mouth: 'This is how it's done – and this indeed is how others do it!'.

In short, through the medium of verbal language, which in effect means speech, *all human beings may in principle partake of all the thoughts of all other human beings through all of time*. Other animals transmit ideas. Old ewes are retained on hill farms to show the new generation of lambs where to graze and how to avoid trouble. Particular packs of wolves have their own ways of doing things; as biologists say, their own 'traditions'. The technology of chimpanzees varies from place to place – they can truly be said to have their own 'cultures'. Various groups of animals have even been observed to *acquire* new skills, which then spread through the whole population and pass to the next generation. Blue-tits in Britain have learned to remove the foil tops from milk-bottles delivered to the doorstep and so drink the cream – and the skill has spread. The macaques of Japan have learned to wash their food in the sea and to take hot baths in the geysers – and they have acquired those skills over the past few decades. But no other animal approaches our degree of collective thought.

This collectivism represents yet another qualitative advance, and one again whose logistic significance can hardly be overstated. For example, it strikes me that in intellectual competitions any one of us ought to have the advantage over, say, a dog. But in addition competitions between dogs and humans could not even start fair – dogs can draw only on their own experience and that of their parents and immediate pack but otherwise must work things out for themselves, whereas individual human beings can draw upon all that they have ever been told and read about, which could in principle represent all that all human beings have ever thought. The children's TV character Dr Who is a 'Time Lord' who can travel through time and may live effectively forever. But it occurs to me that an individual person who lived as long as the Universe *and yet spent his time alone* would never in all that time get around to inventing the computer. Indeed, few of us alone would be likely even to get so far as inventing the wheel – or even the needle. If any of us was alone, in short, then we would probably make no significant progress in a billion years. But for all kinds of easily perceived logistic reasons two heads really are better than one – and a hundred million heads communicating through space and time are a quantum leap ahead of any individual, no matter how venerable or innately intelligent that individual may be.

Thus the communicative skill of the human species represents a qualitative leap in personal ability. But it represents far more than that: the collectivism of thought that such communication allows effectively turns us into a new kind of organism. Each of us has become a neurone in a global brain – a brain that thinks across time as well as space. The power of this global creature is, quite literally, overwhelming. Termites have the same collectivism but with termites the individual creatures are automata, whereas each of us in theory is a free spirit. Our perennial problem, of course, is to reap the enormous benefits of such collective thought while retaining our individuality. Some societies have pulled the trick much better than others but few have managed to sustain the delicate balance for very long.

But there is a second logistical aspect that is even more fundamental, and truly gets to the essence of human success.

HUMAN BEINGS AS TURING MACHINES

John von Neumann's game theory may be seen as the mathematicisation of Machiavelli and its influence accordingly extends through all human affairs and, as we have seen, into ecology and evolution. The English mathematician Alan Turing has been equally influential.

For in 1937 Turing wrote a paper 'On Computable Numbers' in which he showed that in principle a huge array of problems (though not quite all) could be solved by one universal method – or at least by a series of methods each of which was an 'algorithm'. He also described a hypothetical machine which could, in essence very simply, apply all of those algorithms. In other words, he described in theory an (almost) universal problem-solving machine: the basis of the modern computer. Such a theoretical device is known as a 'Turing machine'.

I suggest that the key feature of the human brain is that it functions as a Turing machine. The brains of all other animals are in practice analogous to the ingenious calculating devices of the seventeenth century onwards which could deal only with a set and often extremely limited menu of problems.

Two caveats are worthwhile. First, I am not suggesting that the human brain is literally like a computer or that the abilities of animals are literally to be compared to those of clockwork toys (as Descartes did). Living brains are qualitatively different from any machine that human beings have so far devised. I am merely making an analogy, that the difference between human brains and animals' brains is like the difference between computers and *ad hoc* adding machines.

Second, it is a terrible thing (though the mistake is almost always made) to underestimate the cognitive powers or the emotional resources of other creatures. Many other animals can get their minds around difficult and novel problems. And it is both cruel and poor philosophy to deny the sufferings and moods of animals.

Yet the point remains. There is a logistic difference in the ability to assess problems between us and other creatures, and this has opened a vast ecological gulf and established a new evolutionary principle. Human beings, not quite uniquely but to an unparalleled degree, do not have to wait until the chancy processes of natural selection equip them to cope with a new environment. They simply work out what the problems are and solve them. Indeed they do not need themselves to adapt – or at least only to a limited degree. They can just as soon alter the environment to suit themselves.

For this Turing-esque all-purpose brain is abetted both by a powerful physique and, in the end more significantly, by an ecomorph that has retained all the wonderful versatility of the primate, including in particular the whirling arms and dextrous hands. Nothing more is needed – at least in the present world. We do not need to develop extraordinary teeth to bring down mammoths, as the sabretooths did, or molars for crushing clams, like sea-otters, or snouts for digging tubers, like pigs. With brains and hands we can make weapons and tools that can do all of those things, and a lot more besides, in some cases more efficiently than the specialists.

In short, our universal brain and our generalised physique have made us the all-purpose animal that in principle can solve any problem that any environment can present us with, just by thinking about it. Ecologically, therefore, we are as significant as all other animals put together. None of this gives us *rights* over other creatures. None of this justifies our treatment of them. It is, however, the case.

The key question though, at least as far as our fellow creatures are concerned, is what we have actually done with all this power. Well, one highly significant thing we have been doing ever since we were australopithecines is catching and eating other animals. By the time we had turned ourselves into culturally modern people, about 30,000 years ago, we had already become the most proficient predators the world has ever seen. This point is extremely significant to our own history, and to the fate of all other creatures, and is worth discussion.

THE HUMAN PREDATOR

Rob Foley suggests that hominids made the big swing to meat-eating with *Homo erectus*, and justifies this by a highly ingenious ecological argument. Thus, he says, the number of species in each genus at any one time depends on two features. First, obviously enough, genera that occupy large areas (relative to body size) are liable to contain more species than those that need less space. Secondly, herbivorous genera are liable to contain more species than carnivores, because herbivores tend to be more specialist in their feeding habits and so to speciate more. I would like to add a third point, which is that no population can be viable unless it contains a certain minimum number of individuals, so any one population of predators is bound to occupy a large space because individual predators need far more space than individual herbivores of comparable body size.

Now, says Foley, australopithecines (including paranthropines) are known to have occupied a large swathe of southern and eastern Africa, but nowhere else. Though there are clearly some gaps in the australopithecine record, it seems as if the number of known species of australopithecines roughly corresponds with the number you would expect over such an area. The number of species relative to the area also accords with the notion, arrived at on other grounds, that they were carnivorous up to a point, perhaps obtaining about 10 per cent of their calories from meat.

But the genus *Homo* quickly came to occupy most of Africa - perhaps all of it - plus Eurasia. If *Homo* had had the same kind of diet as *Australopithecus*, Foley argues, then we would expect such a vast area to have contained about thirty hominine species at any one time. But although there may well have been several different species at a time (for example, a whole suite of different 'archaics') no one has ever suggested as many as thirty. Such a paucity of species relative to area occupied is best explained by suggesting that hominines from *Homo erectus* onwards were much more carnivorous than *Australopithecus*; that in fact they obtained perhaps 20 per cent of their calories from meat. For the same kind of reasons, lions, grey wolves, and brown bears spread themselves throughout the world without significant speciation. As I suggested in Chapter 5, the 20 per cent meat intake of the hominines may still seem modest, but it would have vastly increased their ecological options and chances of survival, and transformed their ecological impact.

Foley's argument seems to me to be eminently logical. The archaeological record also shows directly that modern - upper Palaeolithic - *Homo sapiens* were formidable hunters, able to kill elephants, the largest of all their contemporaries on land - and indeed, as the modern Inuit demonstrate, able with very basic technology and huge bravery to kill whales, the largest animals of all. So I am sure we can take it that human beings have always hunted, and that hunting has been a crucial reason for our own success and for our impact on other creatures.

So now two questions are raised. First, how did we manage to be proficient hunters given that we seem fairly feeble physically, compared at least with specialist killers such as bears and sabretooths or even chimpanzees? And secondly, how have we come in the end apparently to defy the ecological law which says that big-bodied predators must be rare?

WHY ARE HUMANS SUCH EFFECTIVE HUNTERS?

To begin with, human beings are not outstandingly feeble. We obviously are deficient in teeth and claws, the standard equipment of specialist carnivores, and we are not as strong as lions, as agile as leopards, or as swift as cheetahs or deer. But we do have our assets. For one thing, we have enormous stamina, and we are better able than many to tolerate daytime heat. Louis Leakey is said to have wagered once that he could run down an antelope – and succeeded, simply by keeping going. Whenever the poor creature stopped to graze there was Leakey, padding over the brow of the hill, starting it up again in the kind of exhausting and increasingly panicky dash that would work perfectly well against a leopard or a lion, neither of whom would follow up a chase once lost. This was probably never a normal method of hunting. However, Laurens van der Post has filmed bushmen in the Kalahari of the 1950s wounding an eland and then pursuing it over several days before it finally collapsed. The stamina and persistence of the human animal, and the mobility that enables us to cover twenty miles and more a day, can clearly form the basis of a hunting strategy that differs from that of lions or cheetahs but need be no less effective.

For another thing, of course, human beings cooperate to hunt, as do lions, wolves, chimpanzees, ground hornbills and a host of other creatures. Such cooperativeness clearly increases efficiency but it also has another logistic advantage: it broadens the prey base. In particular, it enables the cooperative predators to hunt prey larger than themselves, which few single-handed operators are advised to do. Only a few specialists – sabretooths attacking mammoths, weasels killing rabbits – habitually do so. Cooperative wolves may take on moose, and lions may hunt mature African buffalo; but tigers, hunting alone, are not inclined to attack gaur. Humans in concert were clearly happy to take on mammoths.

However, human beings are not mere lions and we know that from at least 30,000 years ago *Homo sapiens* were modern people, at least as brainy as we are. We can reasonably presume that their knowledge of where prey was to be found extended beyond that of lions. Modern humans had the capacity to know in some detail where any one species or herd was liable to be. Furthermore, they could cooperate to a far greater degree than lions are able to. The people of the upper Palaeolithic were already part of the collective human intelligence, able to communicate across space and time. Each group could build on the knowledge of other groups. Indeed they were able to *anticipate* where favoured prey was liable to turn up at some future time. Thus the efficiency of their own foraging strategy was improved enormously – while ordinary predators follow, modern human predators could simply lie in wait. Clive Gamble suggests in *In Search of the Neanderthals* that such a logistic advance in hunting efficiency, brought about by memory, analysis, and cooperation, largely accounts for the eventual 'triumph' of modern humans over neanderthals in Europe. We need not envisage direct confrontation. It is just that the moderns were more efficient: they got more out of the environment with less effort and less risk. Again it looks much like the difference between red and grey squirrels – a conflict not of strength but of logistics.

The third huge predatory asset of human beings seems to me to have been underemphasised. Crucially, human beings developed the use of the missile. If the missile is a stone then it provides significant advantage. Once the missile becomes a spear then it puts the assailant into a qualitatively different league.

The true significance of the spear is once more logistic. With a spear, a hunter can deliver a lethal blow without ever running the gauntlet of the prey's defences. Other predators must 'close' with the opponent. They must slip the guard. They must get past the flashing hooves or the slashing horns. But a man with a spear can hit and run. He can even afford to miss without reprisal, though a mistimed attack by a normal carnivore could result in severe injury. Armed with spears, even single hunters can ignore the rule which proscribes the hunting of prey that is much bigger than the predator. In the forest of present-day Africa a pygmy may kill a forest elephant (though the technique is not to throw the spear but to stab, as with a halberd). With spears, in short, human beings acquired the ability to hunt large and eminently rewarding prey *effectively without risk*. No predator in all the rest of nature has ever enjoyed such extraordinary advantage.

Again we can trace the evolution of this skill. Human beings can throw because they have such wonderfully mobile arms, and great muscles on the chest and back to deploy them with. They have extraordinarily mobile arms because they inherited the abilities of ancestors that evolved in the trees – and instead of abandoning the skill of the arms when they came to the ground as other bipedal creatures have often done, they turned those arms to new purposes. One of those purposes – almost an incidental one, it seems – is throwing. But that incidental skill has transformed the human being from a hunting ape into a predator of a quite new kind: one that has never been seen on Earth before and one that tips the balance absolutely in favour of the hunter. Here is a prime example of the principle outlined at the start of this chapter: that possession of a single 'trick' can change the rules of the game totally – and turn combat into rout. Add the fact that the missile-throwing hunter also has the power to analyse, is also cooperative, and also has stamina and persistence, and we have a devastating killer indeed.

There is one further matter which we have touched upon already but deserves further emphasis. Human beings are not out-and-out carnivores like lions and leopards, but they are extremely accomplished predators – and only bears are comparably versatile. We can subsist on clams or witchetty grubs or bring down mammoths or giant sloths. Paradoxically, because we are so versatile, and do not rely absolutely upon any one prey species, we can be far more destructive of individual prey species than a specialist can.

Thus we have seen how numbers of northern lynx depend entirely on the fortunes of snowshoe hares. But hunters as versatile as us can simply go elsewhere when any one kind of prey becomes rare. Of course, the rarer a species of prey becomes, the harder it is to find, so predation pressure is somewhat relieved. But the smaller number of prey still has to contend with the same number of predators as before. Thus versatile predators can and often do drive some at least of their prey species to total extinction, while they happily subsist on others. Thus feral cats are now wiping out Australia's small marsupials.

The principle clearly applies to Palaeolithic *Homo sapiens* with some even more devastating twists. For human beings are omnivores and may subsist for a time on a plant diet even if the game disappears altogether – but they are there waiting when the prey returns. They can also kill very large animals which are particularly vulnerable because their numbers are bound to be relatively low. Furthermore, rarity is less of a natural protection against human hunters than it would be against, say, lions. Lions would be bound to hunt a rare animal less than a common one simply because it encounters the rare one less often, and on the whole lions are not too fussy what they kill provided the prey is of an appropriate size. But human beings understand the natural history of their prey. If a favoured animal becomes rare – well, they still know where to find the remaining herds if they choose to. And if the rewards and the prestige of the kill are great, as we may assume was the case when mammoths were the target, then they will be tracked down. Human beings are opportunist hunters. But, unfortunately for their prey, they are too intelligent to be *merely* opportunist.

Thus by their ability to switch from food source to food source human beings could maintain relatively high populations even though they were key predators. And if they chose to hunt a rare beast then they had the knowledge and the persistence to do so, as other predators would not. They were able to break the rules, in short. And by these means, in the end, they broke the ecological rule which says that big predators must be rare.

So we can put the whole thing together: a cooperative hunter who not only cooperates but also analyses and anticipates; a predator able to kill animals much larger than himself with little personal risk; a predator that can attack the entire spectrum of potential prey animals from clams to mammoths and can readily switch from one prey to another, or even eschew game altogether for a time; and a predator with the wit, if it seems appropriate, to hound a favoured creature even after it seems to have taken refuge in rarity. In the next chapter I want to discuss the thesis known as 'Pleistocene overkill': the notion that human beings destroyed huge swathes of creatures long before the modern age of obvious destructiveness. Many have attacked this idea because they say that direct evidence is lacking, but since all palaeoanthropological evidence is scarce, and we cannot be sure what should pass as evidence and what should not, such criticism is not entirely convincing.

More cogently, perhaps, many have questioned the *plausibility* of the overkill hypothesis. Palaeolithic hunters just could not have wiped out entire suites of huge and powerful creatures, the critics say. It seems to me, however, that once we begin to apply a little ecological thinking – and in particular compare human hunting logistically with that of other predators – then the overkill hypothesis becomes eminently plausible. It is all too easy to see how creatures like us, with modern human assets and a professional interest in hunting, could transform the fauna of entire continents. That those fauna were indeed transformed as palaeolithic hunters got into their stride seems to me perfectly to match expectation.

But of course human beings did not remain as other animals have - as creatures that simply live off the land, mere hunters and gatherers. Degree by degree our control increased until hunting and gathering became husbandry. A key step in this progression was the harnessing of fire.

FIRE

Human beings evidently harnessed fire a surprisingly long time ago. Evidence of hearths in China and France dating from about 480,000 years ago indicates that *Homo erectus* made use of fire. Recent evidence from Ethiopia suggests controversially that the very first deliberate fire-makers may have lived as long ago as 1·1 million years. *H. erectus* is still the most likely pioneer fire-exploiter although it has been suggested that the Ethiopian fires were made by *Paranthropus boisei*.

It is easy to envisage the many practical contributions of fire. Late in our history, regular use of fire in a variety of venues would sooner or later have revealed to our ancestors that clay becomes hard by firing, which is the key to functional pottery, and that certain rocks when superheated dribble globules and rivulets of metal. Each of these discoveries opened new cultural vistas.

But long before our predecessors employed fire to create new materials they would have appreciated its ability to transform food. That it may detoxify and disinfect may not have been obvi-ous - though they would have reaped the benefits of sterilisation nonetheless. They would certainly have appreciated the ability of fire to tenderise and hence to turn what was unchewable or unpalatable into pleasing and satisfying provender; they would have realised, too, that cooked meat may be stored longer than raw. But again, the logistical point is what counted first: fire increased the range of the human diet even more widely, enabling early people to live in even more places, and squeeze through in even harsher times, than they were able to already.

On the grander scale, however, the overwhelming significance of fire lies in the control it has given the human genus over land-scape as a whole, and over all the plants and animals that live in it. Ecologists now appreciate that over much of the world – wherever it is not permanently wet, it seems – fire largely determines which plants will grow where, whether forest or grassland prevails, and if forest prevails which trees it contains. The point has been beautifully if sadly illustrated from the 1950s onwards by the endeavours of Rutger's University biologists to conserve the much-loved Mettler's Wood, which is the last remaining uncut upland forest in central New Jersey, USA. They protected the oak trees well enough by restricting public access to a single trail with an expert guide. But the trees are now senescent and the forest is not regenerating. It is clear now, as it was not when Rutger's began, that oak forest of this type does not regenerate unless there are regular fires – roughly one every ten years, to judge by the scars in ancient timber. Presumably, if we want this forest to continue for a few more thousand years, we should set light to it.* The other side of the coin is revealed in some of America's national parks, such the wonderful Yellowstone which was designated by Congress in 1872 and is the oldest in the world. Here conservation biologists, farmers, foresters, and local people have very different views on whether or not to try to quell the many fires that arise spontaneously (let alone the many more than are started by human beings). In general, the biologists take a *laissez faire* attitude to the fires which they know are ecologically 'normal', while the people trying to make a local living decidedly do not.†

In dry land, natural fires influenced the distribution and indeed the evolution of plants long before human beings learned incendiary arts. Outside the rainforest of Queensland many of the continent's native plants are fireproof – as witness the rapid recovery of vegetation in New South Wales that has followed the enormous bushfire of 1993, a fire that at times generated temperatures of 1,000°C. Many of Australia's plants escape fire by hiding their storage organs and accompanying viable tissue below the soil surface. Australia's native eucalyptus, with 500 or so species, has become one of the world's most successful genera of flowering plants precisely because it is effectively fireproof. Eucalyptuses

*See *Conservation Biology: The Theory and Practice of Nature Conservation, Preservation and Management*, edited by Peggy L. Fiedler and Subodh K. Jain, Chapman and Hall, 1992.

†See *The Greater Yellowstone Ecosystem*, edited by Robert B. Keiter and Mark S. Boyce, Yale University Press, 1991.

shed their outer bark to form an innocuous tinder on the forest floor while maintaining an iron-smooth trunk on which the flames can gain no hold.

Even more obviously, grassland worldwide is largely controlled by natural fires. Natural fire refreshes the grassland by burning off the rank vegetation, letting in the light, returning minerals to the soil and allowing fresh green pastures to come through.

Modern human beings employ techniques that imitate nature's own fire regimes. In 'swidden' farming, swathes of forest are first burned off and the exposed soil, temporarily nourished by the ash of the trees, is cultivated until its fertility wears off, at which point the farmers move on. Such swidden or 'slash-and-burn' agriculture is sustainable and effectively harmless on a sensible scale although it becomes grotesquely wasteful in the hands of some cattle barons who burn away entire forests to create fragile pasture. Gamekeepers on Scottish moors burn the heather at intervals to restore its leafiness for grouse and to quell invading trees - and it certainly works, though it creates an extremely limited flora and fauna where once was enormous variety. Arable farmers burn stubble - a controversial practice which looks to me like sound grassland management.

More pertinent, however, are the techniques of Australia's aborigines who deploy fire in several very astute ways, primarily to freshen the vegetation in discrete patches and hence encourage small marsupials to recolonise and multiply - and provide the people with food. Australian aborigines do not farm in the conventional sense - which is odd since Australia has at times been joined to New Guinea and the people of New Guinea are excellent horticulturalists who presumably were cultivating plants at the time of the last conjunction. But through their use of fire the native Australians have influenced the flora and fauna of the dry regions for the past 40,000 years.

The true logistic significance of such controlled burning has been summarised by Reese Jones of the Australian National University at Canberra. For the practices of aborigines, he says, amount to 'firestick farming'. Astute deployment of fire raises hunter-gatherers from the ranks of the super-predator to those of the game manager. Fire-raising is not simply a precursor of farming, or a tool of farming: it is a *form* of farming. Hence the deployment of fire has brought about what must be seen as the most profound logistic transformation of all.

Farming, then, must be the next issue to discuss. But as a final parenthesis I am greatly impressed that native Americans traditionally employed smoke signals, and that people in historical times made enormous use of signal fires – especially it seems in times of war when their beacons signalled the approach of enemies. Clive Gamble stresses that much of the success of modern human beings in Eurasia may have depended on establishing good relationships with neighbours. This indeed was one of the 'tricks' that gave our own European forebears an edge over the neanderthals.* Neighbourliness was achieved by diplomacy and trade, and the key to both is communication. I wonder idly (or perhaps not so idly) if people on that vast territory stayed in touch day to day by signal fires, conceivably just to say 'hello' (which is a very useful thing to say) and *inter alia* to pass information on the migratory herds of saiga, bison and horses, which can quarter continents so effortlessly. This is pure speculation. But, on the other hand, the native Americans were Eurasians first.

Taken overall, then, the various manifestations of fire, possibly more than any other single 'invention', bridged the gap between human beings as super-predators and human beings as controllers of all they surveyed. Australian aborigines still represent the transitional state, although perhaps in their harsh and unpredictable continent the native Australian approach is not simply 'transitional' but is ecologically the most appropriate. After all, many a modern farming enterprise has come to grief in Australia and it seems doubtful if large-scale agriculture could have gained a hold on that continent without constant replenishment from the established wealth and technique of Europe.

But over most of the world it has been farming – two logistic steps in advance of mere predation – that finally enabled human beings to break the rule which says that big predators cannot be numerous. Farming deserves a chapter to itself.

*Stringer and Gamble, *In Search of the Neanderthals*, Thames and Hudson, 1993.

7

The End of Eden: Farming

Everywhere you look there is agriculture. That is not quite true of course, for there are still vast deserts and mountain ranges, and a great deal of tropical forest; in fact, the statistics show that agriculture occupies 'only' a third of the world's total land. But the land that is occupied by agriculture includes the temperate valleys and former wetlands and places that once were deciduous forest. In short, agriculture already covers most of the most fertile areas of the world. It also of course fragments what is left of wilderness. So landscape is in reality dominated by agriculture to a far greater extent than the raw statistics suggest. Creatures that are not domesticated or cultivated now occupy the interstices. They survive on sufferance. A thinking animal with the human ability to take an overview would indeed exclaim: 'Everywhere you look: agriculture!'. And out of agriculture has come industry, which in turn has enabled agriculture to become even more productive and prominent — for example able with heavy machinery to plough places that before were left to rough pasture. Here is another positive feedback loop.

As with thinking, as with consciousness, as with speech, agriculture *seems* uniquely human. But when you look more closely you see again that farming is a compound skill, built from components which, taken individually, can in many cases be observed in other animals. Farmers protect their crops — but then so do some coral fish, which stand guard over particular patches of algae. Farmers alter the genetic makeup of crops — but then so do those same coral fish, because algae that are protected from predators at large are bound to evolve differently from algae that are not. Farmers sow seeds of the plants they favour. Well, take away the fruit-bats and orangs from a tropical forest and the fruit trees dwindle too, because those fruit-eaters are also the seed-scatterers. Farmers nourish their crops — but so do termites and leaf-cutter ants, which raise nutritious fungi on custom-built compost heaps. Farmers nurture animals of other species for food. So do ants, which guard 'herds' of aphids and 'milk' them for their honeydew. Farmers plough — so do elephants. Farmers create vast landscapes expressly for their own purposes. So, spectacularly, do beavers, which create entire beaver counties by the sides of obliging rivers. Our special skill, then, our uniqueness, lies in our versatility – not necessarily to do any particular thing that other animals cannot, but to emulate *everything* that they do, and then to mix and match. Again, as the great generalists, we are ecologically equivalent to all the rest put together.

Since farming is so dominating, since it obviously confers such power, and since it has given at least some of us a life of unprecedented ease (for all we have to do to eat is drive to the supermarket), it seems obvious that once human beings realised the advantages of farming they would have thanked their gods for the new enlightenment and got down to it with a will.

That is how traditional archaeologists envisaged matters. Modern scholarship puts the origin of farming in a very different light.

HOW FARMING BEGAN: THE TRADITIONAL VIEW

Archaeologists prefer to deal, as proper scholars should, with the hardest possible evidence, and the earliest hard evidence of true farming dates from the Middle East of around 10,000 years ago. There are caches of grains from this place and period that seem different from their wild relatives. From somewhat later dates come the bones of sheep and cattle which appear domesticated because they are smaller than their wild counterparts – suggesting poor nutrition and, perhaps, the deliberate selection of more manageable runts.

The traditional conclusion has been, then, that this was the start of formal agriculture; from there, the signs of its subsequent spread through Europe are clearly discernible. Whether the techniques spread culturally among people who stayed in the same place like a sound-wave through a cymbal, or whether they were carried from place to place by migrating farmers is still discussed. However, most archaeologists seem to incline to the notion of cultural spread.

The picture is neat and seems convincing as far as it goes, although the archaeological record now reveals what appear to be separate foci of farming beginning in China, the Indus Valley,

Africa, New Guinea and other areas of the Pacific, and North, Central, and South America. All foci, though, are taken to have arisen after 10,000 years ago, a time which is taken to be the end of the Pleistocene and the start of the Holocene or Recent epoch.

On to these archaeological observations, however, a mythology has been superimposed in the manner that Misia Landau described. Thus it was traditionally taken to be self-evident that farming was *better* than hunting and gathering. It produced a more reliable food supply, did it not? It even produced surpluses, which gave people spare time and freed more and more of them from the chore of food production, and so created leisured and specialist classes who seem to be the *sine qua non* of civilisation. The location and the timing seemed right as well. For did not civilisation – at least in its western mode – begin in the Middle East? And is it not the case that an origin around 10,000 years ago would leave plenty of leeway, but not too much, to establish the emphatically agricultural societies of the Old Testament, with its endless references to sheep, cattle, wheat, figs, grapes, and olives?

Yet there are various problems with the traditional scenario. We must assume, after all, that agriculture arose because it was favoured by natural selection. That seems fair enough at first, since the farming societies we know about seem so obviously better off than the hunting societies of which we have direct knowledge. But life is not so simple. For as I stressed in Chapter 3, natural selection deals only with the immediate. It is not prescient. It does not have goals. Natural selection would not have said to the world's first farmers, 'If you start planting crops now, then in a few hundred years people will be able to build great cities, with armies and temples and paintings and music'. If farming did not bring immediate reward then it would not be favoured. Its first stirrings would be snuffed out. And the problem is that farming in its early days seemed to offer very little advantage indeed. In fact more and more evidence suggests that it was ghastly.

Such evidence is of various kinds. First, the diminution in body size seen in the first domesticated animals is also seen in the world's first farmers. Along with that general enfeeblement there is often a bending and thinning of bone which suggests disorders of privation from rickets to tuberculosis. More specifically, at London's Natural History Museum Theyer Molleson has now described skeletons from early Egyptians that show a peculiar and most horrible pathology. The bases of the toes are arthritic and deformed, as if the toes had been constantly bent back upon themselves, and the bones of the lower back are also deformed and arthritic. For a long time Dr Molleson was hard-pressed to find an explanation and then she did – on Egyptian murals which showed young people (few lived beyond thirty in that debilitating age) working at saddle-querns. To use these diabolical devices, the millers would rub an upper stone back and forth across a lower one to mill the grain. They had to kneel on the ground to do this – hence the bent toes as the feet are folded, and hence the horrendous strain on the back. Of course, the growing of cereal is only the beginning of food production and once grown, the grain has to be processed. But it is clear from the rickets that after all that effort the grain-based diet left much to be desired. Besides, living as they did on the edge of the desert the Egyptians consumed egregious quantities of sand. This wore down their teeth by their mid-twenties and produced abscesses which now can be seen as neat rows of holes in the jaw-bones even of aristocrats, who presumably had a better diet than the common people.

The Old Testament confirms again and again that the life of early farmers was harsh indeed; one thinks for example of Ruth at her gleaning, or David fighting the Asian lions (which perhaps did not abound at that time but were certainly present), or the mortal conflict of Cain the tiller of the ground and Abel the keeper of sheep – for arable and pastoral farming have always been at odds. (It is interesting to note in this age of gentle vegetarians that the arable farmer was presented as the murderer.)

Clear too in the Old Testament is a yearning for the old days of hunting and gathering. Eden is seen as the lost paradise, and although it is presented as a 'garden' there is no suggestion that Adam and Eve were called upon to cultivate. The bounty was just *there*. Thus when God expelled Adam from Eden it was with a curse – the curse that Adam must become a farmer (*Genesis* III: 19):

> In the sweat of thy face shalt thou eat bread, till thou return unto the ground ...

'In the sweat of thy face', incidentally, is so much stronger than

'By the sweat of thy brow', which is how this withering dismissal is usually remembered. It has the venom of the modern American: 'Get out of my face!'.

The general impression is growing, then, that farming in its early days was unremittingly harsh; the hunting-gathering days that it replaced, on the other hand, were remembered with affection and nostalgia, albeit in a folk-memory that by the time of *Genesis* was about 6,000 years in the past. This impression has been reinforced in recent decades by studies of modern hunting–gathering peoples. Thus in the Kalahari Professor Richard Lee of Toronto University showed in the 1960s that the !Kung bushmen made a perfectly good living by hunting for just fifteen or so hours per week. The rest of the time they sat around and told stories. John Yellen of the National Science Foundation, Washington, showed in similar vein that the Hottentots, who are essentially the same people as the bushmen, occasionally kept goats but then would decide from time to time to stop keeping them and revert to hunting. In other words the Hottentots were perfectly good husbandmen but to them husbandry was no big deal. Sometimes they decided it suited them, and sometimes not. There was no feeling, as traditionalists would suppose, that husbandry once discovered was immediately acknowledged to be superior. In modern Cape York, the pointed promontory that pokes out of Queensland, the aborigines are said to have an enviable time feeding on both the permanent residents of shellfish and the constant through-traffic of migrating birds which stop by to feed.

Finally, it is clear that advanced hunter-gatherers (or people who seemed to live mainly by hunting and gathering) clearly could and did develop many of the trappings of civilisation, including graphic art, trade (and presumably diplomacy), and indeed the beginnings of cities – Catal Huyuk in Turkey, for instance, may well date from pre-agricultural times. In fact it could well be that the period immediately before the era of agriculture – the time remembered as Eden by the authors of *Genesis* – was a golden age.

So to the fundamental problem – what was the natural selective advantage? – we must add another question: Why? Why should thinking and already civilised people, artistic and doubtless philosophic, have abandoned an apparently easy way of life in favour of one which, until the late twentieth century AD, has remained almost unremittingly awful? What on Earth has been going on?

WHAT REALLY HAPPENED

It is in fact impossible to know how agriculture really began, or why precisely it has come to be the dominating force despite innate unpleasantness that is alleviated only intermittently and only in a few fortunate societies. But again it is reasonable to speculate on the basis of common sense and of observations in other, relevant fields – notably in that of ecology, reinforced by the rigour of game theory. In practice, hunting and gathering are a complementary double-act, and their gradation into pastoralism on the one hand and horticulture (leading to arable farming) on the other require different if complementary explanations.

To begin with the latter, John Yellen suggests that the arts of cultivation probably began not 10,000 years ago but as long as 30,000 years ago, and not in the Middle East with the sowing of cereals but in tropical forest, perhaps Africa, with the simple planting of favoured trees. Why not? We might stress here that at 30,000 years ago we are talking not about australopithecines or even *Homo erectus* but about people who, if they were alive today, would be surgeons or bus drivers or accountants or what you will but in those days just happened to be full-time professional hunter-gatherers. They knew their environment. They knew where things grew and, in a detailed if *ad hoc* fashion, how they worked. Of course they knew that seeds grew into plants: they could see them doing so in the forest litter. Of course they knew that a new plant would grow – almost without fail in a tropical forest – from a stick thrust in the ground. It is inconceivable that they would not have known how to spread the plants they favoured at the expense of those they did not. Add to that their mastery of fire and we have cultivation.

Note just a few points, however. First, cultivation in such a fashion and on such a scale would not show up in the archaeo-logical record. What would there be to see? A change in the frequency of a few trees in a few places in a vast forest would be invisible: the archaeological record is not that precise. Note also,

though, the point made in Chapter 4 on the dates of the first origins of animals: that by the time they appear in the
palaeontological record they are probably already common, and
probably have already been in existence for thousands if not many
millions of years. Thus if clearly cultivated grains are found in the
Middle East from 10,000 years ago, as indeed they have been,
then this by analogy suggests that the true origins of cultivation
probably stretch back for a huge swathe of time before that.

It is the case, however (as emphasised in Chapter 6), that such
an innovation – a slight increase in the reliability of a favoured
food source – can make a huge logistic difference. Creatures that
did just a little cultivation would be marginally but crucially more
likely to survive in the bad times than creatures that had to rely
simply on what nature cared to provide. Again, the grey squir-
rel/red squirrel model discussed in Chapter 3 suggests that such a
tipping of balance towards hanging on in any one place at any one
time is the difference between long-term survival that may lead to
a flourishing population, and oblivion. In short, the ecological
consequences of cultivation bear very little relation to its conspic-
uousness. Just a little touch can make the crucial difference.

The idea that cultivation is indeed as ancient as this seems to
mesh in with three other significant observations. First, the spread
of human beings around the world after about 30,000 years ago –
including way out into the Pacific – has an inexorability about it.
We can imagine that the ability to plant just a few crops to eat
after the emergency rations had gone would make all the difference. In the same way the first act of the Pilgrim Fathers when
they arrived in North America, albeit in a quite different age, was
to sow. Secondly, a propensity for modest cultivation reinforces
the vision of Pleistocene overkill, for cultivation implies the
expropriation of land, usually the best land, and this would
increase the impact of invading human beings wherever they
went. Specifically, the best archaeological evidence suggests that
the first colonists of Madagascar were pastoralists, and although
this was well after the Pleistocene (in fact at about the time of St
Augustine) it shows what *can* happen, and what might therefore
have happened elsewhere. Thirdly, if cultivation of a kind did
indeed arise 30,000 years ago then this solves the significant mystery of why it was that agriculture seemed to arise independently
in many different locations at different times after 10,000 years

ago. The point is that different people were *not* reinventing the skills from scratch. They all knew perfectly well how to cultivate, and had known for tens of thousands of years. Cultivation and perhaps husbandry were skills which they, like the modern Hottentots, invoked when necessary. The apparent first appearance of farming in the archaeological record of any particular place indicates merely that cultivation had become economically desirable at that particular time and so was being practised on a scale that was at last large enough to leave some trace.

It is easy to see, too, in a general way, how advanced Palaeolithic hunters graded seamlessly into husbandry. The 'beating' of game by war whoops and fire becomes indistinguishable from herding. Where initially they might have driven the animals into corners for easy slaughter – or indeed over cliffs, for which there is evidence – they might soon have guided them into custom-built corrals. Eventually, their control extended even to the animal's reproduction. Then passive herding truly became husbandry.

On the animals' side we see two processes at work. The first and less subtle is the traditional view: that the first pastoralists chose the species that were of the right size (cattle rather than mammoths), were least agile (sheep rather than gazelles), and were least aggressive – although the popularity of cattle, or indeed of pigs, is not easily explained in this way. But whatever the species, we can imagine the first husbandmen selecting the individuals that were most passive and, probably, the smallest: the ones they could handle most easily. Temperament and size are to a large extent heritable and so the first husbandmen quickly produced strains of manageable livestock that were distinct from their wild ancestors, just as the first serious horticulturalists quickly produced native varieties – 'landraces' – from their most favoured food-plants.

However, this traditional speculation has been greatly enriched of late by Stephen Budiansky in *Covenant of the Wild* (Weidenfeld & Nicolson, London, 1994). He suggests that the animals played a far more active role in their own domestication. First, he says, the phenomenon of 'commensalism' is common in nature – that is, many species tend to tag along with other species because, in various ways, it suits them to do so. Thus do egrets follow elephants to pick the insects from the kicked-up dust, and cleaner wrasse pick the teeth of predators which know when to strike and when to lie back and enjoy it. Human beings, active and invasive creatures that they are, attract many such commensals, from the gulls that follow the plough to the raccoons, possums, rats and dogs that hang around human settlements worldwide. Secondly, many animals are natural followers – such as sheep, which live on difficult mountain territory, and whose best chance of survival lies in following the most experienced animal; they exhibit no leadership skills themselves, but build mental maps for future reference. All in all, then, it is not at all fanciful to imagine that many of the first domestic animals, including sheep and pigs, essentially gave themselves up. A life of commensalism suited them. Then, bit by bit, their freedom to do otherwise was curtailed.

But here is the final twist. Modern evolutionary theory suggests that natural selection operates at the level of the gene – that is, we should envisage that individual alleles that produce advantageous characters, including characteristics of behaviour, gradually (or quickly) spread through the population. This is what Richard Dawkins meant by 'the selfish gene'. In practice, says Budiansky, individual animals that lent themselves to domestication would have enjoyed greater reproductive success than those that stayed on the outside. So the genes that made them compliant would have spread, while genes that produced stand-offishness would have left their owners out in the cold. Hence natural selection rather than human will favoured domesticity in those animals which were by nature commensal. The proof lies in the modern statistics: domestic cattle and hens are among the commonest large species on Earth – comparable even with ourselves – while many if not most of their wild relatives, which for one reason or another slipped through the domestic net, are now endangered. It may not be dignified for an animal to be domesticated, but at least for the time being it works. And natural selection is not concerned with dignity – only with reproductive success.

We can easily envisage, then, that cultivation of plants and domestication of animals would have developed almost inevitably as human beings became more adept in their gathering and hunting, and as they began to cooperate more widely with each other and in general to operate more strategically. We can see, too, that people who cultivated as a hobby and cooperated with complaisant wild creatures to create the phenomenon of domesticity would have made life easier for themselves, tightened their grip on their own environment, and thereby been favoured by natural selection. Hottentots seem (or seemed until recent decades) to demonstrate the enviable half-way state, in which husbandry is conceived as a take-or-leave option. The people of modern New Guinea often demonstrate a slightly different model, combining living off the land with horticulture. So far so idyllic. But why take the next step, apparently demonstrated in the Middle East around 10,000 years ago, into the drudgery and indeed the misery of virtually full-time agriculture? Where is the sense of this?

In fact there is no 'sense' in it at all – not, at least, if we assume that to be sensible is to move towards greater contentment. Yet again the point is merely one of logistics. People who cultivate a little and who begin the transition from hunting to husbandry are more likely to survive. More than that, because they increase their own food supply ever so slightly and thus – perhaps more importantly – their chances of pulling through the worst of times, their population tends to increase. At the same time, the creatures and plants that have not been caught up in cultivation and domestication are being forced to retreat, reducing the options for hunting and gathering at large. Thus people who begin domestication and cultivation are likely to be forced to do more of it, partly because their population goes up and partly because the options for doing otherwise begin to be taken away. Thus they embark upon another positive feedback loop. The more they farm, the more their numbers rise, the more the wilderness retreats, and the more they are *obliged* to farm. They may not enjoy it. But that is not the point. Natural selection is not concerned with enjoyment, any more than with dignity. Survival is the game.

In practice the transition from part-time farming to virtually full-time – from convenience to reliance – is not inevitable. The Australian aborigines never took to serious large-scale cultivation. Some native North Americans were farming when Europeans arrived but some were not, or at least were relying mainly on hunting and gathering. Hottentots clearly managed to sustain the putatively ideal half-way state until the last few years. Presumably people commit themselves to agriculture only if the conditions favour the switch. Clearly, though, the necessary conditions have arisen many times – as witness the apparently independent origins of large-scale agriculture at many different foci.

In general, I suggest, the conditions that favour the final commitment fall into two categories: general and specific. The general point is simply that people who do farm on a large scale enjoy an overall advantage no matter how hateful they may find their existence. For the whole point of farming is that from any given area it produces more food suitable for human beings. Therefore population does increase. A point made by the traditionalists is also true: the increased population is likely to include a leisured class. In general, then, a farming population is liable to be more powerful, in a crude military sense, than a non-farming group. Thus if your neighbours are farming then you had better start farming as well, otherwise you will be swamped. In short, farmers obliterate non-farmers in exactly the same way that human beings in general tend to override existing faunas when they arrive on fresh continents. They exploit the land more efficiently. They turn more of the local resources into their own flesh. They outcompete the groups that are less efficient. A favourite theme of the movies is the farmers versus the bandits, the setting commonly being Mexico or Japan. Always in the movies the bandits do well for a time, but always in the end they meet their comeuppance. That is how it is in real life. The farmers are still farming and indeed are driving Range-Rovers while the bandits have mostly been hanged. It is sad, perhaps: the farmers in the movies are always miserable wimps while the bandits are given to curly moustaches and wild bouts of mayhem. But that's the way natural selection works. This particular game is to the dour. Theory shows that the race is not to the swift but to the Calvinists and killjoys.

But there must always be special, local reasons why agriculture slides from a part-time convenience to a full-time obsession in any one time and place. In the Middle East, it seems to me, the evolutionary kick from part-time cultivator to committed farmer was ultimately delivered by the same kind of global force that prompted apes to become australopithecines and australopithecines to become humans: yet another shift in climate.

THE MIDDLE EAST: THE FARM AND THE ARK

There are reasons bordering on the mundane why agriculture took off in the way that it did in the Middle East. Among the local fauna, the sheep is particularly compliant: slower than the gazelle, possessed of a wonderful propensity to follow when led, and able to subsist on low-grade pasture. Marvin Harris of the University of Florida suggests that Jews were emphatically forbidden to eat pigs not in fact because pigs are 'unclean' (although this is the reason given in *Leviticus*, XI:7) but because they need a lot of water and are also omnivores, requiring a varied diet.* For desert people pigs would be an economic disaster. Sheep are the thing, able to get by on wisps of grass and browse.

Then again, the hills of the Middle East still harbour a series of wild grasses whose seeds are particularly large and tasty, notably wheat and barley. Seeds are excellent food because they are nutritious and built to last – the plant produces them, after all, as a storehouse for its offspring. Seeds of all kinds have played a key part in agriculture, including many kinds of nut, a host of pulses, various chenopods such as Fat Hen and Good King Henry in pre-Roman Britain and quinoa in South America, and amaranth, also in South America. But the bigger seeds of grasses – the cereals – are unmatched. In any hierarchy, after all, something or somebody has to be top, and wheat, rice, maize, barley and a few others just happen to be outstanding. In short, the cultivators and husbanders of the Middle East had promising raw material: sheep, wheat, and barley, plus the highly nutritious and esculent olives and figs. Embarkation upon agriculture was therefore liable to meet with greater reward than was sometimes the case elsewhere.

Even so, the final reason why Middle Eastern people became committed farmers was, as ever, because they were pushed into it. And what pushed them into it was the end of the last ice age, around 8,000 years ago. For with the end of an ice age comes flood. Water runs off the land, if not directly from melting ice then from increased precipitation, and rushes to augment the sea. People who live near estuaries are caught two ways: by the rivers flooding out, and the seas surging back in. And many people do live by estuaries – the Ganges, the Hudson, the Murray – because in normal times they can be extremely comfortable, with molluscs and crabs, a host of birds, easy navigation and plenty to drink.

Thus it is that 500 or so of the world's mythologies include accounts of flood. The area that gave rise to Sumeria, Assyria, and Babylon and is regarded as the birthplace of western civilisation is

Cows, Pigs, Wars and Witches, Marvin Harris, Random House, New York, 1974.

Mesopotamia, which was and is particularly flood-prone. After all, Mesopotamia is placed between the Tigris and Euphrates – its name means 'midst of rivers' – and the marsh Arabs in what is now southern Iraq live there still, albeit under political siege and the constant threat of land drainage. The particular account of Noah, so graphically related in *Genesis*, is only one of many such stories from that region. Indeed the same story has been traced to *The Epic of Gilgamesh*, Gilgamesh being a Sumerian king who became the world's first literary hero. Sumeria itself is the earliest known civilisation of Mesopotamia, where Gilgamesh reigned over the city of Uruk some time between 2,700 and 2,500 BC.

The Epic of Gilgamesh contains the story of Utanapishtim who, like Noah, was warned in a dream of impending rainstorms and thence of flood; built an ark with family and livestock aboard; floated through the storms, buffeted here and there until the water subsided; and finally was able to hitch the ark to a re-emerging mountain–top. The parallels with the account of Noah in *Genesis* are exact. The story probably came to the Jews via Abraham who, so *Genesis* tells us, began his long journey into Israel from Ur, not far from Uruk:

> And Terah took Abram his son, and Lot the son of Haran his son's son, and Sarai his daughter-in-law, his son Abram's wife; and they went forth with them from Ur of the Chaldees, to go into the land of Canaan: and they came unto Haran, and dwelt there.
>
> *Genesis* XII:31

Abraham and Gilgamesh were probably real people, while Noah and Utanapishtim may be symbolic figures – but of the fact that there were horrendous floods in Mesopotamia, a little before Sumeria came into being, there can be no doubt. The debris of those floods is still to be seen. At Ur itself there is still a three-metre layer of sand and silt which, to judge from the pottery immediately below and above, was deposited around 5,000 years ago. That is the spoor of a huge flood. At Fara (Shurippak) is a 70-centimetre layer dating from somewhat later – still huge, although less horrendous – and at Kish is the debris of yet another flood, later again.

But what has this to do with the birth of Middle Eastern agriculture? Well, consider this hypothesis: that the memories of flood originated 3,000 years before Utanapishtim and Noah, and the evidence at Ur and Fara; that the first memories date, indeed, from the end of the last ice age. After all at the height of that ice age around 18,000 years ago – the last 'Glacial Maximum' – the sea level dropped by 150 metres: nearly 500 feet. Because the shelves at the edges of continents have only a shallow slope, that fall translates into an enormous area – so that at the last Glacial Maximum there was 40 per cent more dry land than there is now. When the ice age ended, that 40 per cent disappeared beneath the rising sea.

Now cast back to the first people in *Genesis*, Adam and Eve, and their banishment from Eden. Where was Eden? *Genesis* tells us (II:10–14):

> And a river went out of Eden to water the garden: and from thence it was parted, and became into four heads.
>
> The name of the first is Pison: that is it which compasseth the whole land of Havilah, where there is gold.
>
> And the gold of that land is good: there is bdellium and the onyx stone.
>
> And the name of the second river is Gihon: the same is it that compasseth the whole land of Ethiopia.
>
> And the name of the third river is Hiddekel: that is it which goeth toward the east of Assyria. And the fourth river is Euphrates.

A little geographical speculation is now required, but not too much. Havilah is in the south-west of Mesopotamia. Gold was mined there, and the aromatic resin bdellium can still be found. The Pison could be the present-day Wadi Batin – now a dry river-bed. 'Ethiopia' in the beautiful King James Version, quoted here, is likely to be a bad translation. It probably relates to an area of south-east Mesopotamia, in which case the Gihon could be the present-day Karun; before this river was dammed it carried most of the sediment out of the highlands of Iran to form the delta of the modern Persian Gulf. Hiddekel is the Tigris, and the Euphrates is the Euphrates. Trace these four rivers back and they converge at a spot that now lies several kilometres offshore in the Persian Gulf. But then, at the height of the last ice age most of the Gulf was dry land. Eight thousand years ago, when the big melt really got under way, half of it was still dry. It would have been a fine spot for hunting, a gathering place of fish and clams, wading birds and antelopes. It would have been a fine place for casual cultivation, too. This, at least, is the thesis of Juris Zarins at the South-western Missouri State University.★

But why the switch to serious farming? *The Epic of Gilgamesh* offers a clue. The narrative is down-to-earth and humane, with stories of forgiveness and tolerance. But also, intriguingly, it warns against the dangers of overpopulation: this at a time when the world population was probably only around 8 million – less than one-500th of its present level. But then, of course, it seemed to the people of Mesopotamia that the world began and ended in the Middle East. What mattered were the people in their own region, and the numbers relative to the local resource. We can imagine that in the original estuaries of the Tigris and Euphrates, way out in what is now the Persian Gulf, human numbers rose as people enjoyed the fruits of a fertile valley. This was Eden indeed. But we can also see how those people must have been squeezed as the rising sea forced them inland. Then the cultivational skills that they had indulged as a bonus had to be deployed as a matter of urgency. Thus they were embarked on the rising vortex of agriculture and population from which there has been no escape.

There has been no escape, either, for our fellow creatures. Agriculture has transformed the ecology of the whole world.

THE *COUP DE GRÂCE*

There are obvious and perhaps not so obvious physical reasons why agriculture has changed the world so completely; transformed its ecology and confirmed the status of *Homo sapiens* as a new life form. But, as ever, the true significance of farming lies in the intangibles of logistics. Agriculture has changed the nature of the game.

Farming is obviously of physical significance because it occupies so much land, which previously belonged to other creatures. Indeed, as I will argue in the final chapter, one of the principal tasks for modern conservationists is to create farms that are more

★These ideas are discussed further in *Tales of the Earth*, Charles Officer and Jake Page, Oxford University Press, 1993.

hospitable to other creatures – or else to make the farms more focused so that more of the wilderness is left alone. But perhaps less obvious is that the habitats of every wild creature are in effect mosaics, with many separate components which may play only an intermittent role and yet are essential. Agriculture is liable to remove components from the mosaic, as in the expropriation of a water-hole, or to introduce a discontinuity – many bats for example will not fly across open fields. (On the other hand, and tragically for all concerned, farms often *provide* essential components of mosaics which have otherwise been removed. Thus the small farms of India now provide essential provender for thousands of elephants whose forests have been swept aside, and the confrontations between elephants and farmers are increasingly desperate.)

More to the point, however, is that farmers have a relationship to their resources that differs from that of hunter–gatherers and of all other animals. Thus other animals, plant-eaters or carnivores, are limited by the generosity or otherwise of nature. To some extent some animals do tend to increase their own food supply as we have seen – scattering seeds or flooding fields – but in general an animal or a hunter–gatherer can eat only what nature chooses to provide. The populations of predators in particular are geared to those of the creatures they feed upon, and even the most versatile predators, with many separate herds to sustain them, remain relatively rare. *But if a farmer wants more food he merely has to work harder.*

In fact, of course, populations of farmers are limited too, and we can see what happens all around the world when the limitations are not recognised. The process of desertification, brought about by over-exploitation, dates from pre-literate times. Yet in broad terms the generalisation applies. The whole point of farming is to convert the food source, and indeed to convert the landscape that produces that food source, until all the nutrients in the entire landscape are pressed to the service of the farmer. A rhinoceros in a forest needs tens of square kilometres, because only a small proportion of a few plants serve it as food. Modern cattle need barely half a hectare each of good grassland because *all* the grass is grown for their needs, and it grows far faster than any wild plant. If human beings eat the crops themselves, without feeding it first to animals, then with intensive cultivation each of us could in theory subsist indefinitely on the produce of a hundred square metres. With farming, in short, the potential food supply per unit area increases not twice or ten times but perhaps a hundred or even a thousand times. Until the limits of the Earth itself are reached, the increase in provender is directly proportional to the work put in.

The crucial logistic point that follows is that hunting and gathering offers only modest reward for extra endeavour, and will quickly stifle whoever is over-ambitious. The !Kung sit around most of the time largely because they have no sensible alternative. It really would not be a good idea to catch significantly more than they do already. Farmers by contrast can reasonably work all the hours of daylight and then some more – and they often have.

This is the sense in which the farmer plays a quite different game from the hunter. The hunter, whether a human being or a lion, has a strictly limited output which in turn defines his sensible input. The farmer has not. Thus to the point that farming increases the human population is added another key factor: *that the ecological impact of each individual human being is increased perhaps tenfold, perhaps a hundredfold – simply because each individual works harder.*

Game theory when applied to the practical world should include the concept of *attitude*. Thus the player chooses whether to play with enormous effort, or to be relaxed; whether to seek to change the environment, or to lie back and enjoy what the environment offers; whether to experiment or to be conservative, and simply do what members of the particular society have always done. For hunters, human or animal, it does not make sense to do more than is necessary, and the attitude that natural selection is liable to favour is one of relaxation, acceptance, and conservatism. But farming favours effort and those who seek to exploit – and because it tends to provide food surpluses, and so gives leeway, it also allows the farmer to take risks, and hence to experiment. In short, with farming the demands of natural selection change. Vigour, exploitativeness, and experimentation take over from laid–back conservatism. To be sure, there have been plenty of laid-back conservative farmers, but game theory shows that sooner or later they will be swept aside, just as traditional farmers are at this moment being swept aside all around the world as more vigorous methods come on stream.

When we put all the points together, we see how it is that human beings have apparently broken the ecological law which says that big predatory animals are bound to be rare; how it is that although we are big predators we contrive to be among the commonest of all land vertebrates. Quite simply, we have invented a new ecology; one in which, to an ever-increasing extent, all the resources of the world that previously nurtured many millions of species are channelled towards just one.

Of course it is clear that the expansion cannot continue forever. The world clearly could support the present human population of 5 billion plus – the cause of the ever-present famines lies in politics and not in the physical limits of the world. But we can seriously doubt whether the world could sustainably support 10 billion, or 20 billion; yet those are the kinds of figures that would be reached within the lifetimes of our children if the present growth continued.

It strikes me, though, that to call a halt we need to do more than change our day-to-day activities. We also need to alter the attitude of endeavour and exploitativeness that has been favoured this past 10,000 years by natural selection and then by politicians. Such attitudes are appropriate to expansiveness. Those are the attitudes that enable a society to get to grips with a landscape, and to drive out the people next door. They are not the attitudes that can allow us to sustain ourselves into the indefinite future in a state of peace. But attitudes are hardest of all to change.

What Difference Do We Make?

In the eighteenth century Jean-Jacques Rousseau established the myth of the 'noble savage' who, whatever he lacked in European graces, was supposed to live in harmony with his fellow creatures. Only 'civilised' people, Rousseau felt, have lost their respect for nature and despoil it so wantonly. The myth formed a powerful strut in the Romantic and indeed the revolutionary movements of the late eighteenth and nineteenth centuries. It persisted, albeit in self-delusory form, in Paul Gauguin's paintings of Tahiti at the end of the nineteenth century – and indeed was a fashionable component of anthropology and green politics in the 1960s and 1970s.

Of course there is some justice in the Rousseau myth. The hunting and gathering peoples who survived into modern times clearly protected many of their prey animals by taboos: some could not be killed at all, while others could be killed only in special circumstances – exactly comparable with the western laws that now protect 'game'. (These latter resrtrictions also may have quasi-religious overtones, as Rudyard Kipling describes in his stories of *Stalky & Co*, which were published in collected form in 1899. Anyone who bagged somebody else's fox in the English shires without a yoicks tally-ho became a social pariah.) It seems obvious, too, that traditional hunter-gatherers could not have been as destructive as modern people are now with their rifles, their heavy tractors, their civil engineering and their all-pervading pollutants.

Rousseau knew nothing of anthropology, of course. He had not seen 'savages' at first hand and certainly had not studied their way of life. All he had to go on were the stories of travellers who, in his adventurous century, were returning from the ends of the Earth with wild tales of strange people. Almost always those people, for all their gaucherie, seemed to live in paradise: surrounded by animals and plants of marvellous exoticism and undreamt-of variety. Many of those animals – the ones that lived on islands – were ridiculously tame. Obviously the people lived harmoniously with them, or the animals would not exist. Contrast the various-ness and apparent tameness of those animals with the narrow suite of nervous creatures in agricultural and citified Europe.

Yet Rousseau was deceived. It just happens to be the case that the creatures of the tropics are more various than those of higher latitudes. The fact is not intrinsically surprising but no one has explained it in a completely satisfactory way. It may have to do with the general opulence of the tropics – the never-failing, high-energy sun. Or it may be an historical phenomenon, reflecting the mosaicism created by the expanding and retreating forests as the tropics responded to the ice ages – mosaicism that encouraged the emergence of new species, including our own. Whatever the explanation, the eighteenth-century explorers were the first Europeans with the leisure to study the natural variety of the tropics – and they encountered it in lands that also happened to be inhabited by 'savages'. So savages and natural ebullience seemed to belong together.

More cogently, however, Rousseau was quite unaware that the variety that was coming to light in tropical lands, and particularly on islands, was generally only a relict of what had existed 100,000 or 10,000, or in some cases only a few hundred years before. Of course the tropics are productive. Of course the vegetation was lush and the animals teemed accordingly. But what Rousseau and his eighteenth-century contemporaries did not begin to suspect, and what indeed is only now becoming apparent, is the sheer scale of destruction that had taken place *before* the Europeans arrived and recorded the remaining fragments. The travellers undoubtedly encountered pristine floras and faunas on some islands – those that human beings had not previously visited. But however wondrous they may be, the floras and faunas of islands never approach the sheer opulence of continents – and no one in historical times has ever seen a continental fauna in its proper state of glory. Only Africa, and then only in parts, remotely approaches the pristine state that obtained worldwide until the late Pleistocene. Ironically, some of the countries that are now regarded as the 'wildest' and most 'natural' are in fact the most degraded. The highlands of Scotland have become a symbol of natural wilderness though they contain effectively nothing but red deer and grouse for shooting – and yet those mountains and valleys would still abound with moose, wolf, lynx, beaver, and bear were it not for our nobly savage ancestors and the zeal of

Tudor ship-builders. New Zealand, which sells its wild landscape so energetically to modern tourists, has in a few brief centuries stripped out the moas, the most wonderful suite of ratite birds the world has ever seen – them and the great eagle that preyed upon them; and transformed the flora.

In short, the modern hunter-gatherers who were newly discovered in the centuries before Rousseau may seem to have lived in harmony with the creatures that still surrounded them, but those creatures were only the vestiges of former glories. Eighteenth-century 'savages' lived harmoniously with them in the way that, say, the Saxons of England lived among the ruins of Roman Britain. It was picturesque, but it was devastation nonetheless.

But were our ancestors truly responsible for the deaths of the animals with which they once shared the planet? After all, the demise of the animals can be explained in other ways. Notably, there could have been changes of climate – changes that favoured the spread of human beings but simultaneously compromised other creatures. So before we abandon the kindly, Rousseau-esque view of our 'savage' forebears, we should give them a fair trial.

OUR ANCESTORS ON TRIAL

The facts of the matter are only now coming fully to light. First, a huge number of creatures all over the world disappeared during the late Pleistocene and continued to die out *en masse* well into modern times. Secondly, this die-off coincided with the spread of human beings around the world, initially from Eurasia into the Americas and Australia and then into the islands of the Indian Ocean and the Pacific, including Madagascar and New Zealand, and those of the Mediterranean.

The charge is that the deaths of those extinct animals were caused by the diaspora of modern humans – in other words, that our ancestors, wilfully or inadvertently, killed the creatures. In fact this putative scenario has been called the 'Pleistocene overkill' although it actually extended well beyond the Pleistocene.

The chief prosecutor in this trial is Paul Martin, Professor

Emeritus of Geosciences at the University of Arizona.★ Of course, the evidence he can bring to bear is bound to remain circumstantial but – just to anticipate – it has three powerful features. First, there is an awful lot of it: the sheer magnitude of the extinctions now being revealed by fossil and subfossil evidence is staggering (subfossils being the remains of dead creatures that have not yet had time to become completely fossilised). More and more creatures are coming to light whose existence was unsuspected. Secondly, there is bias in the pattern of extinction – for *large species suffered far more in the putative overkill period than small ones* ('large' here being arbitrarily defined as 100 pounds, or 44 kilograms and above). Yet, as Martin argues, if climate caused the extinctions then we would expect the small creatures, such as shrews and mice, to suffer more. Thirdly, although there are often problems with dating and sampling (it is difficult or impossible to identify *first* events) it seems that the extinctions in each particular location generally occurred soon after the arrival of human beings.

So let us examine Professor Martin's thesis, continent by continent, and island by island.

NORTH AMERICA

People arrived in North America via Beringia some time after 13,000 years ago. Their direct descendants are still there, now known as 'native Americans'. The large mammals that survived their coming, and are with us still, span twelve genera. There are moose, wapiti, white-tailed and mule deer, bison, musk-oxen, mountain goats, bighorn sheep and pronghorns among the hoofed animals; and pumas, wolves, and various bears (black, brown, and polar) among the carnivores. There are several 'feral' types as well – domestic animals gone wild – including burros (donkeys) on the Rockies, left over from the Gold Rush days, and 'mustangs', scattered here and there over centuries. Thus the native North Americans that are left to us form a wonderful line-up, particularly from the perspective of denuded Britain where

★See 'Prehistoric Overkill: the Global Model', in *Quarternary Extinctions*, edited by Paul S. Martin and Richard G. Klein, University of Arizona Press, 1984.

the red and perhaps the roe deer are the *only* large native terrestrial mammals that remain.

So where is the problem? Well, until at least 100,000 years ago North America had *forty-five* genera of large mammals – and several of those genera embraced several species. Those that have been lost include a glyptodont, *Glyptotherium*; at least four genera of giant sloths; the spectacled bear *Tremarctos* (which still survives in South America) and the formidable short-faced bear *Arctodus*; *Smilodon* the sabretooth and *Homotherium* the scimitartooth; *Acinonyx* the cheetah (which of course survives in the Old World); *Castoroides* the giant beaver; *Hydrochoerus* the capybara which still lives in South America and *Neochoerus*, which is a capybara that has gone altogether; several species of *Equus*, both horses and asses; *Tapirus* the tapir, which also has survived elsewhere; two genera of peccary, *Mylohyus* and *Platygonus*; the camel *Camelops*, the llama *Hemiauchenia*, and the short-legged llama *Palaeolama*; *Sangamona* the fugitive deer and *Cervalces* the stag-moose; *Tetrameryx*, which was a pronghorn; *Saiga* the saiga antelope, which still abounds on the Russian steppe; *Euceratherium* the shrub-ox; two genera of woodland musk ox, *Symbos* and *Bootherium*; the yak, *Bos*, still found in Tibet; and three proboscideans from three different families – *Mammut* the American mastodon, *Cuvieronius*, which is a gomphothere, and *Mammuthus* the American mammoth. Note too that in some of the above cases entire *families* disappeared from North America, although they survived elsewhere. These include the glyptodonts and the giant sloths; the Equidae, Tapiridae, and the Camelidae (all of which had originated in North America); and the three proboscidean families. The loss of the proboscideans represented the passing from North America of that entire order. Some of those losses may have taken place before human beings arrived, but many clearly occurred soon afterwards.

Note, finally, that the large mammals that survived the advent of human beings were largely of Eurasian origin. In other words they were accustomed to human beings: they had already been hunted by them for tens of thousands of years. Many of the survivors, too, are either solitary, as are moose, for example, or given to unpredictable migrations, for instance bison and caribou. In either case, this makes them difficult to hunt in a concentrated fashion. These points seem to me to be highly significant –

especially in the context of Africa, as we will see later.

SOUTH AMERICA

South America was hit even harder at the end of the Pleistocene than North America – harder indeed than any other continent. Now it has only twelve genera of large native wild mammals. Again they are wonderful to behold, and include llamas, guanacos, alpacas and vicuñas plus various deer and the Brazilian tapir among the hoofed animals, with jaguar, spectacled bear and maned wolf among the bigger carnivores, the huge capybara among the rodents, and the giant anteater among the edendates. Of course there is also a host of other creatures, including the New World monkeys, but although they are equally wonderful none of those others is large.

Yet until 100,000 years ago South America had no fewer than *fifty-eight genera* of large mammals. These of course included descendants of the true South American natives that had survived the Great Interchange of the Pliocene, plus the descendants of the northern Pliocene invaders. With these two mingled faunas South America was even richer than the North, which is not surprising as we would in general expect to find more species nearer to the Equator. But the southern continent lost far more than the northern. No fewer than forty-six genera out of the fifty-eight disappeared after 100,000 years ago.

In the late Pleistocene the losses are again biased towards large mammals. In the Pleistocene as a whole South America is known to have lost thirty-two genera of small and medium-sized mammals, including marsupials, armadillos, rodents and carnivores. However, as in North America, these smaller animals were mostly lost in the *early* Pleistocene. In the late Pleistocene, when the large mammals were hit so hard, South America lost not a single genus of mouse – though mice can be extremely sensitive. By contrast, too, the losses of large mammals in late Pleistocene South America greatly exceed those of the previous 2·7 million years. As Professor Martin says, 'While South America became a refuge for some large mammals that had ranged widely in North America, such as tapir, camelids, and spectacled bear, it became a graveyard for far more.' But again the fossil records show that the commoner types of large mammal had survived at least to between 15,000 and 8,000 years ago.

The late Pleistocene extinctions of large South American mammals – and note once more that we are talking genera, not mere species – again include about nine glyptodonts; about ten giant sloths; *Macrauchenia*, the last of all the litopterns on Earth; and *Toxodon*, the last of all the notoungulates. *Neochoerus*, a capybara, disappeared from South America as it did from the North. Carnivore losses again included *Smilodon* the sabretooth and *Arctodus* the short-faced bear – the total end of two formidable creatures whose like we do not see today. Gone also were at least five genera of camelid; four deer genera; two genera of peccaries; and three genera of horses, including *Equus* and two hipparions, *Hippidion* and *Onohippidium*. A gomphothere and three mastodonts also disappeared. We have been brought up to believe in a vague sort of way that these elephant-relatives were ancient creatures whose day had come, like Triassic dinosaurs. But they were modern animals (albeit from ancient lineages) which belong in the modern world, and could have been with us still.

So what can explain these losses? Again, climate has been suggested. Yet the losses were of allegedly *tropical* animals – which disappeared at a time when, so the pollen records show, the climate was getting warmer. The aftermath of the American interchange has also been blamed. But this took place 3 million years before the late Pleistocene collapse, and if invading animals have an effect at all it is generally quick. Besides, the fossils show no signs of long-term conflict. Both the glyptodonts and the giant sloths generated several new genera in South America *after* the northerners arrived – and of course spread and diversified in North America as well. Litopterns and notoungulates were apparently declining since the Miocene but some at least were doing well in the late Pleistocene and remains of *Macrauchenia* are found alongside those of the North American camelid invader *Palaeolama*, which does not suggest that there was conflict between them. Thus twenty of the forty-six genera that went extinct in late Pleistocene South America were themselves of North American origin.

So again, circumstantial evidence implicates human beings. Climate and competition between different species of animals seem implausible causes. Common observation suggests that only human beings could select large mammals to destroy. The bulk of the extinctions apparently occurred soon after human beings are thought to have arrived in South America 11,000 years ago. There remains a lack of direct evidence – the archaeological record does not abound with the relics of butchery – and we have still to show that human beings *could* have wrought such destruction.

AUSTRALIA

People came to Australia at least 40,000 years ago, and perhaps as long as 80,000 years ago. Either way, they were late Pleistocene arrivals. As with the Americas, Australia also suffered huge losses in late Pleistocene and Recent times.

Australia began the Pleistocene with far fewer genera of large mammals than either of the Americas, and all of them were marsupial; thus it had far fewer to lose. Yet it did lose thirteen genera of large mammals and they were extremely speciose – so Australia may in fact have lost almost as many large *species* as either of the Americas, and the *proportion* of loss was even higher. In fact only one genus of terrestrial mammal of more than 44 kilograms now survives in Australia – that of the large kangaroos, *Macropus*. This includes four species, of which only two, the red and the great grey, can truly be considered large.

The large mammals of Australia which went extinct in the Pleistocene included *Thylacoleo*, the 'marsupial lion', the most impressive of all the Australian marsupial carnivores; three genera of wombat; nine genera of kangaroo, some of which were fleet of foot like the surviving *Macropus* and some of which were more like giant sloths; and four genera of the ponderous diprotodontids, of which *Diprotodon* was like a two-tonne but unarmed rhinoceros. The losses of mammals continue in Australia, of course. Most of those that are now disappearing are small and 'unimpressive' to the non-zoologist. But as late as the 1930s Australia lost the last of its thylacines, *Thylacinus*, which was the size of a small wolf and was the only Australian marsupial predator that could truly have been a runner.

In Australia, too, more than in the Americas, non-mammals have played significant roles among the large terrestrial fauna (though we should not forget the phorusrhacoids of South America – the giant relatives of the moorhen discussed in Chapter 4!). Many of them also disappeared in the late Pleistocene. The losses include *Megalania*, the giant monitor lizard; *Meiolania*, a giant horned tortoise; *Wonambi*, a python-sized snake; and *Genyornis*, a giant ratite bird. Two big ratites do remain, of course: the emu and the cassowary.

Although the dates are far from clear, these Australian creatures apparently disappeared some time before the late Pleistocene col-lapses of the Americas. But then, people had arrived in Australia much earlier than in America. Present evidence suggests that in Australia, as in the Americas, the die-offs peaked after the human invasion. It is hard to ascribe those extinctions to changes in cli-mate, and in Australia there is no question of invasion from alien animals apart from humans. Again the evidence against human beings is circumstantial but again, as I will argue later, the cumu-lative case seems inexorable.

So Australia and the Americas show a similar picture: a rash of extinctions of large mammals – though not of small ones – appar-ently following hard on the heels of the first human invasions in the late Pleistocene. The remaining continents, Africa and Eurasia, show a different pattern of Pleistocene extinctions: far fewer and far earlier in Africa, and far more spread out in Eurasia.

AFRICA

In the whole Pleistocene – from 1·8 million to 10,000 years ago – Africa lost thirty-seven genera of large mammals – but no fewer than thirty of those occurred in the early and middle Pleistocene, which means they occurred *before* 130,000 years ago. In Africa as elsewhere there is a bias of extinction towards large mammals, for in the whole Pleistocene only ten genera of small mammals are known to have gone extinct.

The large mammal losses in the early and middle Pleistocene of Africa included at least eight species of primate, including various baboons and the hominid genera *Australopithecus* and *Paranthropus* (though of course the former did leave descendants in the form of *Homo*). Three hyaena genera disappeared in that time, includ-ing *Percrocuta*, and four cats, including the sabretooths and scimitartooths – *Machairodus, Meganteron* and *Homotherium*. Proboscideans lost the gomphothere *Anancus* and the true elephant *Mammuthus*, the mammoth, which of course survived elsewhere. The deinotheres disappeared altogether, as *Deinotherium* went extinct. The only perissodactyl lost in the early Pleistocene was the last of the African chalicotheres, *Ancyclotherium*. The moose-like giraffe *Sivatherium* disappeared, plus five pigs and six genera of bovids. This makes a grand total of thirty.

But in the late Pleistocene (after 130,000 years ago), in stark contrast to Australia and the Americas, only seven large mammal genera disappeared from Africa. These include the genus *Elephas*, which of course survives to this day in Asia; the three-toed horse *Hipparion*, which left its footprints alongside those of Lucy's relatives; the camel, *Camelus*, which of course lives on in Arabia; the giant deer ('Irish elk') *Megaloceros*; and three genera of bovids.

Some of these Pleistocene losses could have been due to competition between animals – for example between the relatively diminutive hipparion and the emergent middle-sized ruminant antelopes. *Mammuthus* may have lost out early in the Pleistocene to *Elephas*. Overall, however, Africa *gained* in general during the Pleistocene – notably because the bovids continued (and continue) to radiate. The continent now remains as the richest in large mammals, with forty-two genera – of which nineteen are bovids, mostly antelopes.

Clearly, then, Africa has retained far more of its late Pleistocene fauna than the Americas did, or Australia. How come?

Several explanations have been put forward, all of which are attractive and all of which may in part be true. For example, one proposes that the forest animals of Africa survived because they are solitary and elusive, while the surviving savannah species, like the survivors of North America, tend to be unpredictable migrators.

I like the notion that infection has played a large part in curbing the zeal of human beings in Africa, and hence of protecting the animals. A high proportion of major human infections have arisen in Africa, including the malaria parasite, yellow fever, and trypanosomiasis. The reason seems fairly obvious: the infectious agents have to evolve themselves, and they have had longest to evolve in the continent in which human beings arose. By the same token, infections in general arise initially by transfer from other species, and humans in Africa have been in contact with other animals that carry potential pathogens – notably with monkeys – since before the time that they were human. We know that human beings in Africa have evolved specific defences against parasites even at great cost to themselves: there is a widespread tendency to anaemia, which protects against blood parasites in general, and the specific condition of sickle-cell anaemia clearly protects against malaria in particular. Such an apparent sacrifice of physical ability could not have come about except in response to enormous selective pressure. Even today African wildlife gains some protection from invasion from domestic cattle because of the trypanosomes which cause the bovine equivalent of sleeping sickness. I suspect there have always been places – many places – in Africa where human beings could not survive because of the sheer weight of infection, which means that other animals could. In general, ecologists are only now beginning to realise that infection plays a huge role in the organisation of the natural world; that parasites can be among the leading players. The human beings who migrated out of Africa left many of their infections behind them, just as domestic crops may do when taken to a new location, and they sometimes flourished better away from their land of origin, as many a crop has done.

But the third explanation for human and animal coexistence is surely the strongest: that human beings and the post-Pliocene African fauna evolved side by side. Prey animals can of course survive in the presence of evolving predators: if it were not so, then there would be no predators because there would be nothing for them to prey upon. So the big African animals have been adapting to hominid hunting for 3 million years or more, and their various evasive tactics – including erratic migration – were probably shaped in large part by the hominid presence. But the human beings who first came to the Americas and Australia were fully-fledged hunters with novel tactics, thrown suddenly among creatures which were entirely naive. As has been demonstrated time and time again in recent years, there is a world of ecological difference between predators and prey which have evolved side by side and co-adapted, and the clash of naive natives with introduced exotics. Thus it is that mice and rats have flourished in Eurasia in the presence of wildcats while the descendants of those cats, tamed, transported, and returned to the wild, wreak havoc among the ecologically comparable marsupials of Australia.

There is a similar contrast between the coevolution of hominids and other animals in Africa, and the sudden imposition of fully-fledged hunting human beings among the innocent faunas of the Americas.

EURASIA

The recent fate of Asia's fauna is still largely unknown but that of Europe is well understood. In Europe as in Africa there have been steady losses (and gains) throughout the Pliocene and Pleistocene but losses have not been particularly concentrated in the late Pleistocene: just thirteen genera went at that time, of which eight still survive elsewhere (tahr, rhinoceros, horse, the wild dog known in India as the dhole, the hippopotamus, the musk ox, the spotted hyaena, and the saiga). The five late Pleistocene losses from Europe are the scimitartooth *Homotherium, Megaloceros* the giant deer, *Mammuthus* the mammoth, *Palaeoloxodon* the elephant (though this genus may be the same as *Elephas*), and *Coelodonta* the woolly rhinoceros.

Overall, then, we have three continents in which widespread extinction of large mammals seems to have followed hard on the heels of human occupation: the two Americas and Australia. We have one, Africa, in which the extinctions were much more drawn out and were mainly focused on the start of the Pleistocene – but in explanation this is the continent in which humans were getting into their stride in the early Pleistocene, and in which animals and hominids had the chance to coevolve. And we have one continent, Eurasia, that seems intermediate, with a more erratic scattering of extinctions. But here hominids arrived early – at least a million years ago – and through that long time they had other things to think about, including a periodic engulfment under ice. In short, the pattern of extinction worldwide is exactly what you would expect if human beings had been directly responsible for the animals' demise.

Of course we need more evidence. It would be good to produce unequivocal traces of human assaults upon animals. It would be good to show that other factors – notably climate – could not have been responsible, or at least not entirely. And of course we should show that stone age hunters *could* have eliminated other animals on such a scale – that the overkill hypothesis is plausible.

I will come to all this. First we should finish the litany of circumstantial evidence. For the pattern of extinction perceived on continents has been mirrored in microcosm, time and time again, on islands.

ISLANDS

Continents are huge melting pots. Space is not a problem. Whatever is biologically possible may occur. Lineages and eco-morphs let rip. Islands are much more confined. They are qualitatively different.

The key problems with islands are severalfold. One is that they are not big enough to sustain many viable populations of large animals – or certainly not of large land mammals, each individual of which needs a great deal of energy. Another feature is that they are by definition cut off from continents. The creatures that finish up on islands do so very much by chance. Some islands arise by splitting from continents and their fauna evolves from whatever happens to be marooned or manages to float or fly in before the divide becomes too wide – Madagascar budded from Africa with a cargo of proto-lemurs and, fortunately for the lemurs, no monkeys. Some islands grow as volcanoes in the middle of oceans, and never have contact with continents. They acquire their faunas very much by chance: for example the partula tree-snails of the high volcanic islands of the Pacific were probably carried in from ancient Gondwana on the feet of birds. In general, then, the fauna of islands is a ragtag and bobtail: a random scattering of creatures from which there is liable to be an absence of large terrestrial mammals, albeit with a commensurate flourishing of less-demanding reptiles. Furthermore, the assemblages on islands bear less and less resemblance to the fauna of the nearest continent the further they are from the shore.

On each island, the random scattering of founding creatures evolves in sublime isolation. But islands impose a logic of their own, and the evolutionary paths on different islands tend to run in similar directions.

On the one hand we find that if big mammals become stranded on islands then they either go extinct or else adapt to the reduced food supply by becoming smaller. The logic is simple: small individuals eat less than big ones, and it is easier to accommodate a viable population of small individuals than of large ones. Thus, as a homely example, we find tiny sheep and horses on the Shetland islands. Far more intriguingly, we find dwarf elephants on islands all around the world.

On the other hand, because islands cannot support large mammalian predators, the prey animals no longer find it advantageous to be really small: after all, mice evolved their exiguousness principally to be elusive. So while the big mammals become small, the tiny ones tend to grow larger. Thus Malta once had dwarf elephants and giant dormice; perhaps, with time, the two would have met in the middle. On the continents of Europe or Asia such ecomorphs would have made no sense at all. But islands impose their own rules.

Many reptiles, too, become giants on islands. Predatory reptiles need far less food than mammalian carnivores and in the absence of mammalian competition seem to come into their own. Thus Australia − an island continent − once had an impressive suite of land crocodilians and a truly massive goanna. Today the largest lizard of all lives on the Indonesian island of Komodo − and we saw in Chapter 4 that it may have evolved originally to feed upon dwarf elephants. Tortoises, too, in the absence of hyaenas or bears which could bite their heads off, become giants on islands. Now they exist only on a few islands such as Galapagos in the Pacific and in Aldabra in the Indian Ocean but once they abounded also on Madagascar and in the Mediterranean.

In the absence of mammalian predators, too, island creatures commonly abandon the apparatus and the techniques which ensure their safety on continents. We discussed a host of flightless birds in Chapter 4. Many such birds and other island creatures have also lost the reflexes and the elaborate programmes of behaviour that once protected them. In short, they are often ridiculously tame. The dodo seems to have given itself up to seventeenth-century voyagers to Mauritius. The booby bird still exists. It is a fabulous flier − a gannet − but acquired its name from the sailors who used to invite it to jump into the cooking pot.

Island creatures, in short, are innately vulnerable. Their populations are invariably small and so they are always closer to extinction. They have nowhere to run when threatened. A fire, a hurricane, a flock of goats can wipe out their habitats altogether. They often lack the reflexes of more street-wise creatures that might have enabled them to adapt. It hardly seems surprising that scores of island creatures worldwide are now on the endangered lists, including the kakapo and the Pacific partulas and a huge variety of fruit bats and Madagascan lemurs. What is surprising and indeed shocking is the mass of creatures that have already died out within the last few centuries and are only now coming to light. We should look at a few.

ISLANDS OF THE MEDITERRANEAN

Mediterranean islands have the typical fauna of inshore islands that may be joined to the continent when the sea-level drops. Their faunas look like a fairly random but much reduced sample of the mainland, and the individual species show typical island modifications. Nowadays the biggest mammal of the Mediterranean islands is the acrobatic ibex, and connoisseur visitors on some at least of the islands delight in the black vulture (which has now been reintroduced to Mallorca). But what remains in the Mediterranean is a sad relict of what was there until just a few thousand years ago.

For the fossils and subfossils that are still coming to light on a total of eleven Mediterranean islands, including the Balearics, Sicily, Malta, Sardinia, Corsica, Crete and Cyprus, reveal giant land tortoises, so typical of warm islands in general – and, wonderfully, a bizarre array of dwarf elephants, dwarf hippos, and dwarf deer. These last include (ironically) a miniature version of the formerly giant deer, the so-called 'Irish elk' *Megaloceros*. At least one of the dwarf elephant species (or subspecies) was less than a metre high when adult – an astonishingly inappropriate ecomorph for such a small creature but proof, if proof were needed, that natural selection is *ad hoc* and simply goes to work on whatever is around. The youngest of the known dwarf elephants disappeared on Tilos around 4,500 years ago – the time of the earliest pyramids.

In the last few thousand years, too (almost in historical times), there have been dwarf proboscideans on islands off the coasts of Siberia, south-east Asia, and California. They came from several different lineages – mammoths, stegodonts, *Elephas*, and mastodonts. Elephants in fact, having gone to such great lengths to cope with hugeness, seem very good at dwarfing. It would be interesting to come back in 10,000 years and see what has happened to the erstwhile working elephants that are now living feral on the Andaman Islands, 1,500 kilometres or so off the east coast of India – assuming, that is, that our descendants prove more enlightened than our ancestors, and allow them to live.

WRANGEL

Wrangel is a high spot of Beringia that now pokes above the Arctic Ocean 200 kilometres or so off the north-east coast of Siberia. It has long been known for its mammoth remains, which hardly seemed surprising as Siberia was the principal centre of mammothdom. The first surprise has emerged since 1989 as Sergei Vartanyan, geologist from St Petersburg, showed that some of the tusks dated from the time of the Pharaohs – indeed that the latest of all are only 3,700 years old. Thus mammoths survived on Wrangel for at least 5,000 years longer than on continental Eurasia. The second surprise has emerged as Vartanyan and Andrei Sher from the Institute of Animal Evolution in Moscow have shown that the later mammoths were dwarfs: again the bizarre elephantine propensity for miniaturisation is evident.

Once more we must ask what killed them. People? – or a change of climate and hence of habitat? Well, as discussed later, it does seem that vegetation change played a large part in the extinction of Eurasian mainland mammoths. But the mammoths survived in Wrangel precisely because the island retained the ice-age grasses and sedges that suited them so well. People are known to have lived on Wrangel around 3,200 years ago, which seems too late to account for the mammoth's demise. But then Wrangel has not been intensively studied: it is too remote, too expensive to get to, and has been politically sequestrated. The earliest *known* people were probably not the first. It would seem rather an extraordinary coincidence that the mammoths departed from Wrangel so suddenly after 5,000 years of adaptation at a time so close to the known arrival of human beings. It would be surprising, would it not, if people were not involved. Besides, as cited in Chapter 1, there is a picture on a wall of a pharaonic tomb which looks remarkably like a dwarf mammoth. There is no very good reason to doubt that it is.

MADAGASCAR

Madagascar is the fourth largest island in the world – large enough to be acknowledged, like Australia, as 'an island continent'. It has a tremendously varied terrain, with upland, lowland, wet tropical forest, savannah, desert, and of course a rich and various coast. At the time of Christ it had a commensurately rich fauna – what Robert E. Dewar writing in *Quarternary Extinctions* calls 'a magnificent bestiary'. The fauna is still wonderful, and includes entire suites of 'endemic' creatures, which means that they exist nowhere else in the world. There are endemic insectivores, rodents, carnivores and, outstandingly, the unique lemurs. But at the time of Christ there was also a dwarf hippopotamus and giant tortoises in the genus *Geochelone*, plus a range of giant and robust ratites, the Madagascan equivalent of New Zealand's moas, collectively known as 'elephant birds'.

We do not know what happened to the Madagascan fauna more than a few thousand years ago or how it came into being except in the broadest terms, for there are *no* Pleistocene fossils on Madagascar – in fact there are no Cenozoic fossils at all. All that remain are subfossils, taken from a narrow band of time. But as usual there is a bias in these subfossils towards the larger animals, and indeed there is bias here towards primates – the mammals which in most locations have generally preserved so badly. Thus of the living Madagascan primates, only two small genera, *Microcebus* (mouse-lemurs) and *Phaner* (fork-marked lemurs), are unrepresented among the subfossils. But of the seven genera of carnivores on Madagascar only two have been recovered (one of which belongs to an extinct species). Only one of Madagascar's seven endemic rodent genera has turned up as a subfossil, and only one of the eight or nine endemic insectivores.

But let us focus on the primates, which in Madagascar means 'lemuroids'; lemurs and a few similar prosimians. Now there are ten genera. Two thousand years ago there were seventeen. Since these creatures are endemic, a loss from Madagascar means total loss. Two of the genera that do survive, *Varecia* (ruffed lemur) and *Daubentonia* (aye-aye), are known to have lost species: *V. insignis* and *D. robusta*. Each was the largest in its genus.

In fact all the extinct lemuroids were large by lemur standards, for the biggest of the living types, the indris *Indri indri*, would just about have matched the smallest of the extinct species for size. The largest of all the extinct types was *Megaladapis edwardsii*, whose skull was about thirty centimetres long – getting on for a foot. The adult males must have weighed fifty to a hundred kilograms. The existing lemurs are largely nocturnal, but to judge from the shape of their eye-sockets all the extinct types were daytime animals. They moved in more varied ways than modern types. The huge *Megaladapis* was probably a ground-dweller which also climbed trees, vertically and clumsily, like a koala or a bear. *Archaeolemur* was a quadruped, like a modern baboon – though it may have had a flexible snout. *Paleopropithecus* probably brachiated, like a gibbon or a spider monkey. Between them, in short, the lemurs as a whole have mimicked the ecomorphs of the monkeys and apes on other continents – creatures that might have out-competed them, if ever they had found their way on to Madagascar. In one sense the lemurs outstrip the monkeys and apes, however, for in places up to seven different genera evidently lived side by side. Nowhere else in the world do we find – or have we ever found – such a coexistence of so many different primates. Perhaps, Dewar suggests, the lemurs were even more varied than they otherwise would have been because there were no bovids or deer to fill the niches of the middle-sized browsers.

Three non-primate mammals are also known to have gone extinct on Madagascar in the last few thousand years – though there were probably many more, given the obvious sparsity of the non-primate subfossil record. They include the only two wild Madagascan artiodactyls – a hippo in the same genus as the existing African type, but only two-thirds the size, and an extinct bush-pig. There was also an endemic aardvark, *Plesiorycteropus madagascariensis*. Finally, there was a civet in the same genus as the modern fossa, *Cryptoprocta*. The fossa is a handsome beast, remarkably cat-like, right down to the pointed ears and the retractile claws: a striking piece of convergent evolution. The extinct *Cryptoprocta* was bigger, like a low-slung puma. A sad loss.

There were two genera of the giant elephant birds, *Aepyornis* and *Mullerornis*, with six to twelve species between them. The biggest, *A. maximus*, was like a massive ostrich, almost two metres high: this was probably the 'roc' of Arab mythology. The smallest was *M. betsilei* – also robust, but the size of a small emu. Their robustness probably reflects their life in the forest – or the general lack of large predators, which reduced their need for speed. Perhaps most striking of all, however, were their eggs, the biggest of which held eleven litres: two gallons. The elephant birds were grazers and browsers, largely filling the gap occupied elsewhere by deer and antelope.

Finally, two giant tortoises are known to have gone from Madagascar: one with a shell about 80 centimetres long, and the other reaching 1·2 metres. Smaller members of their genus, *Geochelone*, still exist.

Carbon-dating is appropriate to these subfossils, and shows that most of them had gone extinct by about AD 900, though there are odd historical accounts from as late as the seventeenth century of huge birds, hippos, and a calf-like creature with a human face – which could have been *Megaladapis*. A few, then, possibly survived until three or four hundred years ago.

It is clear that many and probably all of the extinct types lasted until human beings arrived and died out soon afterwards. For archaeological records show that people did not settle in Madagascar before the time of Christ, and possibly not before AD 500. Indeed the oldest known sites whose age is beyond question date from the ninth or tenth centuries, but these already show a varied culture – one group were coastal fishers, one gathered shellfish, and one was pastoralist – so the initial settlement was almost certainly some time earlier. The people probably came from east Africa, though the language and culture owes much to south-east Asia.

Even with this evidence, of a flourishing ecosystem reduced to fragments within a few centuries of human arrival, some scientists have suggested that a change of climate killed the animals. But there is no evidence for such a change and besides, on such a varied island, the animals would surely have had room to manoeuvre. Then again, the plants of Madagascar are as wonderfully endemic as the animals. They include many unique members of the Euphorbiaceae and one entirely endemic family of peculiar cactus-like trees known as Didieraceae. Stands of these plants have evidently stood in the same places for thousands of years. There is no evidence of climatic disturbance here. Once more, powerful circumstantial evidence implicates the human invasion.

HAWAII

Hawaii has provided the stage for one of the classic conservation endeavours of the twentieth century: to save from extinction the native goose, alias the ne-ne or *Branta sandvicensis*. In 1952 only thirty-two individuals remained, and they were under siege from introduced mongooses. Then Sir Peter Scott and his colleagues at the Wildfowl Trust (now the Wildfowl and Wetlands Trust) at Slimbridge, Gloucestershire, undertook to begin breeding them in captivity. Now there are thousands. They can be found in parks and reserves worldwide. Although the final phase has yet to be fully realised – to re-establish a self-supporting, viable population of ne-nes on Hawaii – this has truly been a brilliant conservation success.

However, what Sir Peter could not have realised – what no one knew until recent studies of subfossils – was that the ne-ne was merely one of a whole suite of waterfowl that recently included several other geese and at least six ducks, some of them flightless and all now extinct. Besides these, too, there were flightless ibises, flightless rails, a new genus of long-legged owl, a species of sea-eagle, a number of perching birds including honey-creepers and at least one crow, and a new species of petrel. In short, the richness of Hawaii's birdlife was once truly astonishing; the ne-ne was just a lucky survivor, which happened to be able to live (though not very happily, it now seems) high on the Hawaiian volcano. All of these birds, so the evidence increasingly suggests, disappeared after the Polynesians first arrived on Hawaii around AD 500.

The same kind of story is repeated again and again throughout the Pacific and Indian Oceans: the archaeological evidence suggests that the native birds and other creatures apparently disappeared soon after people first arrived. There are a few islands, too, that were not colonised by prehistoric people, and so can serve as controls. Lord Howe Island, for example, still contained two flightless birds, a woodhen and a rail, when modern Europeans first arrived. But at the same latitude the comparable but colonised Norfolk Island and the Kermadecs had lost their flightless species.

The evidence that implicates human beings in a Pleistocene and post-Pleistocene overkill may be circumstantial, but every year the pile of evidence grows deeper and it all points in the same direction. The best-known example of all can close our case: a country as large as Great Britain that escaped colonisation until the European Middle Ages.

NEW ZEALAND

Until a thousand years ago New Zealand contained one of the finest suites of creatures that has ever evolved in any country – one that shows what evolution can do, given a promising gene pool and a free hand. That fauna largely consisted of the moas: somewhere between thirteen and twenty-seven species (depending on who is doing the counting) of flightless ratite birds that ranged in size from a big chicken to a very large and heavy ostrich. These birds were the principal herbivores and hence the driving motor of the ecology on both islands.

Now of course they are all gone. Gone, too, from those halcyon and not-so-far-off days are various rails, of which several were flightless and one was a giant; a flightless coot; a swan and at least three geese, of which two were flightless; some ducks; a crow; a large shag; two raptors generally classed as harriers which in fact may have been goshawks; and the giant short-winged eagle that preyed upon the moas in what must have been among the most dramatic confrontations in nature.

Besides the ones that are gone forever, a whole range of creatures which formerly held sway on the mainlands are now marginalised – which in many cases means literally banished to islands. These include the remarkable kakapo, and the even more remarkable tuataras – reptiles that look like large lizards (up to two feet long) but which in fact belong to an ancient order as distinct from all other living reptiles as the dinosaurs were.

As ever, the subfossil evidence continues to mount, and as it does it increasingly suggests that these extinctions followed hard behind the first human colonisation by the Polynesians known as Maoris, beginning in the tenth century AD. In this case, in fact, the extinctions were not quite as rapid as might be expected. Indeed there were reports of moas as late as the nineteenth century, and although it now seems that these were simply mistaken some moas at least may have survived for five centuries or so after the Maori arrival, say until the time of the Tudors or the Stuarts in England. But then, although there is clear evidence that the Maoris hunted moas – indeed for a time they had a 'moa culture' – they were not full-time hunters. In the main they were horticulturalists, fishers, and gatherers. As I have suggested, such part-time hunting to some extent favours the prey species since the hunters do not focus upon them exclusively, but in the long term it probably ensures that their elimination is the more inevitable. Maoris also compromised the moas and other creatures through the fires with which – intentionally or not – they cleared much of the forest.

In one striking respect the extinctions and diminutions of New Zealand contrast with the first wave of destruction in the Americas and Australia. On those continents, only the big animals apparently suffered. In New Zealand it is clear that some marine fish and shellfish, plus crayfish and a range of giant flightless insects, also suffered badly. But then, the Maoris were gatherers of crayfish and shellfish. And, crucially, they brought with them the Polynesian rat, which winkled out the small creatures that would have escaped the attentions of humans.

It is for similar reasons that the invasions of modern Europeans have often been even more devastating than those of prehistoric peoples – though now of course there is less to devastate. The creatures we have carried with us, which in Australia have included rabbits, cats, foxes, camels, water buffalo and cane toads, may be even more destructive than the human beings themselves. Indeed, speakers at a symposium held at Britain's Royal Society in February 1986 concluded that 'biological invasions' – of exotic creatures introduced by human beings – have now become one of the most significant causes of species extinction, second only to habitat destruction. The Australians with their dingo, around 5,000 years ago, and the Maoris with their Polynesian rat, were among the first to demonstrate that humans-plus-hangers-on are even worse than humans on their own. Hawaii, incidentally, was originally free of ants, but now several species have inadvertently been introduced and have transformed the insect fauna, wiping out scores and possibly hundreds of species, including some that were essential as pollinators of native plants.

Overall, then, the circumstantial evidence that indicts our ancestors seems powerful indeed. The dates do not always correspond as neatly as a prosecutor might like, for it is not always possible to say that such-and-such a creature or suite of creatures definitely disappeared within a few years or centuries of human arrival. The principal problem here is not technical – events of between a thousand and 15,000 years ago can often be dated extremely accurately – but the usual one of logic. The archaeological evidence cannot tell us precisely when human beings first colonised a particular place, but only that they must have arrived by a certain time. The palaeontological evidence cannot tell us precisely when the last animal lived – it can tell us only that a particular animal was still extant at the date of the fossil or subfossil. In general, though, the evident pattern of extinction coincides remarkably with the evident pattern of human colonisation, and whenever human beings came to new places, among native creatures, the shock of novelty seems invariably to have been devastating.

But no jury should convict on circumstantial evidence alone. All other accessible lines of inquiry should be pursued. These in this instance are of three kinds. First we should seek alternative explanations for the Pleistocene extinctions – among which a change of climate and hence of habitat is overwhelmingly the most obvious. Secondly we should seek *direct* evidence of human guilt: where are the signs of slaughter? And thirdly, and I think most importantly, we should address the issue of plausibility. Could our ancestors, who were not particularly numerous and were armed only with stone-tipped spears, really have wiped out so many creatures in so many places?

ALTERNATIVE EXPLANATIONS: CLIMATE

To explore the notion that climate killed the creatures of the Pleistocene, we might reasonably focus on elephants. Thus Andrei Sher (who revealed the dwarfing of Wrangel's mammoths) believes that change in climate and hence in habitat was at least the principal reason for the final demise of mammoths on mainland Siberia. Fifteen thousand years ago, when the mammoths abounded, the habitat was 'tundra steppe': grassland over permafrost. When the ice age ended the permafrost melted and the grass gave way to a misty, ghostly landscape of lakes, moss, and a monocultural forest of larch, albeit with an understorey of birch and blueberry. Mammoths evolved as mass consumers of grass and sedge and as Dr Sher says, 'We don't see any source of forage for woolly mammoths in this forest'. We know, too, as related in Chapter 2 that when an ice age ended in any one place it could end fast over a wide area. Twenty years could see a 7°C rise in temperature – the difference between a frozen landscape and a temperate one.

The Siberian mammoths did try to make a getaway. They moved north, to the high Arctic. But, says Sher, 'By 9,500 years ago larch forest and wet tundra spread almost everywhere, and I believe this was the main reason for mammoth extinction.' Wrangel Island, far to the north even of northern Siberia, happened to be the place where the old tundra steppe stayed longest, and the mammoths chewed on for another 5,000 years.

The general picture to emerge from mainland Siberia is that the mammoths were creatures of the cold – as indeed is suggested by the anatomy of the occasional frozen corpses that still come to light, with their thick layers of fat and big pumping hearts. They are adapted also to the grass and sedge that such cold promotes. Warmth is not their thing at all.

But the point does not apply universally. Near Oxford in England Adrian Lister of Cambridge University has discovered late Pleistocene mammoth bones from a former river bed in association with the shells of molluscs – molluscs of species that now live only in the Mediterranean or the Nile. Here, in short, the mammoths flourished in a climate that was clearly more balmy than today's. On the Colorado plateau, too, Larry Agenbroad and Jim Mead have discovered mammoth dung from around 13,500 to 11,600 years ago and have found that it is rich in the remains of grass, sedge, spruce, sagebrush, and saltbush. In the place where this dung was found these plants no longer exist for the climate now is hotter and drier, and so we may conclude as Andrei Sher has done in Siberia that the elephants disappeared because their favoured plants had gone. But the Colorado plateau is not flat, and as you go uphill it becomes cooler: a change of altitude is like a change of latitude. And the plants that the last of the Colorado mammoths were eating, 11,000 or so years ago, are still to be found just 4,000 feet up the slope. Whatever those elephants died of, then, it was not lack of food – or that at least could not have been the sole cause.

In short, although Siberia was the principal home of mammoths, it may ecologically have been a special case. The mammoths flourished because there were miles and miles of flat grassland of precisely the kind they preferred. But when the grass retreated the vegetation that replaced it happened to be particularly unhelpful – for larch is not exactly succulent and it is deciduous, so there is nothing to eat in winter. Because the land was flat there were no hilltops to repair to; we can imagine the grassland retreating uniformly over a vast area, like the tide going out over a flat beach. In short, the flat uniformity that had allowed the mammoths to flourish also brought about their demise, for there were no microclimates to duck into or – as it happened – any lush new plants to enjoy. In the intricate landscapes of England or America enterprising mammoths could clearly scratch a living even when the comforting cold was taken from them – if only something else had not added to their woes.

Neither can the demise of dwarf elephants on the islands of the Mediterranean be readily explained by climate. As Paul Martin points out, there were no known changes at the time of their going that would have had such an effect. Besides, at the trough of the last ice age, 18,000 years ago, the surface of the sea in the eastern Mediterranean is known to have cooled by more than 6°C, which in ecological terms is huge – and yet the elephants and their miniaturised neighbours came through those harsh times. 'Ironically', says Martin, 'the last European elephants appear to have [survived] an environment viewed by biogeographers as especially prone to the hazards of natural extinction', and, 'Holocene extinctions in islands in the Mediterranean would be quite mysterious without the likelihood of overkill'.

It is clear that climate was a factor in the late Pleistocene extinctions. But taken alone, except here and there, we seem to need some additional cause. But if that cause was indeed overkill – where is the evidence?

DIRECT EVIDENCE

In science, direct evidence is always a good thing. The overkill hypothesis would gain from middens of butchered bones, crushed skulls, and arrow heads trapped between subfossil ribs.

But evidence of this kind is sparse and what there is is equivocal. In Siberia, for example, Olga Soffer from the University of Illinois and her colleagues are excavating houses that were built around 18,000 to 12,000 years ago not out of wood – for of wood there was precious little – but of mammoth bones. One of them, at Mezherich, is ingeniously cobbled from more than 400 large bones including 93 lower jaw-bones: an awful lot of mammoths. Here was a 'mammoth culture' comparable with the 'moa culture' of New Zealand – and, as in New Zealand, the apparent profligacy implies carnage.

In practice, though, Dr Soffer suggests that people and mammoths lived side by side for several thousands of years on mainland Siberia. This does not seem to me to offend the general overkill notion. For one thing, as we have noted, the animals of Eurasia were exposed to hominids in a low-level way over at least a million years and had time to adjust: *H. erectus* and *H. neanderthalensis* before *H. sapiens*. For another, 18,000 years ago represents the height of the last ice age, and human numbers could not have been great, although mammoth numbers could have been very high. As we will see later, a high initial number does not protect an animal from extinction once the tide starts to flow against it, but it does take longer to wipe out a lot of animals than a few.

We might argue, too, as I will argue later, that the people of the late Palaeolithic were not at all stupid. If they relied upon mammoth bones for housing then they might assiduously have avoided killing them – they could have found all the bones they needed just lying about. In fact there were places where the bones accumulated and, according to Dr Soffer, they used these as lumber yards: 'They just settled next to a lumber yard and used that lumber for construction, for fuel, and for tool-making.'

In North America, where continental overkill seems least equivocal, direct signs of human attacks on animals have been found at five sites. However, while some of these signs – including, for example, stone arrow-heads lodged between the ribs of

elephants – do give pretty convincing evidence of human
involvement, other alleged evidence now seems somewhat shaky.
For example, crushed mammoth bones from young animals have
been found with peculiar scarring and spiral fractures – for all the
world suggesting butchery, with a bias towards the most
amenable prey. But archaeologist Gary Haynes has studied piles
of elephant bones in Zimbabwe that result from deaths caused by
drought in the early 1980s. At that time the animals gathered
around the dwindling water-holes and as their desperation grew
their social structure broke down and the smallest animals, normally cossetted, were pushed to one side and were the first to die.
Then the frantic animals trod on their fellows' corpses – producing precisely the kinds of marks and breaks that have been seen in
North American mammoth heaps. There is every reason to suppose that at the end of the North American ice age mammoths
would have gathered around the dying streams and fought and
panicked just as they sometimes do today in arid Africa. We
should not drag in notions of human butchery gratuitously.

Yet I feel that both sides, the prosecution as well as the defence,
are equally entitled to treat such evidence cautiously. We all
know how sparse the archaeological record is – and the further
back you go, the sparser it becomes. Do we really expect to find
a cave marked 'Butcher's Shop'? Any direct evidence at all seems
to me a bonus. Only a few flint spear-heads have been found in
skeletons but a few, in this context, seems an awful lot.

So we must say that climate alone certainly does not seem
always to explain the deaths of Pleistocene animals: certainly not
of mammoths, which were among the most cold-adapted animals
of all. The direct archaeological evidence, as ever, is hard to read:
either side can bend it to their advantage. That leaves the last
great issue of plausibility.

COULD STONE-AGE HUNTERS REALLY HAVE KILLED SO MANY
ANIMALS?

The theoretical case for the prosecution which says that
Palaeolithic and recent hunter-gatherers *could* have killed vast
suites of large animals rests on three main points: that large animals are much more vulnerable than they seem; that human

beings are even more destructive than they seem; and, as is increasingly suggested by the modern science of theoretical ecology with its computer modelling, that surprisingly modest pressure of the kind that humans can bring to bear can all too easily drive sensitive creatures to oblivion. We should look at these points in turn.

BIG ANIMALS ARE FAR MORE VULNERABLE THAN THEY SEEM

Three outstanding biological features militate against big animals. First there is the one we have met throughout this book, the importance of which can hardly be overstated: population. Animal populations need to be big if they are to be viable in the long term. Populations smaller than a few hundred seem almost bound to go extinct in centuries if not in decades, through physical accidents such as epidemic or statistical accident such as a skewed sex-ratio; in the longer term, lack of genetic variation will prevent their further adaptation when conditions change. In reality, 'a few hundred' may mean several thousand. Thus Tom Foose, when he was with the World Conservation Union, calculated that unless wild populations of black rhinoceroses contain at least 2,500 individuals then they are liable to go extinct. A population that size requires vast undisturbed space: on normal territory, at least, perhaps around 25,000 square kilometres. Just a little disturbance here and there can reduce the effective size of the territory below the size needed to support viable numbers.

Furthermore, and secondly, large animals are generally reproductive 'K strategists': that is, they produce only one or two offspring at a time, and only at longish intervals, in the expectation that most will survive. They stand in contrast with 'r strategists', such as mice and flies, which produce big or even vast litters at short intervals in the expectation that only a few will live. K strategy reproduction is commonly associated with slow maturity and a long life.

It can pay to be a K strategist. In Australia wedge-tailed eagles can override the droughts that commonly last five years or more simply by stopping breeding until the good times roll. The small rodents and marsupials have no such option because they do not live that long. The slow maturation of the K strategist leaves

plenty of time for learning, so that clever animals such as elephants and apes have time to hone their survival and social skills.
Human beings demonstrate the ultimate merit of K strategy.

But K strategists pay a huge price for their carefulness. When
their populations are reduced, they are slow to recover. If the
stress that reduced their numbers continues in the years when the
population is low, then the animals may not recover at all.
Continuous pressure, even apparently low continuous pressure,
can erode them little by little until, inexorably, they crash.
Modern orang-utans illustrate the point beautifully – or tragically.
Their reproductive rate in the wild seems astonishingly low: only
one offspring every eight years or so. Even human beings in a
state of nature improve on that, with one every five years or so
(and a total of five in a twenty-year reproductive life). Simple calculations show that if only one in twenty female orangs of
reproductive age is killed each year then the population will
crash.

Thirdly, and most obviously, big animals are conspicuous.
They are easy targets for spears or (later) arrows. They do not
need to die immediately: the hunters are so well rewarded that
they do not resent a two- or three-day follow-up.

In short, we may begin with a fairly small population, innately
vulnerable; we pick off just a few easy targets; and, because the
animals have so little spare capacity and are quite unable to
rebound as mice or herring may do, then little by little or indeed
quite rapidly they dwindle to nothing. Once you apply a little
theoretical biology or indeed observe what is happening now
among elephants, rhinos, orangs, big whales, and slow-breeding
birds such as cranes and birds of prey, you see how easily the most
conspicuous and impressive creatures can be brushed aside.

Why has this not been obvious? Why have ecologists only
recently framed such ideas? In part, I suggest, it is for the logical
reason that the big animals that now remain to us are, for one reason or another, the least vulnerable. The more vulnerable ones
have already gone. We have already explored various specific reasons why creatures might escape immediate extinction: the
solitary elusiveness of the moose, the erratic and rapid migrations
of bison and caribou. In general, the ones that survive now are
the ones that were least easy to wipe out. Although this makes
sense it was not immediately obvious. The tough survivors have

given a false impression. The creatures that are long gone were far more sensitive than the survivors – and far more typical.

There is another, more subtle, general point. Unlike many modern biologists, I do believe that competition is a real and powerful phenomenon. Of course animals in an ecosystem eventually settle down and live far more amicably as neighbours than the metaphor of 'nature red in tooth and claw' would have us believe. Yet each kind lives within bounds set by the others. The corollary is that when two creatures are competing for the same resource then the removal of one can allow the other to expand. This, I am quite sure, is what happened after the late Pleistocene extinctions of North America. With the removal of horses, elephants, camels, and a host of antilocaprids, the animals that were left – the deer and bison – could spread themselves as never before. The first creatures that European naturalists encountered in North America were these luxuriously expanded survivors: tens or even hundreds of millions of bison. It seemed implausible indeed that stone-age hunters could have wiped out such herds, and of course they did not. But the Pleistocene fauna that the stone-age hunters encountered was not like that. It was an assemblage of many different creatures each of which had a far smaller population and was far more easily pushed over the edge. The apparent swarm of survivors is an artefact – like a rash of ragwort on a bombsite. The ragwort would hardly get a look in if the other wild plants had not been wiped out first.

In short, big animals are vulnerable, and in general the survivors are the less vulnerable but also the less typical. Now add to that the fact that human beings, who are obviously destructive, are even more destructive than they seem.

HUMAN BEINGS ARE EVEN MORE DANGEROUS THAN THEY SEEM

The hunters of the upper Palaeolithic – the late Pleistocene – were obviously proficient. But it is difficult to judge just how proficient they were. Were they simply good predators, like wolves or lions, but with a few extra tricks thrown in? Or were they more than that? Might they have qualified, in modern parlance, as game managers?

There is a spectrum of possibility. The notion that our ancestors functioned as just another predator is the conservative view, while the idea that they were game managers is clearly more bold, and I have not heard it stated so explicitly. Some scientists feel that it is innately virtuous to be as conservative as possible, and would not consider the game manager hypothesis until the simple predator idea was exhausted. But actually I think that is bad philosophy. It is at least as acceptable, and in the end more economical, to consider the whole spectrum of possibility together. So let us ask: were our late Pleistocene ancestors – those of around 30,000 years or so ago – merely predators, or were they perfectly competent game wardens?

Well, even if they were 'merely' predators, they clearly would have been very adept indeed. We explored their assets in Chapter 6. We know they could think, cooperate, remember, and share experience. It is not foolish to imagine them lying in wait for prey whose habits they understood well, or dividing themselves into beaters and killers, as many hunting–gathering people do today (and which is the technique employed by shooters of pheasant on Norfolk heaths). It is sometimes said that we should not extrapolate too readily from present-day experience to the past but this is sometimes helpful and necessary. Indeed the same inferences can be made at least as cogently the other way around. We know from their anatomy and from all other signs – including their weapons and their paintings – that the upper Palaeolithic people of the late Pleistocene were as clever as us. They lacked the thousand years of experience and accumulated infrastructure that we have now inherited, but as people they lacked nothing. If they were alive now they would hold down jobs as builders and tycoons, bank managers, scientists, and coaches of tennis. Well, in those days circumstance obliged them to be full-time hunters. I see no reason to doubt that they practised the crafts of their time as efficiently as their descendants practise those of the present. In short, we know that they were hunters, and there is absolutely no reason to doubt that they were extremely good at it.

This general aptitude was augmented, I suggest, by one technical attribute that is undeniable, and one ecological possibility that is highly speculative but at least worth thinking about. The technical attribute was of course the missile, as discussed in Chapter 6. The ability to hit and run – to strike the mortal blow with little or no personal risk – is unique among large predators and rare in all of nature. Here was an innovation indeed: a 'trick' that transformed the nature of the game almost as profoundly as that, say, of speech.

The ecological possibility, discussed in Chapter 7, is that from about 30,000 years onwards (and maybe before!) our late Palaeolithic ancestors were perhaps already practising horticulture: not on a scale large enough to show up in the archaeological record, but certainly enough to make a crucial difference to their survival in any one place and at any one time. The art of survival is not simply to flourish in the good times, but to get through the bad times. If those stone-age hunters *were* cultivating, then their efficacy as hunters would have been greatly enhanced, simply because the alternative food source would have allowed them to maintain their population when the wild prey became rare.

This principle can apply to late Palaeolithic hunters even if we do not admit that they might have indulged in cultivation. For the key to human ecology is our versatility. If the supply of mammoths fails, then we can get by on crayfish. If the meat fails altogether, we can at least subsist on plants. The same argument applies, or seems to apply, to true carnivores versus creodonts. The carnivores on the whole are *less* committed to meat, and so can survive in more circumstances than could the creodonts, and so in the end were bound to oust them. Human beings have a more varied diet than any carnivore except the bears – and if we cultivated as well, as at least is possible, then we could outstrip them as well. Besides, the use of fire and of stones for bashing sinews and bones would have made us more efficient than bears even at the meat–eating.

The fact that humans are supremely clever gives them a crucial advantage that is denied to all other hunters. In general, other predators are merely opportunist. They may have some preferences but they will take whatever is suitable and most available. They cannot afford to waste time seeking out what is rare. This creates a balance of a kind because the species that are overhunted are protected by their scarcity and have a chance to recover. But we can imagine that human hunters were not such slaves to opportunity. If mammoths were rare – so what? The hunters were astute enough to know where the few remaining herds could be found. And it is doubtful if hominids ever regarded hunting merely as a source of food. Always there was kudos attached to it – just as is obviously the case among present-day chimps. There would be kudos indeed in killing a creature that was not only huge and powerful but was also hard to find. In short, it is eminently reasonable from all that we know about hunting people to assume that our late palaeolithic ancestors were uniquely capable of hunting rare animals to extinction – or, more to the point, of hunting them until the populations were too small to be viable.

There is one final ecological scenario. All animal populations fluctuate in the wild. Species experience good years and bad years, and on a grander scale we can probably envisage that elephants experienced good centuries and bad centuries. Thus we see that at any one time animals go 'locally extinct', which means that they disappear from part of their range, but hang on in another. When times improve they begin to spread again from their refuges, and reoccupy the places they have vacated.

But an extremely versatile animal like the human being is less liable to be driven out of any one place by any one set of circumstances. In the same way – demonstrably – grey squirrels are less likely to disappear from any one spot than the more pernickety reds. Competition, however, is pre-emptive: in general, it favours the creature that is already in residence. Thus the red squirrels found it harder to get back into the places from which they had been made locally extinct, because the greys had never left and were already in residence.

I find this kind of picture eminently capable of explaining the erosiveness of human invaders in North America. People occupied spaces and then had little need to vacate those places in the bad times because they were so resourceful. But the less versatile creatures were obliged to leave from time to time. When they tried to get back in, however, the human beings were already ensconced, ready and waiting. This would not happen every time, and the human beings would not always win. But they would win often enough. The process worked as a ratchet. Little by little the human range and population grew, and the other animals diminished. Furthermore, because human beings are so versatile, the same scenario could be enacted in a hundred different habitats: in the forest, by the river, in the mountains, on the plain. The importunate primate was always there.

Finally, modern observations show that it is not necessary to kill an animal directly in order to make its life intolerable, and hence cause it to retreat, and hence in the end drive it to extinction. There are two main points. First, animals construct their habitats as mosaics: a collation of essential components. If any one component is made unavailable, then the whole habitat collapses. The mosaic exists in four dimensions – time as well as space. If you make it difficult for an animal to drink in peace at the waterhole, then its whole habitat is compromised. If you occupy some favoured spot in which it feeds at one particular time of the year or in which it hibernates – an estuary or a cave – then again, the whole territory becomes inhospitable. If *parts* of a territory become inhospitable then the population can be fragmented. And if it is fragmented then each of the divided subpopulations may be too small to be viable and again the whole population collapses, fragment by fragment. This is what seems to be happening today with Asia's wild elephants.

Secondly, most animals are extremely sensitive to disturbance. In the Pleistocene, orang-utans occupied a vast swathe of southeast Asia; indeed they must to a large extent have coevolved with giant pandas, which in those days were similarly extensive. Now the pandas are confined to a few hillsides in China while the remnant orangs are thousands of miles away, on Sumatra and Borneo. But the modern orangs are now demonstrating the extreme vulnerability of animals that are large and apparently formidable. Their reproduction is egregiously slow. They are also outstandingly stand-offish. When human beings move in they tend to move out: not necessarily because they are molested, but simply because they are accustomed to having the forest to themselves. I wonder if this is because the males stake out their territories by a call that for all other orangs is terrifying – and find that human beings call their bluff by ignoring them, and thereby announce their own dominance. Whatever the psychology, we know that orangs vacate vast areas that they could perfectly well inhabit simply because they resent having neighbours. They cannot afford to be so choosy but choosiness is built into them.

In general, human beings are far more disturbing than any other predator. Lions may walk in full view within a hundred yards of antelope without disturbing them. Provided the antelope can keep them in view they know they are safe. But prey animals are not stupid. They know that human beings have missiles. They know that, uniquely, human beings can kill from a distance. So human beings cannot walk openly within a hundred yards of wild antelope. Indeed on walks in agricultural land if you keep your eyes open you can see crows and pigeons take off from trees half a mile away. You normally do not notice them. But they notice you, and they act accordingly. They would not respond that way to a fox or even an eagle. But then the fox or the eagle has to get in close in order to kill. Indeed, old Africa hands such as zoologists David Houston of Glasgow University and Brian 'the lion' Bertram, tell me that you can stride up to lions at a kill and shoo them away. I cannot believe that lions find human beings innately terrifying. But they are experienced, and although wild animals lack the detailed communicative skills of human beings they do have traditions. They know, therefore, that human beings have tricks up their sleeves – if not spears then guns. The safest option is simply to give our species a very wide berth.

In short, it seems reasonable to suggest that our late Palaeolithic ancestors not only killed their fellow creatures but also made their lives difficult, upsetting their patterns of feeding and reproduction, and generally compromising their habitats, to a far greater extent than an ordinary predator would have done. For large, vulnerable, slow-breeding species, that could have been all that was required.

Yet all we have assumed so far is that human beings were proficient predators: the conservative hypothesis. If they were more than that – if they were proto-managers of game – then their influence could have been even more acute.

PALAEOLITHIC GAME MANAGERS

The notion that late Pleistocene hunters veered towards game management must be seen to be speculative, yet in part seems largely a matter of definition or of degree. We could argue, after all, that people who are conventionally considered merely to be proficient hunters, and yet are anticipating the movements of their prey both in the long term and the short, and are employing beaters to drive their prey into corners or into the paths of their partners, are managers of a kind – just as we can argue that people who stick twigs in the ground in the expectation that they will grow at least have their foot on the ladder of horticulture. But it seems reasonable to me to speculate that Upper palaeolithic hunters were more organised even than this.

We can again learn from present-day hunter-gatherers, and in particular from the aborigines of Australia. For they above all are astute deployers of fire. In their early days they may well have used fire to drive diprotodonts and giant kangaroos and now they use it to freshen the vegetation and attract small animals for prey. As we have seen, Reese Jones of the Australian National University of Canberra suggests that this is a fine way to manage that vast, uncertain continent. I see no reason to doubt that people of the upper Palaeolithic all over the world could have used fire to create amenable landscape: less forest, more open space. It seems eminently likely too, that they knew perfectly well how to adjust the landscape to direct and manipulate their fellow creatures.

Why should we doubt, either, that those advanced stone-age hunters preferred some creatures to others – and knew how to advance the cause of those they liked and undermine the ones they did not? It is easy to imagine such people imposing close seasons on their favoured creatures through laws of the kind that we choose somewhat snootily to call taboos, which were designed to keep the favoured ones in good heart. And if, on the other hand, they decided that some other creature was bad news, why doubt that they might have targeted them? They knew perfectly well – they were modern people after all – that it is the young females that give birth, and if you want to eat meat sustainably then it is wise to kill only the ageing males; contrariwise, they knew that if the animal is of a kind you feel you would be better off without then you should kill the ones with the swollen bellies. Perhaps – only perhaps, but the idea is at least worth considering – the first colonists of North America set out to eliminate the mammoths. Perhaps they decided that smaller animals were of more use (since on this tree-rich continent they did not need the elephant bones for timber). Perhaps they decided too, with even greater sophistication, that they would be better off without large rival predators, and set out to remove the principal prey-base of those predators. Get rid of mammoths and giant sloths and you eliminate sabretooths and the giant running bears. In similar vein many modern historians now argue that the government of nineteenth-

century America set out to eliminate the bison – the most tri-
umphant survivor of the Pleistocene pogrom – so as to destroy
the economy of the 'Indians', who were themselves the descendants of the Pleistocene invaders. I see no reason to suppose that
the original Pleistocene invaders were less astute than the
American government of a few thousand years later.

As I have already said at least once too often, however, the
idea that upper Palaeolithic hunters were game managers – that
they consciously manipulated their prey and encouraged some at
the expense of others – is speculation. It merely represents one
point, the extreme point, on the spectrum of possibility and
therefore (it seems to me) should at least be considered. What
seems to me to clinch the case for the prosecution, and show
beyond reasonable doubt that our ancestors certainly could have
perpetrated the late Pleistocene overkill and therefore (in the
absence of a more convincing culprit) probably did, are the theories that emerge from computer modelling. These show that
big and therefore vulnerable animals can be wiped out by hunting even when the hunters are merely predators – even when
they fall short of game management.

In particular, Steve Mithen of the University of Reading has
devised a model to show what would happen to populations of
mammoths when they are subjected to various stresses. The population dynamics of the animals – the rate of birth, the interval
between births, the age at sexual maturity, and so on – are based
on those of their living relatives, African and Asian elephants in
the family Elephantidae. The stresses Dr Mithen invents for them
are hypothetical but nonetheless realistic: a changing climate that
diminishes the food base, and hunting pressure.

The model shows that remarkably little hunting pressure
quickly drives mammoths to extinction (just as we have already
noted is the case with orangs). Dr Mithen posited a reasonable
population of human beings in North America and showed that
if one mammoth were killed per year for every twenty people
then, sooner or later, the mammoths would go extinct –
especially if, as seems likely, they were already under climatic
stress. The original size of the population does not affect the issue.
It takes longer to eliminate a big population, but it will crash
sooner or later. In the interests of conservatism, however, he proposed that the rate of hunting would diminish as the mammoth

population went down, and so in his model the rate of hunting never exceeded 2 per cent of the mammoth population per year. Still it dwindled to extinction. A mammoth population under climatic stress cannot increase at 2 per cent per year, and so it cannot withstand a loss of 2 per cent. Perhaps, too, as I have already suggested, the model does not need to be so conservative. Determined or bloody-minded human hunters with something to prove could well have hunted mammoths into the ground even after they had become rare. A good number of modern creatures – great auks, dodos, passenger pigeons, moas and grey wolves, and many a bird of prey over much of their range – have similarly been hounded past the point of rarity and into the grave. Besides, rarity by definition implies a small population – and small populations tend to dwindle on their own account.

So we know that in the late Pleistocene many large animals died out on three great continents, while in the late Pleistocene and Holocene entire suites of creatures disappeared from islands worldwide. We also know that the creatures we see today, wondrous as they are, are a shadow of the faunas of comparatively recent but 'prehistoric' times. We know that the extinctions tended to follow the incursions of human beings. Did the animals simply fade away or did we kill them?

Of course we killed them. Or at least, our immediate ancestors did. I do not know whether they did it inadvertently as highly competent hunters who were also insouciant; or whether they did what they did with regret; or whether they set out, as proto-managers of game, to weed out the species they found least helpful and leave the others to flourish – a scenario which does not seem too fanciful. But whichever way they approached the task, the jury must find them guilty.

The evidence that implicates our ancestors is flawed because it is circumstantial, and yet it seems overwhelming. The direct evidence – of arrow heads stuck in mammoth ribs – is sparse, but the wonder is that it exists at all. The issue of plausibility seems to me to be open and shut. It would be amazing indeed if predators as competent as our ancestors had not had a tremendous impact. All that has become apparent these past few years in ecology and population dynamics, including the mathematical modelling that shows how creatures like orangs and mammoths will decline under what seems to be only moderate pressure, proclaims that for big, slow-breeding animals extinction is always imminent. Other factors did play a part in the Pleistocene and post-Pleistocene extinctions, of course. Climate alone might have done the trick here and there. But the *coup de grâce*, and often the sole operant, was ourselves.

And now the pace of extinction has increased. Now the world is so arranged, if arrangement is the word, that the existence of every other creature is to some extent in our hands. The animals that serve us directly are overwhelmingly successful, if the criterion of success is indeed the replication of their genes – cattle and chickens too are far more numerous than they would ever have been in untamed nature. By contrast, the ones for which we have no use are pushed aside – unless they discover some human niche, as aphids and rats have done, and become 'pests'. So now we have the world at our feet, where do we go from here?

The Next Million Years

Throughout the Cenozoic most species of mammal lasted roughly a million years and then went extinct or evolved into something else. There are no innate mechanisms to limit the span of a species, at least that are known about, but that is the way things have tended to turn out. After a time conditions change and species must also change or go to the wall, and the cycle of change averages around a million years.

So what are the chances of *Homo sapiens* lasting a million years? Of course the question is arbitrary because there are no rules. There is no *a priori* reason why our species should survive for so long. On the other hand, there are some very good biological reasons why we might last in recognisable form until the dying of the planet – because in theory there is less cause for us to alter and also less opportunity. So at least in the spirit of intelligent provocation we might ask: 'What *are* our chances of lasting a million years?'. But at the same time we must ask: 'And what will happen to our fellow creatures along the way?'.

Already, of course, we have had some of that arbitrarily allotted span. But not much. The species *Homo sapiens*, as distinct from the 'archaic' heidelbergensis and the neanderthals, has been anatomically modern for about 100,000 years. So if we define ourselves in anatomical terms, which after all is the criterion that palaeontologists apply to other species, then we can reckon that we have had only one-tenth of our time at most. Although our impact has already been frightful and for many other lineages has been decisive, we are very much at the *beginning* of our run. We still have 900,000 years to go – as near to a million as makes no difference.

Mao Tse-tung commented that a journey of a thousand miles begins with a single step. Our journey of a million years into the future must begin with the next century or so. This will be a particularly testing time.

THE NEXT FEW HUNDRED YEARS: THE HUMAN SPECIES

All times are unique; all times are special. But some are more special than others and the age we live in now is crucial. The next
century or so – the next ten centimetres in the kilometre of time
we still have to run – will show whether or not it is possible for
the human species to regulate its own numbers by means that are
voluntary and, as we might say, 'benign' – and whether, in doing
so, we can preserve at least a fair proportion of our fellow creatures. If not, the coming century will produce a collapse of
humanity and of the environment that in ecological terms is
entirely comparable with the death of lemmings, or with algae in
a pond when the nutrients are gone – but on a far, far greater scale
than either. Nature's rules are universal, and nature has no taste.
We may find our own collapse unthinkable simply because it is so
horrible to contemplate, but repugnance provides no protection
at all, any more than incredulity protects against flood or the
encroachment of ice.

Populations of all creatures grow exponentially. 'Exponential'
does not mean 'fast'. It simply implies growth by compound interest – not by a fixed amount each year but by a steady proportion
of whatever was there before. In practice, with most creatures
most of the time, this exponential tendency is countered by the
hazards of life, of which limited resource is the principal one:
either because the resource simply is not there or because some
extraneous factor, like a rival species, prevents access. Eventually,
even the most favoured and rival-free populations must stop
growing as they exhaust the capacity of their environments to provide more. But when everything is going well – in halcyon days
when there is no practical limit on resource – populations grow
maximally, the only limit being imposed by the reproductive
capacity of the animal (which usually in effect means of the female
animal). The maximum expansion of elephants, which mature in
their 'teens and produce only one infant at a time after a two-year
gestation, is many times less than that of mice, which can produce
litters of six or more at age six months after a gestation of about
three weeks. The maximum reproductive capacity of human
beings is somewhere between those two.

Until humans beings were finally obliged to commit themselves
more or less fully to agriculture, about 10,000 years ago, the

restraints on their population growth were all too obvious. Resourceful as they undoubtedly were they still had to compete with bears, and the supply of mammoths and gazelles was all too fragile. It seems, indeed, that by about 10,000 years ago the human population had reached a maximum of around 5–10 million.

But the final commitment to agriculture removed the restraints. After all, the whole purpose of farming is to divert the highest possible proportion of the land's output into human food. And up to a point – a point which even now we have not yet reached – more food can be produced simply by expending more effort. Thus, by farming, human beings can increase their effective resource by a factor of ten, a hundred, or with modern intensive methods at least a thousand. So by the time of Christ, after a mere 8,000 years of large-scale, full-time agriculture, human numbers worldwide are estimated to have reached somewhere between 100 and 300 million.

After this, with the baseline already substantial and farming techniques already advanced, the exponential growth of the human population finally entered its rapid phase. The billion mark was passed by about AD 1800. By AD 1900 the world population reached 1·7 billion. By AD 2000 numbers will exceed 6 billion. Thus agriculture has allowed a thousandfold increase in numbers over 10,000 years. In short, in recent millennia the exponential potential of human beings has more or less been unrestrained. Indeed at times, as in Kenya in recent decades, human population growth has approached the maximum that is conceivable for our species, at around 4 per cent per year – a rate that doubles population in less than twenty years. Worldwide, the numbers now added each year are equivalent to about twice the current population of the United Kingdom.

The question is not whether this growth must stop, but when, and how great the numbers will be by the time it does – and whether we can call a halt by means that are voluntary and benign, or whether the eventual restraint will be out of our hands. If things simply get out of hand we might ask how much damage is liable to be done as we enter our maximal phase and then collapse out of it, and whether or how much of that damage could be repaired in the following centuries. Soil erosion might be countered to some extent, for example, by fresh weathering of rock – but the loss of elephants will be permanent. Those

who feel, as some clearly do, that matters can be left to chance
or to God might simply consider some statistics that emerged
from Princeton University in the 1960s, when the proportionate
increase in population was somewhat higher than now (although
the absolute number added each year was smaller). The
Princeton demographers calculated that the growth rate then
current would produce within 700 years a world population of
17 *trillion* (a trillion being a million million). Such a figure is
clearly fantastic: several thousand people for every one that now
exists. But 700 years is a trivial period of time – two-thirds of a
metre, in our time-into-distance scale. *Something* has got to happen between now and then, and either that something will be a
tight and clever policy, benignly expedited, or it will be very
nasty indeed.

In practice there are some clear and perfectly acceptable routes
to population control which could bring about the necessary cur-
tailment within a half-century or so and level the human
population at around 10 to 12 billion. That number would still be
uncomfortably high, putting more strain on world resources than
truly seems desirable. But those same policies, if maintained,
would then bring the world population steadily downwards to
whatever figure our descendants feel is desirable. However, there
is in populations the property of *momentum*: that is, trends that fall
short of massacre take several decades to show a serious effect. For
example, at least two-thirds of the people now on Earth are under
sixteen years old and have yet to reproduce, so the world population will increase markedly even if they all decide to have only
one or two children per couple. Taking momentum into account,
modern demographic projections suggest that it would take about
500 years for the world's maximum population (10–12 billion) to
fall again to current levels (5–6 billion) if reasonably benign policies were put in place.

Once population begins to drop, then people can decide the
figure to which they want it to fall, and at which, roughly, it
should be maintained. I have asked various conservation biologists what kind of world population they feel is reasonable and
their answers ranged from 2 billion down to about 300 million.
But all the biologists brought the same principle to bear: that the
population should be small enough to be sustainable indefinitely,
leaving plenty of leeway for ourselves and other species, but large

enough to sustain a variety of healthy civilisations. Three hundred million may seem draconianly low (it is barely more than the present population of the United States) but it is the same as the *world* population at the time of Christ and at that time there was certainly no shortage of genius or of cultural variety (any more than there is in present-day America). Incidentally, too, this 'low' figure is 10,000 times higher than the present population of Asian elephants and 10 million times higher than that of northern white rhinoceroses. But whatever figure our descendants consider desirable, it could be reached within a few thousand years from now – more than 1,000 but less than 3,000 – simply by applying policies that most people would consider eminently benign.

But of course, there are 'pronatalists' who maintain that anyone who seeks to reduce human reproduction must in some sense be 'anti-humanity'. To prevent the birth of possible babies is, they say, to 'deny life'. Some religious people argue too that all babies are born 'for the glory of God' and that more babies means more glory. Such arguments can be answered even by crude statistics. Let's suppose, for example, that we do survive the looming demographic crisis, and that our descendants finally decide that a world population of around 1 billion is a reasonable sustainable target. With such a population there is no reason to doubt that our species could last a million years. In such a case, the human species will enjoy 1 billion × 1 million (that is, a million billion) person-years. But if we allow our population to rise to, say, 20 billion then we must surely doubt whether we could survive in recognisable form for more than another 10,000 years or so. If we faded after 10 millennia then our total presence through the time still to come will have been 20 billion × 10,000 (a mere 200,000 billion) person-years – at *most*. In other words, if we exercise restraint then the total number of human beings who will have trodden this Earth could be at least five times greater than it would be if we allowed populations to run away with us. Who, then, are the misanthropes?

But what are the 'benign' policies that could reduce human population so dramatically, without pogrom or epidemic or ecological collapse? Well, common sense reveals that if each couple (which effectively means each woman) elects to have only two children then the population cannot grow (except for the first few decades, because of momentum). In practice, if two children per family was accepted as the preferred maximum then the population would eventually fall, since some people would die before they reproduced, and some would elect to have only one child or none at all. So long as the *average* number of offspring reaching reproductive age is less than two per mother, the population is bound to level out and then to fall. Recent experience – for example from West Germany, before the reunion with the East – shows that when people are rich they commonly do elect to have only two children. Large families are associated either with particular fashions (the Kennedys initiated a minor baby boom in the US) or, more commonly, with deprivation: that is, large families are commonly seen (a) as a status symbol for women in societies in which females can gain respect only through motherhood; (b) as a source of support in old age; and (c) as a buttress against high infant mortality. Thus, the only sure as well as the only benign route to small families is via increased wealth and security, and *reduced* infant mortality.

Common sense plus the experience of the past few decades show that several preconditions must be met if the two-child family is to become the norm worldwide, all of which are difficult to realise but conceptually undramatic. First, all efforts must be made to minimise infant mortality. People must *know* that two children out of two are liable to survive. Secondly, everyone worldwide needs a pension, so that they do not need to rely upon their children when they stop working. Thirdly, the trend in rich countries towards earlier and earlier retirement must be reversed, for if people retire earlier *and* the birth rate goes down then within a couple of decades or less we will find there are too few young recruits for the job market and indeed that only a small minority of the population is actually working. In many countries this is already a problem. We therefore need to employ people of sixty-plus in ways that retain their dignity but do not (as in the past) hold up promotion and clog the heights with gerontocracy. Lastly, we need to ensure that the women of the world who have already declared an interest in the technologies of family planning have that technology available, and preferably should control that technology. As modern family planners say, the point is not to coerce but to 'empower'. Coercion is obviously undesirable – but modern experience shows that it is also unnecessary. People do not actually want to have more children than they can reasonably support, or than they need for their own security.*

In short, the policies that could enable the human species to keep its numbers within sustainable bounds are clear in principle, and they are all benign. Indeed, the pleasant truth is that no policy that is not benign can possibly succeed. High infant mortality, for example, tends to be countered by high birth rate, and leads not simply to misery and sadness but also to biological disarray and extreme wastefulness. War, famine, and pestilence have often produced dramatic blips in populations – but again, people invariably respond to these setbacks by breeding their way out of trouble. Wars are commonly followed by epidemics and also by baby booms.

Finally, we must of course acknowledge that to curtail the growth in human numbers is only half of the equation. The other half is to place a ceiling on human acquisitiveness. Thus people on the receiving end of family planning policies are wont to point out that a well-regulated, well-planned nuclear family in Los Angeles, with Mom, Pop, and two kids, consumes about twice as much as the average Bangladeshi village. We cannot all aspire to live like middle-class Californians: indeed such a standard must be seen to be anomalous, just as the pending world population of 12 billion must be seen to be anomalous. A world standard closer to that of, say, a Mediterranean village is more realistic – a way of life which can be very agreeable indeed and which has produced more than its share of geniuses, from El Greco to Jesus Christ. We need have no fears for the future of civilisation if we managed to achieve the material standards of traditional Greek farmers. But we can improve dramatically on traditional standards and certainly on cultural horizons simply by adding electronics. Energetically-speaking, electronics is cheap and so is sustainable indefinitely. The internet could be run many times over on solar power, if such was considered desirable. To live with the physical

---

*Of course, contraception for men is desirable, too. But for good physiological reasons, and not simply for reasons of male chauvinism, male contraception is a far more difficult trick to pull than female contraception. Fertility in men is far more closely interlinked with secondary sex characteristics than is fertility in women and most male 'pills' produced so far have tended to emasculate if not frankly to poison. So far – apart from condoms – vasectomy remains the only safe male contraceptive option but it is not fully reversible.

simplicity of a Greek villager and yet to be in touch with the culture of the whole of the rest of the world seems, at least to me, to be a very reasonable prospect. I think a lot of Californians would agree. Many, indeed, already aspire to living that way.

In short, if we were to address our own biology seriously then we could secure a future for ourselves that could last indefinitely – though, whatever we do, the next few centuries will be difficult. What, then, of our fellow species?

THE NEXT FEW CENTURIES: OUR FELLOW SPECIES

The survival of other species depends to an extent that is hard to overestimate upon ourselves. Of course we do not exercise absolute control. Of course there will be some that are liable to survive even though we may do our best to eliminate them – for instance mosquitoes and cockroaches. Others seem likely to slip through the net simply because we are too remote from them, for example the creatures that swarm around the hydrothermal vents in the ocean floor. But the creatures of which we are most directly aware – grand survivors of the Pleistocene overkill, the elephants, rhinos, tigers, lions, cheetahs, bears, camels, antelope, deer, koalas, kangaroos – none of them has a prayer unless we take their cause seriously. Some of them, including tigers, have no conceivable long-term future in the wild even as things are.

Why should we care? In fact, there is no space in this book to address this issue at proper length, although I have discussed it more fully in *Last Animals at the Zoo* (Hutchinson Radius, London, 1991). But in general there seems to me to be a hierarchy of reasons why we should care, extending from the materialistic to the spiritual. The materialistic argument I feel is the least interesting, although I now think it is weightier than I once did. This simply says that other creatures – or, more generally, the genes that they contain – are a resource which, increasingly, may be pressed into human service, for drugs, food, or what you will. The materialist argument also suggests that biological diversity provides some protection against ecological collapse, but although this point seems intuitively obvious it is actually quite difficult to defend. The most obvious weakness among several in the materialist argument is that it might tempt us simply to seek to preserve those species that we perceive to be most useful – and although the list of perceptibly useful creatures might extend to tens of thousands it would fall several orders of magnitude short of the number that now live on Earth. Thus we could conserve the 'useful' creatures yet perpetrate a mass extinction nonetheless. In short, if we want to conserve more than a tiny fraction of present-day creatures then we have to conserve them *whether or not* they are of obvious 'use' to us.

So what other reasons are there? Next in the hierarchy of reasons is aesthetics: that other creatures are beautiful, and they bring us pleasure. This point is far from feeble. What a shock it would be to contemplate a world in which there were no more tigers! The fact that *Homo sapiens* has already despatched so many fine beasts of comparable beauty would not lessen the sadness. But aesthetics does not seem a strong enough reason. If nothing else, it is too anthropocentric. Again it suggests that we suffer other animals to live only in so far as they bring pleasure to us. There should be deeper reasons.

So then we have to make this a question of ethics. It is simply *right* for us, as the world's most powerful species, to look after the others. If you ask, 'Why is it right?' then a great list of arguments may follow but in the end we would simply be forced to say that it *feels* right. This may seem unsatisfactory but, ultimately, this is the true reason behind every ethical stance. All ethical positions rely in the end upon conviction. Moral philosophers offer reasoned arguments but these arguments in the end merely justify the underlying conviction. They do not provide the foundation of that conviction. David Hume made this point in the eighteenth century and although many have tried, including Immanuel Kant and J. S. Mill, no one has yet significantly improved upon it.

But mere 'convictions' – feelings – tend by their nature to be inchoate. They need to be encapsulated in verbal form so that they can be discussed and conveyed. A useful, 'heuristic' device is to embed the underlying feeling within a narrative. The narrative that works for me is the traditional notion which runs through most of the great religions, that we and all other creatures on this Earth are part of a Creation. I do not want to argue that there is a literal Creator, or to argue that there is not. I merely want to suggest that the *idea* of the Creation and the *idea* that we are part of it provide the framework we need on which to hang the notion that we *ought* to seek to conserve our fellow creatures. With this established, we need to add just one other principle: that of *noblesse oblige*. We are the most powerful creatures within that Creation and as such we must accept our obligation to look after the rest. It is our proper role to act as guardians; not as plunderers.

There is one final kind of argument of a more pragmatic nature which some may find easier to accommodate. This refers to the principle espoused by the World Conservation Union: that of 'minimum regret'. The meaning is self-evident. We do not *know* what effect the elimination of elephants will have upon the future world – upon the Earth's ecology, or upon the wellbeing of our descendants. But there are many conceivable reasons for preferring a world that contains elephants to one that does not. At the very least it seems perverse to substitute the impoverished world for the richer one, if we have a choice. We do have such a choice, and we surely would have less cause for regret if we endeavoured to save elephants than if we did not.

It has been suggested, however, that the kind of debate presented in this book makes a nonsense of all conservation. For example, there is the argument that even if we do precipitate ecological disaster *something* is liable to survive, and whatever survives will evolve again to provide new life forms, some of which will refill at least some of the niches that will have been vacated. If any mammals at all are left, even if only rats and mice, then their distant descendants will surely include some huge terrestrial forms that will emulate the elephant, even including the proboscis. But throughout this book I have also emphasised the role of chance. There is a fair chance that elephantine creatures would appear again, but no guarantees. It is certain, too, that history never repeats precisely. If present-day elephants disappear, then we can be sure that the Universe will never again see a creature that is precisely comparable.

Then again, we have seen the evidence that life on Earth has been interrupted at least five times by mass extinctions, possibly occasioned by collision with asteroids. We can be reasonably certain that such a disaster will strike again. So what will it matter then if the elephants have already gone? They would be wiped out anyway.

But this argument fails on at least two counts. First it is clear that some creatures *do* survive mass extinctions, for if it were not so then there would be no animals now. But nothing comes through a period of mass extinction that did not enter it. If there are elephants around at the time of the next mass extinction, then their descendants *may* come through to help repopulate and enrich the ecosystems that come after. But if they have already disappeared then of course they will not. In short, the elimination of elephants could alter the ecosystems of the world until the dying of the planet. There need be no time limit on our depredations.

In the first chapter I mentioned John Maynard Keynes with disapproval for his dismissive, 'In the long run we are all dead.' Well, according to Jack Sepkoski and Dave Raup, who first suggested that asteroid collisions occur at intervals of 26 million years, we are not due for the next collision for another 13 million years. Even I would admit that that is 'the long run'. I just think it is worthwhile to think about the next million. During that time – brief or vast, depending on how you look at it – elephants should be significant players, provided that we let them live now.

That at least is a lightning resumé of the reasons for caring about other animals. If we do want to conserve them, however, then we must do a very great deal more than we are doing now.

WHAT MUST WE DO TO SAVE OUR FELLOW CREATURES?

We have to think first of ourselves. Any policy of conservation that does not take full account of the reasonable needs of the human species is doomed. The human activity that affects the planet most is that of food production. So we need to devise systems of food production that meet our own needs and at the same time leave room for our fellow species.

I first started thinking seriously about world food production in the 1960s, but my thoughts achieved some coherence in 1974 when I attended the World Food Conference in Rome, which was convened after a series of particularly vicious famines in the late 1960s and early 1970s. First it became clear that the famines of the time (as now) were caused not by an innate inability to produce food but by misdirected policy. Then I began to realise that most of the nation states at the conference were not actually addressing the issue of food production but were simply defending their own position: 'It's not our fault'; 'We cannot afford to help'; 'We do enough already'. That was fairly shocking: I was more naive then. But then the final realisation dawned that was even more astonishing: that *the agricultural systems of the world are not actually designed to feed people.*

Well of course that is a slight exaggeration. Feeding people overall is what agriculture is *for*. But, in general, agricultural systems throughout the twentieth century have been designed primarily to fit in with prevailing economic norms, or to justify some political conceit or other. Thus western agriculture is designed in the end to maximise profit, and the agriculture of the old USSR was intended to show that collectivisation is best (which in the context of agriculture was shown, spectacularly, not to be the case). If the prime concern of the human species was to feed people, then we would do things very differently. There are two main changes we would make, both of which would increase our own security and also leave more room for our fellow species. The first, which in fact has been much bruited over the past two decades, would be simply to produce less livestock. We do not need to contemplate worldwide vegetarianism, but we certainly should not be producing mega-quantities of grain and pulses specifically to feed to livestock, as we do at present. By doing this, we effectively double the population we need to feed: ourselves, plus the livestock that is supposed to be feeding us. There is certainly a case for feeding *some* cereal and pulses to livestock, but the true ecological niche of livestock is to eat things that human beings cannot eat, such as grass, and to live in areas where we cannot grow cereals and horticultural crops.

The second change would be to apportion the land surface of the whole world more efficiently, using some for highly intensive food production (which takes up less room), some for 'extensive' agriculture (combining food production with wildlife conservation), and designating some specifically as 'wilderness', devoted principally to wildlife. This, I believe, is the essence of future conservation. But there is much more to it than meets the eye. The difficulties are such that if we really want to conserve more than an arbitrary smattering of our fellow creatures then we need to dig very deeply indeed into all of present-day politics, economics, and attitudes to the world at large.

THE NEXT THOUSAND YEARS OF CONSERVATION

It seems all too obvious that animals and plants should live and hence be conserved in their natural habitats in the wild, and this implies 'wilderness'. But wilderness these days is a much-compromised concept. At best it tends to imply a protected area, or 'reserve'. Reserves range from esoteric patches (in Britain called 'Sites of Special Scientific Interest' or SSSIs) which may contain just a few recondite bushes or a pond or two, up to national parks which in some cases, for instance South Africa's Kruger or America's mighty Yellowstone, are the size of a small country.

Unfortunately, no reserve in the world can ever enjoy cast-iron and permanent legal status. Reserves are created by governments, and governments fall. Besides, as Tom Paine pointed out to Edmund Burke at the end of the eighteenth century (they were discussing the French Revolution), no society has the right to lay down rules that bind *future* societies – which means that there are sound reasons of law why no reserve can ever have permanent status. Even within its own time no government has absolute power (which in general we take to be a good thing, for the obverse is tyranny) and the limitations of governments imply that they sometimes bow to pressures that are not benign. So it is that tropical forest may be sold for logging, or islands in the Great Barrier Reef for quarrying. Sometimes reserves are compromised for reasons that may seem benign or at least temporarily necessary, for example when traditional pastoralists are allowed to graze their cattle in woods and on grassland which, on the map, are marked as wilderness. Many a 'reserve' in Asia contains more cattle than wildlife. Even at its best, then, the legal status of reserves is precarious, temporary, and in various ways compromised.

Even the reserves that are given the best possible legal protection that their governments can provide are unsafe. In the early 1990s the conservation of the black rhinoceroses of Zimbabwe seemed to provide a model for the world. Wildlife provided wealth for the country, so it was in the people's interests to protect them – and protect them they did, with teams of dedicated wardens whose optimum distribution was planned by computer. But between 1992 and 1994 about half of the rhinos have apparently disappeared, which means they have fallen to poachers. The more space the rhinos are given the better, but the more widely they can roam the harder they are to protect. The animals of North America are safer. Many may be poached for meat and trophies but none provides the incentive of a black rhinoceros whose horn may be worth a lifetime's wages to the poacher – the difference between lifelong security and lifelong privation. The protective system of law in the United States is more intricate, more multi-layered, than in most countries of the tropics. There is more wealth around to enforce that law. But space is at a premium in the US. Even Yellowstone, which with more than 3,000 square miles is about one-fourth the size of Holland and is the biggest US national park outside Alaska, is apparently too small to sustain a viable population of grizzly bears. In fact very few national parks anywhere in the world can truly sustain viable populations of large carnivores. If tigers lived *only* in the wild – if there were no back-up populations in zoos – then we could seriously doubt if the species would be with us in a hundred years. Yet tigers are prestige animals which many people, including the rich and powerful, would like to preserve.

The principal mistake that non-biologists make is to assume that a national park created in the midst of a continent can be an ecological microcosm of that continent. In practice the boundaries of the park might embrace some populations in their entirety, but they will cut through the populations of many others. The number of any one species that is left inside the reserve may simply be too small to sustain itself. The effects will not be felt at first, for if the species is long-lived then it may take a decade or so before the animals that are inside the reserves start to die off. Close observation will reveal, however, that as time passes too few youngsters are being born, and eventually – and often quite suddenly – the senescent population will just fade away. Many of the deceptively healthy flocks of cockatoos in Australia consist mainly of old birds, waiting to die. At least half of Asia's remaining elephants are liable to die without further issue. We can expect a crash early in the twenty-first century.

For the fact is that a change in size of habitat alters the ecological rules. If an entire island is declared a reserve, fair enough: the island animals continue as before. But the designation of a reserve that is surrounded by farmland and cities effectively creates an area with island conditions to which continental animals, especially large continental animals, simply are not adapted. Then we must add a basic fact of geometry: that a small patch of land (where 'small' is a relative term) has a very long margin relative to its total area and to its diameter. For these reasons, small reserves are subject to 'edge effects'. Weeds, pollutants, and alien animals such as cattle, people, and feral cats encroach from all sides and do not have far to go before they reach the very centre of the habitat – a place that before might have been many miles from the madding crowds. Put everything together and we see why it is that reserves – even the biggest and best-run of them – are liable to succumb to 'species relaxation', a quaint and almost cosy term that describes the steady loss of species over time.

What can be done about this? Well, in practice our impact is bound to become even greater than it is already as our numbers rise and 'species relaxation' continues to take its toll. So it is all too easy to give way to despair or to indulge in the pretence that the collapse of other species is somehow inevitable or 'natural' – that indeed it is simply a manifestation of natural selection, as 'inferior' life forms give way to ourselves. Despair, however, cannot be allowed on to the agenda. Hope, as St Paul suggested, is one of the great virtues of humanity, and in the context of conservation it is a *sine qua non*. In positive vein, then, there are two prime routes to conservation, the first being to focus upon landscape and habitats as a whole, and the second, complementarily, to concentrate on particular species – which should probably be those of outstanding ecological significance, and those that represent the larger branches of evolution.

We have to begin by conceiving all the world's landscape as a whole and as a mosaic: that is, not simply as an arbitrary patchwork, but as a patchwork in which the different elements complement each other. Some land of course must be city and road. Some should be preserved or recreated, and then managed, as closely as possible, as natural wilderness. Some must be devoted to 'extensive' agriculture, designed both to produce food and to maintain wildlife. Some should be apportioned to intensive farming, its task being to produce the maximum food possible in the smallest space. It is wrong to assume, as so many 'environmentalists' have apparently assumed in recent years, that intensive agriculture is innately wildlife-unfriendly. To be sure, wild creatures are not welcome among the crops themselves, and intensive farms are certainly unfriendly if they are allowed to pollute their surroundings. But intensive agriculture is not innately polluting, and if agriculture is practised truly intensively, and cleanly, then it is benign precisely because it releases land for other purposes, including the conservation and creation of wilderness. The current policy of 'set-aside' in Europe shows this principle in action. In truth it is *extensive* agriculture that needs to justify its existence, and it can do so only if it does indeed benefit particular wildlife. This can be the case – as in the south of England, where traditional grazing of sheep preserved the short grass of chalk downland, and allowed a suite of ice age species to survive that otherwise would have been swamped by advancing forest.

Perhaps the most vital requirement, however, is to create 'corridors' between areas of wilderness so that small and unviable populations are, as far as possible, linked into larger units that might collectively be viable. In Britain and Australia farmers are now encouraged to leave or create hedgerows, to guide woodland bats across open fields. In India biologists dream of creating broad 'jungle corridors' to link the sequestered pockets of elephants.

Some reserves are designed with particular species in mind – for example it is now intended to establish larger prairie-dog 'cities' in the Badlands reserve of South Dakota, with a view to reintroducing the black-footed ferrets which prey upon them. Increasingly, in all parts of the world, animals must be and are 'translocated' from areas where they are temporarily too crowded to places where they are too sparse. Some otherwise unviable populations will perhaps need constant reinforcement. Increasingly the wild populations must be backed up by captive populations – in the case of tigers, the captive already outnumber their wild counterparts. The objection is often raised that captive populations inevitably drift from the wild state, both genetically and in behaviour; that indeed they become adapted to a captive state and cannot then be reintroduced. Certainly this often happened in the past but, as I discuss in *Last Animals at the Zoo*, this is avoidable. If the reproduction of animals is properly controlled (arranged marriages are necessary) then it is possible to maintain almost all of the genetic variation contained within the initial population (the founders) more or less indefinitely. Furthermore, if the animals are kept appropriately they can maintain most of their original behavioural repertoire, and more and more species are being returned successfully to the wild. The objection which says that such return is impossible is simply out of date. To be sure, reintroduction has often proved a great deal more difficult than was at first appreciated, but the difficulties are there to be overcome. Species returned successfully to the wild now include several that were once considered impossible, including 'higher' primates such as woolly monkeys and orang-utans. Increasingly, indeed, wild and captive groups must be managed together as single 'metapopulations', with a regular flow of individuals and genes between the two. It is effete to be purist, and object to such practices on aesthetic grounds. The next few centuries at least will be desperate times for all of us – and desperate measures are called for, unless we choose simply to give up and allow the tide of extinction to engulf the few big animals that are left to us, and a great many others besides.

Yet the measures discussed so far, difficult though they will be to carry out, address only the problems of the present. We know – it is perhaps the principal lesson of history – that the world will continue to change. So the task is not simply to correct present ills but also to create resilience: a system that can cope with future pressures for evermore, whatever they may be. This is a very tall order indeed, and requires new depths of thought.

A WORLD BUILT FOR RESILIENCE

The lessons of history are inevitably broad, for no set of circumstances can ever be repeated precisely. But the lesson that resonates through all of geology and the historical science of palaeoclimatology is that the world changes, and is bound to change in the future. In particular, we know that the world is liable to warm in the immediate future as increasing levels of carbon dioxide give rise to a greenhouse effect, just as the fall in carbon dioxide that was brought about by the uplift of the Himalayas has left us with an icebox world. In detail we cannot tell precisely how any one place will change: in a new greenhouse world Antarctic ice may expand and Britain could theoretically freeze. Even if things turn out as simply as possible, however, and without too much discomfort – a Mediterranean climate for the north of England, for example – living things will still need to adjust. In high latitudes they will have to face peculiar combinations of high temperatures and dramatically changing daylengths, a pattern without precedent during the previous 100,000 years. At some time in the future we may reasonably expect another ice age.

History tells us, too, that animals can survive such radical changes in three ways: they may move, and in particular shift latitude; they may evolve into something else; or they may alter their behaviour. The trouble is that even the best of modern conservation measures, at least as now enacted, remove at least two of those options. So present policies, even at their most enlightened, provide no more than a stay of execution – and that, perhaps, for no more than a few decades.

For how and where will the animals move as the world warms, or freezes? I do not see wildebeest migrating across Nairobi. It is hard to envisage reindeer crossing Paris. Lions failed to reinvade northern Europe after the ice age not because they are innately tropical animals but because human beings and their farms were already too populous. Lions would now be living if France if it were not for us. But many animals are sensitive to climate and for them the present reserves are potential death-traps. However beautifully we manage them the creatures they contain will die if we do not allow them to move out as the climate alters. If we truly care about our fellow species we must create north-south corridors of far grander proportions than are now envisaged. Either that, or we will have to translocate the animals on a truly fabulous scale, and indeed recreate entire ecosystems in different latitudes.

As for the animals' second option – to evolve, and hence to re-adapt to the changing conditions – that will generally prove impossible in the foreseeable future for at least two reasons. First, the changes that we are liable to cause would generally be far too rapid. We might cause significant greenhouse warming in a few decades and we are reducing the size of habitats by the day, so there is no time for the evolution of dwarf races. The second reason is probably even more decisive: that present populations, particularly of big species, are generally too small and/or too uniform genetically to provide adequate raw material for natural selection. The kind of pressures that might produce greater adaptation in big, resilient populations are far more likely to drive the precarious herds of the present into oblivion.

This leaves only the third option: that the animals might change their behaviour. Here there are crumbs of encouragement, as some species at least have shown that they can live far more closely to human beings than seemed the case only a few decades ago. If they are left alone for long enough then they become more trusting and so may reduce what they consider to be a reasonable 'fleeing distance'. The more that other animals can learn to tolerate human beings, the greater the space that is theoretically available to them. Thus vixens in modern-day Britain play with their cubs on suburban lawns. A few decades ago they would rarely be seen by day, and never in cities. Carrion crows and woodpigeons, famously aloof in the countryside, are at home in modern suburbs just as foxes are. In more romantic vein, parts of the United States are seeing the return of the bald eagle: their national bird which they used to like to shoot is now to be seen around many a picnic area. We need a few more decades of enlightenment before such tolerance becomes the norm, and some creatures will always remain standoffish. Marsh harriers, for example, simply cannot hunt when there are people around. But in time, if we learn to value their company, wild animals will increasingly surprise us with their complaisance. After all, wild animals do not generally run from other species the way they flee from us. We are the only creatures that kill at a distance.

However, a few more animals round human settlements is small compensation for the threatened losses elsewhere. Clearly, if we want our fellow creatures to survive in worthwhile numbers – if we want more than the odd zoo, and we want zoos to be more than 'living museums' – then we have to take conservation very seriously indeed. It would be a huge leap forward if we were able to bring our present-day wildlife reserves up to scratch; to make sure that there were enough, of the right size and in the right places, to serve present-day creatures. But in a world that we know is changing we need to do far more than that. If we were truly to take our fellow creatures seriously we would have to design the landscape of entire continents with them in mind; not only to designate areas of wilderness but also to provide corridors between them. That, of course, would mean a huge economic and political commitment – far greater than anything that is so far on the agenda.

WHAT POLITICS? WHAT ECONOMICS? WHAT ATTITUDES?

Is it actually possible to redesign the world in ways that will enable wild animals not simply to survive in viable populations but also to migrate from place to place as the climate changes? Is that possible in a world which begrudges even the meagre reserves that we now accord to wildlife – and in which every postponed marina or diverted motorway is seen as a 'major triumph' for the conservationists? Possibly not. But then, despair cannot be allowed on to the agenda. We must begin with the conceit that even this apparently Sisyphean task is possible, and then ask what would need to be done.

The central trouble, it seems to me, is that people who are seriously interested in the conservation of our fellow creatures are all too easily laughed out of court. I have tried arguing the conservation case in influential circles and found that it is generally dismissed as 'unrealistic' – even, I have been chastened to find, within a society that includes the word 'conservation' in its 'mission statement'.

The problem is that *as things are* the jeremiahs are probably right, at least in global matters. There are a hundred competing claims on any one piece of land, and the idea that a patch of, say, India – a patch that might be the size of an English county – should be left as a 'jungle corridor' for elephants can seem not only ludicrous but inhumane. As it is, the farmers try to make a living from half a hectare – and they are the well-off ones. What happens to them when their last scrap of land is given back to the elephants? In western countries the argument takes a different form but the end result is much the same. Why keep a mangrove for crabs and manatees when it could in the short term be used to farm jumbo shrimp at 20 dollars a kilo and in the longer term could be drained for hotels and casinos? One may attempt at least to seize the moral high ground by saying – 'Well, I don't think we should simply be indulging the whims of people who are too indulged already!'. But this kind of high-mindedness is easily countered. Hotels and casinos provide jobs. In theory, they create 'thriving communities'. They offer an alternative to the village life that can no longer be sustained. It seems just as inhumane to oppose the casino as it would be to create the elephant corridor. In both cases, the argument goes, poor people would suffer – and *as things are* that argument is probably true. *Ergo,* radical attempts at conservation do indeed seem unrealistic. You may put a notional fence around a desert or a mountain that nobody can make immediate use of and call it a reserve, but as soon as somebody finds oil or sees a chance to build a ski resort then the conservation arguments go out of the window. The idea that we might actually *increase* the area devoted to wildlife, and indeed in some cases increase it by an order of magnitude, seems nonsensical indeed – morally as well as economically. What hope is there then?

I have written about this before and editors and publishers have sometimes said, 'Well, what's the answer? If you cannot provide an answer, why raise the matter at all?' But no solution will ever be found unless we first state the problems clearly – and this is what I am trying to do. As I see it there are two broad issues. First there are the biological realities – the ecological and evolutionary facts which ensure that our fellow creatures are even more precariously placed than they so obviously seem, and need far more space and protection than we have afforded them. So far, only professional ecologists have appreciated that this is the case.

The other set of reasons embraces the point I made above in the context of agriculture. It is that the present political ideologies and economic systems of the world simply do not acknowledge the existence of any species apart from our own. This is equally true of all of them, in different ways. Thus although there are pleasant 'socialists' with sandals and beards who espouse 'animal rights', the powerful mainstream of socialism, for example as represented by Karl Marx or indeed by the British trade unions, has been fiercely anthropocentric. Conservation has rarely been on the agenda. China is a conservational disaster, while animals survive in eastern Europe mainly by default, basically because the agriculture has been too backward to wipe them out.

Apparently in complete contrast, the essentially feudal squirearchy of England boasts of its 'stewardship'. The gentry justify their ownership of land by the principle of *noblesse oblige.* These days they tend to acknowledge that to own entire counties or thereabouts may seem a little anachronistic, but claim nonetheless to have created and maintained a landscape in which everyone can delight. This is true. The 'traditional' British landscapes are 'man-made', the landowners can claim much of the credit, and at its best in the Scottish highlands and the English lowlands that landscape is indeed glorious. I chauvinistically suggest that there is none more beautiful in the world.

Yet this is the glory of devastation. Britain is the northern temperate equivalent of denuded Crete, whose beautiful pastel rocks shine in the sun – but which, just a few thousand years ago, was covered in forest that might have harboured dwarf elephants and hippos. The soft purple hills of Scotland with their melancholic accompaniment of pipes were formerly smothered in ash, pine, and birch in the warm, damp west, and oak, pine, birch, and rowan in the Grampian mountains. The green lush fields of England were once covered by open oak forest – the temperate equivalent of australopithecine country – practically from border to border. In fact Britain retains less of its pristine forest than any country in Europe. We also retain fewer of our large animals. There were wildcats around London in Roman times, the bear survived in Wales until the Middle Ages, there were beavers in Loch Ness in the sixteenth century, there were wolves in England until the sixteenth century and in Scotland until the eighteenth, the white-tailed sea-eagle, the biggest and once the commonest of Britain's larger birds of prey, was wiped out from its last Scottish stronghold in the nineteenth century to make way for sheep, and the black kite which was once common in London now occurs only as a vagrant. Other natives, such as the red kite and the otter, have been all but wiped out in recent decades. We even managed for a period to drive out the osprey, and almost eliminated the peregrine, two of the most widespread birds of prey in the world. About half of our bats hang on by a whisker. On the other hand, many of the most conspicuous animals in Britain were imported, for instance the rabbit and the pheasant, while vast areas of 'wilderness' are maintained for the traditional pleasures of the gentry: hunting, shooting, and fishing. The rich wildlife is reduced to a virtual monoculture of respectable targets: pheasant, grouse, deer, and imported trout. In short, Britain's conservational record approaches being the worst in the world although we are rapidly being overtaken by Australia. So much for *noblesse oblige*. So much for stewardship.

Finally, of course, traditional landowning feudalism is now being replaced by modern capitalism which, I would say, is no worse or better than the old squirearchy or than collectivism.

Like them, it is merely insouciant. Oddly, the arch exemplar of capitalism, monetarism, could be adapted to serve the needs of conservation very well. After all, one key difficulty at present is that the things the conservationists treasure are outside the mainstream economies; as the adage has it, 'The best things in life are free.' But so long as they are 'free', they are abused – because they simply are not taken into account. Monetarist conservation does have its grisly side – an accountant behind every tree. However, so long as we live in a world in which the only things that are truly valued are those that have a discernible price it is worthwhile at least to attach some prices. I often wonder, whimsically, why people pay thousands for Fabergé eggs and tread on beetles. Looked at closely, and objectively, the beetle is more beautiful.

But if the conventional economic systems cannot provide long-term security, what can?

ECONOMICS WITH WILDLIFE

For the next 500 to a thousand years, while the human population rises, stabilises, and then with luck begins to slide down to a sensible level, everything we do to protect wildlife must in effect be seen as an emergency measure. The prime concern must be to retain as many different species as possible, and within those species to maintain as much genetic diversity as possible, in the hope that the remaining lineages can pick up the threads again after the biologically anomalous human bloom has subsided. In practice, we have to modify the desire to keep as many species as possible, and decide priorities. But that is merely a conditional clause. The overwhelming requirement is to hang on to what we can in the face of appalling odds. Measures that we might undertake *now*, for short-term purposes, do not necessarily represent ideal long-term solutions.

In the short-term – perhaps the next millennium – there seem to me to be two overwhelming economic desiderata. Both have been discussed at length, for which we may be grateful, and are still being discussed. But neither has yet been taken seriously enough by the politicians who are actually in power. Just to be parochial, I have never heard Mr Major or Mr Clinton speak seriously on either issue.

The first is the overwhelming and urgent need to integrate wildlife conservation into the concept of 'development'. Most species of animals and plants live in the tropics, which means that most endangered species live in the tropics, and most of the tropics is occupied by countries that collectively form what Pandit Nehru referred to as 'The Third World', and almost all of them have horrendous problems among the chief of which is human poverty. The survival even of tigers and rhinoceroses, let alone of mice and parrots and snakes, is rarely high among their perceived priorities. Yet wild creatures have little hope of survival until the people of 'developing countries' are in a position to see them not as rivals, or as irrelevancies, but as assets.

In practice of course this nettle has been grasped, not least by the World Conservation Union, and all around the world we now find groups of 'native people' earning their living from crafts that are based upon their natural resources. These activities tend to form only a marginal component of the national economy (which of course makes them extremely vulnerable) but 'ecotourism' as a whole, which is another aspect of sustainable exploitation, can make a huge contribution. Thus for Kenya tourism is the greatest single source of foreign exchange, and at least half of the income from it can be ascribed not to the beaches but to the wildlife. Zimbabwe's farmers – uniquely in the world – now find it more profitable to return their farms to wildlife than to raise cattle.

But the problems are huge. In Kenya the swarm of tourist buses threatens to destroy the creatures they are supposed to support. There is deep ideological and hence practical conflict between Kenya and Zimbabwe, the former banning all hunting and trading in elephant ivory, the latter feeling that the sale of tusks from superannuated bulls is a potentially huge resource that could fuel the economy and hence give the people the reason they need for keeping elephants. For few countries can benefit as easily as Kenya can from merely showing off their wildlife – no other country has its wealth of savannah where the animals line up to be photographed. You could spend a lifetime in Indonesia and never see either of its two native rhinoceroses (and indeed people have done PhDs on Sumatran rhinos in the field without actually seeing one). Ecotourism in tropical forest, which is disappointingly uniform when you get close to it and is nothing like the floral floor of Harrod's, is extremely difficult to sustain. Perhaps such countries must simply create super-zoos, on the margins of the forest proper, to show what the animals inside are like. Once the novelty has worn off, western tourists also object to the long forest treks and the luke-warm evening shower in a hut. First-class hotels are needed to go with the super-zoos. But this is all expensive.

In short, it will not be at all easy to integrate wildlife into growing economies. Yet it is vital. People must have a reason for looking after their native creatures. A live hyacinthine macaw must be seen to be worth more than a hyacinthine macaw that is shot and barbecued. Overall, this is not a problem that developing countries can solve by themselves, if only because the start-up costs can be so great (not least the cost of establishing ecotourism of a kind that would actually attract westerners). First world cash must be injected. The Brazilians are quite right to accuse the British of hypocrisy, as we lecture them on the joys of tropical forest and wild animals. 'What have you done with your own wild animals?' they tend to ask, and with absolute justice. In the parts of the world that are now so beleaguered we (and the Americans and Australians) could make some amends for the devastation we have wrought at home.

The second prime desideratum, of course, must be to devise economies that are truly sustainable. In the short term – the next few hundred years – we do have coal and oil, but they will not last forever. After Chernobyl we must at the least treat nuclear power with caution. Perhaps it is premature to smother the landscape in windmills, or to fit suburban houses with solar panels. But if we are serious about the future we should regard the next few centuries' worth of fossil fuel largely as start-up money, providing the means to create technologies that will enable future generations to live safely on renewable power. There is no panic on this. Indeed it would be a great error to panic: it might lead us, for example, to build too many precipitate dams. But the development of renewable energy must be firmly on the agenda.

More broadly, however, the notion of sustainability requires new kinds of economics: economics that can be called 'green'. There are university departments and institutes of green economics worldwide. Strength to their arms and brains. We will know the world is making progress when a Nobel Prize for Economics is won by someone who can show convincingly how the world can live well, and can indulge its ambitions, without the constant goad of material growth. Put that together with sustainable energy and – provided we also control our own population – there is some hope of surviving the next thousand years in tolerable and recognisable form, and hence of thinking seriously about the following 999,000 years that our descendants should live to enjoy.

Still, though, the jeremiahs will cry, 'Unrealistic'. And still, *as things are*, they will probably be right. Everyone knows – surely? – that we need a sustainable world and a controlled population. Everyone knows that the world as a whole cannot live in the style of California, so that we must either ask the Californians to modify their lifestyle or accept the extreme inequity. Everyone knows these things, yet nothing serious is done to bring about the necessary changes. Why not? In the end, the jeremiahs say, it is because present political and economic systems respond to the needs and aspirations of *human nature*. The Californian lifestyle is acknowledged to be the great good, and present-day economic systems are geared to the Californian goal because *that, in the end, is what people want*.

But this, surely, is not true. Nobody I know who has any knowledge of the world seeks to be poor because poverty really is not ennobling, unless you can live in the glorious and fundamentally wealthy simplicity of some Italian Franciscan monastery (for who needs to be rich when the sun is shining and everything is taken care of?). But equally, nobody I know wants to be filthy rich. 'Comfortable' is the kind of word most people use. 'I just don't want to have to bother about money,' is what the thinking classes tend to say.

So in truth, I submit, the Californian lifestyle is not an aspiration that is universal or even, probably, particularly widespread. If it were, then nobody would become a schoolteacher, a nurse, or a musician; yet thousands and thousands of extremely intelligent people choose these careers. People go along with economies that seem to hold wealth as the prime ambition largely because, well, such economies seem to work, at least up to a point. In reality, people who do not care too much about money survive by hanging on to the coat-tails of those who do – or that at least is what the people who sport those coat-tails hold to be the case.

Nonetheless, the notion that the world's dominant economies are based on the aspiration to live like Californians does contain a significant germ of truth. Only a minority in any one society may hold that ambition overtly; but that minority drives the economy. Even if the intelligentsia do not espouse the notion themselves, they still acquiesce in systems that are propelled by it. It is true, then, that the dominant economies of the present day reflect at least a component of 'human nature'. They reflect a widely held *attitude* to life, and attitude is all-important.

So in the end we are obliged to admit what the jeremiahs maintain: that the present-day economies prevail precisely because they reflect the underlying attitude of a significant proportion of society. If we feel that the economy is unsuitable to present needs, or at least to long-term needs, then we have first to change the underlying attitude. Any attempt to alter the economy without changing its attitudinal underpinning can indeed be considered 'unrealistic'. To change our underlying attitude it is necessary first to understand it. The history of the human species – the proper history: the 5-million-year overview – can again provide worthwhile insights.

HUNTERS AND FARMERS: ATTITUDE

Psychologists like to devise matrices by which to define personality. Such matrices invariably include an axis that extends from extrovert to introvert, and sometimes another from assertive to compliant. Some qualities (such as assertiveness and extroversion) seem naturally to go together while others (for instance assertiveness and introversion) seem at odds. I have no views on whether such matrices truly help us to understand ourselves and fellow human beings but I would like to steal the technique. The approach can usefully be applied to the life strategies of animals, including the human animal.

One highly pertinent axis on the life-strategy matrix would extend from 'acceptance' to 'manipulation'. Snails (like mosses, among plants) are acceptors: their lives are dictated by the weather. If it rains they come out and feed and reproduce. If it is dry they hide, and if it stays dry for too long they plug the aperture of their shell with mucus and hope for the best. Most mammals suffer in unfavourable weather but at least they get on with their lives: deer graze in the rain, cheetahs may hunt in the heat. Human beings are at the manipulation end of the axis. We do not put up with the weather, or simply hide when we do not like it. We dress ourselves appropriately and out-face it. Indeed we go further: we create controlled environments where the weather does not matter. More even than that: some people (including the Israelis) are already seeking to control the weather itself and most governments would probably elect to do so if they could. With control of course goes exploitation: we try to make the world do what we want it to (just as the English gentry have created what is essentially a garden). On the acceptance-manipulation axis, most animals fall somewhere between the extremes of snails and human beings.

Another highly pertinent axis would run from 'conservative' to 'experimental'. Duck-billed platypuses would be close to the conservative end of such an axis (along with snails and earthworms and a great many other creatures), while human beings would be close to the experimental end. Duck-billed platypuses behave exactly the way that their ancestors did in the Pleistocene, and indeed in the Pliocene and probably in the Oligocene did we but know, while we live very differently from our Pliocene forebears.

We could also set up such a matrix purely for our own species. Even today we can see that some societies tend to accept what the world throws at them, while others seek to change whatever is inconvenient; some behave as their forefathers did, and indeed make a virtue of it, while others constantly try new approaches and equate novelty with 'progress'.

In practice these two particular axes tend to run more or less in parallel. Acceptance seems to go with conservatism, while manipulativeness/exploitativeness obviously demands some experimentation.

All life strategies have their advantages and disadvantages. The advantage of the exploitative/experimental approach is obvious. We see it in the triumph of our own species. We do not simply dominate the world in the way that the dinosaurs are said to have 'dominated'. We are not *merely* numerous and ubiquitous. We directly manipulate the environment in ways that ensure our populousness and ubiquity: notably by farming. The disadvantage of the explotative/experimental approach is also obvious.

Exploitation is potentially damaging, in a way that acceptance is not; experimentation, by definition, is likely to produce unforeseeable consequences. Contrariwise, accepting/conservative creatures leave the world just as they found it, which is a safe thing to do, and operate on the assumption that whatever behaviour allowed their parents to survive has a fair chance of ensuring their own survival as well. This policy is not foolish. Snails, one might point out, have been around a lot longer than human beings and are likely to be around in various forms long after we have gone. In short, acceptance/conservatism is a safe policy, while the exploitative/experimental approach is innately risky. On the other hand: nothing ventured, nothing gained.

So now we can ask, in the manner of a game theorist, when is it likely to pay to be accepting and conservative, and when is it better to push the boat out? The general answer is that the exploiters/experimenters need leeway. They need to be able to make mistakes and then recoup. They also – crucially – need a resilient environment that is resistant to over-exploitation (although 'resistant' of course can never mean 'invulnerable'). Over-exploitation is equivalent to an experiment that fails.

When we apply this particular exercise in game theory to the history of human beings, a whole number of otherwise confusing issues begin to fall into place. We can begin by asserting, commonsensically, that all human beings have the capacity to behave conservatively and acceptingly, or to be primarily exploitative and experimental. The question then is: 'Which circumstances most favour which approach?' The broad general answer, it seems to me, is that hunters and gatherers really have to be conservative acceptors. This is true whatever their individual personality or *mien* may be; however fiercely they shake their spears. If they try too hard, if they invent ways of killing that are *too* efficient, then they simply wipe out their prey. In the end, so long as hunters remain as hunters, natural selection will favour the lazy ones who tell stories and hunt the way their forefathers have always hunted.

But it is in the nature of farming to be exploitative and experimental. The whole point of farming is not to accept what nature has to provide. The whole aspiration is to manipulate other species and eventually to till the ground so that the environment provides more than it otherwise would. Furthermore, the harder the farmer works, the more he or she is rewarded. Farming, in short, turns an unimprovable resource into one that in principle can be increased indefinitely, just by stepping up the effort. In addition, by increasing output, farming societies create the surplus food and hence the leeway that allows them to take even greater risks. So here we have yet another positive feedback loop: experimentation favours farming which provides greater scope for experimentation.

Thus it is that over the past 30,000 years, which we may take as the rough date of the first deliberate cultivators, natural selection has increasingly favoured the exploitative/experimental approach. The advantages of this approach have become more and more apparent as the feedback loop has begun to bite, until nowadays we take it for granted that farming must be backed by agricultural research which in turn partakes of the highest technologies. By contrast, however fancy hunting may become, with the infra-red sights and helicopters of the millionaires, it will always be a marginal pursuit. The resource – the population of deer or grizzly bears – is simply too fragile. Hunting becomes economically significant only when the prey animals – like grouse and pheasant in Britain – are essentially farmed, and fed to the guns.

But the party really is over. This truly is a special time in history – a critical time. The first full-time farmers of 10,000 years ago were perfectly capable of over-farming (we can see evidence of ancient soil erosion) but, even so, they could effectively regard the world as a limitless resource. There were entire continents still to be discovered, and it would take another 10,000 years to find all the fertile spots and dig them up. But now we have had that 10,000 years. The fertile spots *have* been dug up, and we know there are no more continents to be had; that indeed the land will shrink as the world warms. Agriculturalists can argue about details – can we feed 10 billion people sustainably? Or could we manage 20 or 30 billion if we really put our minds to it? – but no sensible person can seriously doubt that the finishing post is now in sight. The world is not indefinitely large. We cannot simply hurl ourselves at it with the abandon of the past 10,000 years.

In short, the attitude that has been so appropriate this past 10,000 years, and that has allowed the most exploitative/experimental people to rise inexorably if fitfully to the top, has simply ceased to be appropriate. Yet our economies are geared to the exploitative/experimental approach, and so are our political systems. All of a sudden, or so it seems, our political and economic institutions and philosophies are out of synch with the biological and physical realities of the planet. It might be 'unrealistic' to devise new systems that are radically different, with a radically different motivation, but if we do not do this then we cannot seriously contemplate long-term survival. But surely it cannot be the case that the only 'realistic' course is to head pell-mell for disaster? Is that what the level-headed, sober-suited people are arguing? Our position seems not merely precarious but ludicrous. It invites parody. It brings to mind an image that appears in all the best cartoons: the one where Jerry or Tom runs over the edge of a cliff, seems for a moment to defy the laws of physics, realises something is amiss, turns to the camera, gulps, holds his nose, and is seen from above plummeting to the depths of what looks like Death Valley, to carve a perfect outline in the all-too-solid rock below.

So how do we get out of this mess? I am inclined to say, 'Don't ask me.' If you think that is a cheat, I can only repeat that the first stage in finding a solution is to state the problem clearly – which I am trying to do. In fact Jesus Christ expressed the essence of the issue almost 2,000 years ago when he said, in his Sermon on the Mount, 'The meek shall inherit the Earth.' It would be nice to believe the 'shall'. But it is surely true to say that if anyone at all is going to inherit the Earth then it can only be the meek. On the other hand, St Peter identified the snag, just as the modern jeremiahs do: that we live in the here and now, and in the here and now the meek get bashed. Well, it is time to re-address the problem. The task is to create economies that are 'conservative' with a small 'c', and yet robust and able to withstand the pressures of short-term aggressiveness. More broadly, the task is to develop what might glibly be called 'the politics of reverence', as opposed to the politics of exploitation. It is a tall order, just as it was when Christ preached to the five thousand. It is also necessary.

However, the practicalities of the next thousand years are only the immediate problems. There are broader issues.

WILL THE EARTH ALWAYS BE BENIGN?

The Earth has existed for the past 4·5 billion years, which is probably almost a third of the total life of the Universe. Latest evidence suggests that life has existed on Earth for almost 4 billion years. The earliest life forms must have been radically different from today's – although there are many creatures with us still, broadly classed as 'bacteria', which demonstrate at least in part how the earliest types must have lived. Like many modern-day denizens of swamps, the earliest organisms obviously thrived in an atmosphere free of oxygen. They must have fed not by photosynthesis or by eating other things but by various forms of 'chemosynthesis', as still practised by some modern-day microbes. Ultra-violet must have poured through the ozone-free upper atmosphere; so the early types either stayed out of its way or else evolved protective mechanisms, like the pigments of modern-day corals and slime-moulds. Such pigments were presumably a prerequisite of photosynthesis, for unpigmented organisms could not have exposed themselves to the Sun in the first place. We may indeed suppose that chlorophyll itself, which now serves to convert electromagnetic solar energy into chemical energy, evolved originally as a protective pigment. If this were so, it would be another pleasant example of nature's opportunism. Some of the early organisms, too, may have been able to withstand extremes of temperature, like the 'thermophilic' bacteria that nowadays live in hot springs and deep-sea vents.

But however tolerant those ancient creatures were we can be sure that the conditions on Earth, although extreme and in several ways lethal by the standards of modern animals and plants, were modest by the standards of the Universe as a whole. Living forms in general operate at maximum efficiency at around 40°C – roughly the core blood heat of most mammals and birds. Mere survival is possible at much lower temperatures, and some organisms easily survive deep freezing – it is not a particularly difficult trick to pull. Living creatures of some kind or another can survive the coldest conditions of which the Universe is capable, the 'absolute zero' of −273°C. But as the temperature falls below 40°C metabolism slows.

Heat is more of a problem. As the temperature rises above 40°C or so proteins start to break down and indeed to 'denature', which effectively means 'cook'. The metabolism of thermophilic bacteria runs very fast to stay in the same place: the thermophiles contrive to make fresh proteins as fast as the old ones are broken down. Even so, these organisms do not survive for long at much above 100°C. But 100°C is gentle by the standards of the

Universe. The core of the Earth itself is far hotter than that. The surface of our nearest planetary neighbour, Venus, can reach several hundred degrees centigrade.

In short it is a minor miracle, or at least a matter of extreme statistical unlikelihood, that the Earth has maintained conditions suitable for life through 4 billion years. To be sure, the conditions have been very different at different times – requiring an almost complete change in living personnel when the atmosphere first began to acquire oxygen. But always the temperature and moisture content of the Earth's surface – these in the end being more important than the details of chemistry – have been within the very narrow compass required even by the most tolerant of organisms. There are trillions of stars in the Universe, and many of them have planets, and many of those planets have moons. Only a tiny minority are likely to provide conditions suitable for living things, but that minority must still number many millions. The key raw material of life is ubiquitous: carbon is one of the commonest elements in the Universe, and space contains many billions of tonnes of complex organic molecules of the kind from which living things are compounded. It is inconceivable, then, that Earth is the only planet with living organisms. Indeed, as Christian de Duve comments in *Vital Dust* (Basic Books, New York, 1995, p. 284), 'Life is an integral part of the Universe.' There are probably millions of planets with living creatures on board. De Duve speaks purely as a scientist: a Nobel-Prize-winning biochemist who knows better than most what life entails.

Even so, Earthly conditions are unusual, and – relative to the total number of planets in the Universe – must be extremely rare. Life seems inconceivable on a planet without an atmosphere – but only planets of a particular size have gravity enough to cling on to one. Liquid water seems vital – but water is liquid only in a band of temperature, 0–100°C, that is ridiculously narrow by the standards of the Universe. Temperature is extremely labile. The greatest influence on temperature, at least within the range of circumstances that are relevant here, is the chemistry of the atmosphere. A little manoeuvring either way can send it way beyond the compass of Earthly life, or indeed of any conceivable organic life. The awfulness of Venus results not from its proximity to the Sun (though it is closer than we are) but from the greenhouse gases in its atmosphere.

We have seen how the rise of the Himalayas since the Eocene has steadily leached the atmosphere of its carbon dioxide and so produced an icebox world. We have seen the sudden 'catastrophic' falls along the way which have demanded and prompted the appearance of entire new suites of creatures – including ourselves. History shows us, in short, the *power* of atmospheric chemistry – and also its subtlety, for the changes that have caused such radical shifts in the ecology and evolution of living creatures do not seem spectacular: a halving perhaps of an atmospheric gas whose concentration is measured only in parts per million.

We have also seen the phenomenon of catalysis, through which minute intrusions into the chemistry of the atmosphere can have huge consequences. The effect of CFCs on ozone and hence on the radiations that reach the Earth provides a spectacular example. Yet until a few years ago it would not have been possible even to detect CFCs in the atmosphere. We have seen, too, how chemical and physical changes, once set in train, can take decades or even centuries to unfold. It will take decades for the oceans to absorb all the heat now being supplied by our mildly greenhouse atmosphere. It will take decades to leach the last of the CFCs from the stratosphere. Finally, history has revealed the phenomenon of catastrophe: that steady changes can produce sudden effects. As we watch the changes taking place we might bear in mind that in theory, as some threshold is reached, the world might lurch into some quite new state far more quickly than we can cope with, and certainly more quickly than our fellow creatures can come to terms with, trapped as they are in their reserves.

It has come as a shock to realise that we, puny creatures though we sometimes like to think ourselves, can influence the atmosphere of the whole world. Perhaps it should not have been too much of a surprise: after all, it has been obvious for several thousand years that we can transform entire landscapes, not least by cutting down the trees. Yet I am not sure that we have been shocked enough. For although our influence is huge, our control is minimal. Having set the warming of the oceans in train, there is not a thing we can do about it. Having initiated the breakdown of the ozone layer we can only sit and wait – and hope that the chemists have calculated accurately, and that their understanding is now complete, and that the ozone will recover before we are all radiated literally to death.

Overall, history tells us that the beneficence of this planet cannot be taken for granted. It has always been hospitable to life of a kind, but not always to our kind. Conditions on Earth do not have to be the way they are now. The laws of physics will always apply but when those laws operate under different circumstances they will produce a different outcome. We absolutely cannot assume that the Earth will always in the future provide the kind of conditions that suit us. Given that our requirements are so narrow and that our influence is far, far greater than our control, we have at least to consider the possibility that we ourselves could generate global conditions that we, and creatures like us, would find impossible. In short, by our own manipulations of the atmosphere we could create a climate that was suitable only for the bacteria that have now retreated to the marshes and the hot springs, or perhaps, as on Venus, was unsuitable even for them.

This is not gratuitously sensationalist. I am at least as tired of gloom-and-doom as everybody else. It is, however, a modest plea that we should take the lessons of history seriously. Our planet, like all other planets that we know about, is perfectly capable of being an extremely nasty place – and it is a huge mistake to take our present good fortune as a 'given'.

Suppose, though, that our species does survive the next thousand years. Suppose we do indeed embark upon our allotted one million years, our kilometre of time. The human genus has changed radically over the past million years – from *Homo erectus* into us. Would the next million bring comparable change?

THE FURTHER EVOLUTION OF HUMANKIND

Of course human beings will continue to change culturally, and this might be considered to be 'evolution' of a kind. After all, if we entertain different ideas, and behave differently, and have a different *attitude* to the world – if for example we practised the 'politics of reverence' – then we would be ecologically quite different. Our impact on our fellow creatures would be altered, and from their point of view at least we would effectively be a different kind of creature. We can argue too (as others have argued) that the infusion of new ideas to some extent occurs by natural selection. The ideas that produce worldly success do indeed tend to spread, just as science and capitalism have spread these past few centuries (and the present growth of Islam is certainly interesting). But we can also point out (as others have done) that the growth of new ideas proceeds according to Lamarck's fourth law: that is, ideas 'acquired' by one generation are passed on to the next. Darwin himself would have had no problem in accepting that Darwinian and Lamarckian mechanisms might proceed in tandem and indeed, as we have seen, he more than toyed with the notion that Lamarckian systems of inheritance obtain generally.

The issue here, however, is that of *bona fide* neodarwinian evolution: whether it is possible to change the overall gene pool of human beings to such a significant degree that our descendants can properly be considered a different species. The short answer, on purely theoretical grounds, is Yes. Remarkable creatures though we are, we are manifestations of our collective gene pool just like any other animal, and it is possible to subtract alleles from that pool, and add them, and go on doing this until we have a new creature – just as it was possible, by these means, to turn a gomphothere into an elephant or *Australopithecus* into *Homo*. But it is not as easy to envisage the circumstances, or at least the natural circumstances, in which such a change could be brought about.

It is obvious, after all, that the human gene pool *is* changing. To our shame, rare tribes of 'aboriginal' people worldwide continue to disappear, and they seem bound to take at least a few recondite alleles with them. Mutation continues as well, and since the human population is now so large the gene pool as a whole must be accumulating mutations more rapidly than ever before. Some groups, too, are now breeding much faster than others – Kenyans faster than Germans, for example – so some alleles are becoming relatively more common than others. Even so, we cannot argue that such fluctuations truly represent 'evolution'. The loss of alleles, sad though it is, is genetically marginal. At the same time, few of the new mutations contribute significantly to the life of our species. The shift in frequency of alleles within the pool is only the usual 'noise' in the system. No one seriously supposes, after all, that north Europeans are going to disappear altogether.

In short, the fluctuations of the human gene pool are providing raw material for evolution – the genetic variation. But the key ingredient is missing. Natural selection is simply not acting forcefully or consistently upon that variation. The loss of alleles in aboriginal peoples is random – at least, we cannot argue that *particular* alleles are being lost because they are disadvantageous. At the same time, the people who seem to be 'successful' are not necessarily breeding particularly quickly. Neither can we argue that the success of particular present-day groups is correlated with their genes. The materially successful people of California belong to all conceivable human genotypes. Finally, and I think crucially, the human population is just too big to change significantly by neodarwinian mechanisms. Natural selection works best on middle-sized, isolated or semi-isolated populations, like those of the australopithecines on the margins of Africa's retreating Pliocene forest. It is hard to see how it could operate on a population of 5 billion individuals who, by courtesy of the world's airlines, are all in close genetic contact with each other.

There are, however, two feasible sets of circumstances in which we might envisage neodarwinian change. The first is if there is after all some kind of world catastrophe: an ecological crash. In such circumstances we might envisage that the human species would be reduced to patchy populations, separated by various kinds of 'badlands'. Excess ultra-violet radiation, or the still-present spectre of nuclear war (or even peacetime nuclear catastrophe) might provide the conditions. Then we could envisage the isolated groups evolving afresh, just as hominid groups of comparable size, with comparable degrees of stress, evolved in the past.

It is interesting to speculate *how* those isolated groups might evolve. There is absolutely no good reason to assume that the trend of the past few million years would be continued: that intelligent human beings would produce a race of super-intelligents. That is actually an unlikely option, since it is hard to see why natural selection should favour geniuses in the straitened circumstances of a devastated future, any more than it would favour the emergence of a literary codfish beneath the Arctic ice. Besides it seems likely (though nobody knows) that genius is a genetically difficult trick to pull. Overall, indeed, isolated human populations of the future seem far more likely to generate a significantly *less* intelligent lineage. The brain, physiologically, is an expensive item. One way and another it is said to commandeer 20 per cent of total metabolic effort. Unless this prodigal brain can be put to good use, it is a luxury which future hominids in harsh circumstances may prefer to do without. In the same way, many island birds from many different groups have abandoned the apparently self-evident advantage of flight. How glorious to fly! But if you do not need to fly because there are no predators to escape from then you are advised to stay on the ground because it is cheaper. In the same way *Australopithecus afarensis* apparently gave rise to the robust paranthropines, as well as to the hominines. Of course we cannot tell at this range whether the paranthropines were less bright than afarensis. The point is, though, that the hominine emphasis on brain was only one of the options open to the hominids. Muscularity was another. Neither can we assert that the paranthropines were a failure. They lasted a million years and it is not obvious why they went extinct. Nor were the hominines *bound* to succeed. I believe that we can identify their clear advantages, as outlined in Chapter 6. But advantage does not come with guarantees. Every lineage needs good luck. 'Time and chance', as *Ecclesiastes* reminds us, 'happeneth to all men.'

We can, however, envisage a second quite different set of circumstances in which human beings might continue to evolve – not by natural selection, but by artificial selection. In other words, our descendants could in theory *breed* a new kind of hominine, probably (to speed things up) with the aid of genetic engineering. However, I mention this only in the interests of logical completeness. Discussion of its ramifications belongs in other books.

But the theoretical possibility of future evolutionary change does raise an issue that is of universal significance. What, in theory, *might* human beings evolve into? More broadly, of what is life capable?

PROGRESS, POTENTIAL, AND DESTINY: WHAT MIGHT LIVING THINGS DO?

I argued in Chapter 6 that the concept of progress in evolution is worth entertaining. Some creatures really are demonstrably better than others at carrying out definable tasks: better both in engineering terms (for example extracting more useful calories from a given quantity of food) and logistically (according to the analyses of game theory). On the whole, too, the 'better' creatures evolve from the less good, even though there seem at times to have been some interesting reversals.

But one reason why these somewhat obvious and I believe useful ideas have become unfashionable is, I suggest, because people seem to confuse 'progress' with 'destiny'. 'Progress' in general is likely to happen. 'Better' creatures are bound to appear through the chance processes of mutation, and having appeared they are liable to succeed. Furthermore, as discussed in Chapter 4, some lines of development are more likely than others. Animals must obey the rules of engineering, which are founded in the laws of physics, and in practice only a limited range of body forms, or ecomorphs, is feasible. Put the ideas together and it looks as if the gene pools of ancestral creatures are bound to be pushed in particular directions. Indeed as de Duve comments in *Vital Dust* (p. 287), 'Should things start all over again, here or elsewhere, the final outcome could not be the same. But how different would it be?'

In other words, we can predict to a large extent that any suite of creatures given the freedom to evolve will eventually fill at least some niches and that they will do so in at least some of the ways that we have already observed. But we cannot in the least predict *which* particular creatures are liable to evolve. It would never have been possible to predict that life on Earth would have produced *Homo sapiens*, or indeed the hominids as a whole. I have presented the story of human evolution as one of opportunities taken: of the right gene pool in the right place at the right time. What was always absolutely unpredictable, however, was that such a set of circumstances would ever arise. If India had not crunched into Asia, there would be no Himalayas. If there were no Himalayas, then the world might still be covered in tropical forest. Given that there were plenty of primates around in the Eocene, we can reasonably predict that there would be plenty around now. But the predominant forms surely would be monkeys, supremely adapted to the trees. There is absolutely no reason to assume that any of them would have developed along hominine lines. More generally, there is no reason whatever to suppose that intelligence of human proportions would ever have appeared among any lineage. Indeed there is no reason to assume that such a quality would have appeared before the next meteor collision, which if Raup and Sepkoski are right is due in another 13 million years. In fact the world might have begun its final cooling, with the death of all life, before circumstances ever arose that could produce creatures like us. In short there is progress *but there is no destiny*. Time and chance always play their part.

Yet there is another notion that seems to me intriguing and relevant. It is obvious that nothing can happen of any kind except the things that are possible. To put the point more simply: everything that does happen must be possible. Perhaps this seems too self-evident to be worth stating. Yet it is interesting. For if it is possible for phenomenon B to result from phenomenon A, then we have to conclude that phenomenon A *had the potential* to produce phenomenon B. Indeed we might argue, as I think Aristotle essentially did, that the potential to produce B must be numbered among the innate properties of A.

With such notions we might produce an argument that seems to me very close to the thesis of Teilhard de Chardin, who contrived to be a palaeontologist, a Darwinian, and also a Jesuit priest. Thus it seems to me entirely unexceptionable to point out that intelligence of the kind we recognise in human beings is a product of living flesh. Intelligence can be seen as 'emergent property', something that results when some of the molecules contained in flesh are suitably arranged. By the same token, we can argue that the molecules of that flesh must have had the potential to produce intelligence. Look at those molecules more closely and you find they are compounded from carbon, oxygen, hydrogen, nitrogen, phosphorus, sulphur, and a few metals: a pretty commonplace array. Yet, in Chardin-esque fashion, we have to concede that this chemistry-set collection, suitably arranged, has the potential to produce thought. We could go even further back and observe that these elements are themselves compounded of fundamental particles. These particles, then, had the potential, once suitably arranged, to produce the highest flights of genius.

Why is this relevant? Well, earlier in this book I mentioned the children's TV character Dr Who, the extraordinarily accomplished scientist who is able to travel through time. Suppose he travelled back to the time of the Big Bang, when the Universe began, and all the fundamental particles were still separate. Could he have predicted just by looking at those particles (and leaving aside for a moment his knowledge of the future) that they had the potential to form themselves into the elements of the periodic table? I am not at all sure how. I feel he would have to have waited a few years, or a few million years, to see how things turned out. Once the elements had formed, in the depths of successive generations of stars, could he have predicted that they would when suitably combined produce living things? Again I think not. If he visited Earth 2 billion years ago or so, and saw the first organisms with nucleated cells, could he have predicted that from these humble creatures would evolve animals that can think? Again one asks, 'How could he?'. Where are the clues in those primitive creatures to indicate future possibilities?

So I would like now to make precisely the same point in the context of present-day creatures, and indeed of ourselves: that is, *we simply cannot tell, by looking at existing life, exactly what life is capable of.* We have seen that Robert Broom and other eminent biologists of the twentieth century felt that human beings, bright creatures that we are, represent the 'ultimate' in biological evolution. The same point, stated only slightly differently, is made in the Old Testament: we are supposed to have been created 'in God's image' and God, by definition, is ultimate. But what reason do we have to assume that this is the case? What do we really know of life? I submit that we are no more able to predict the possibilities – the *potential* – of life than Dr Who would have been able to predict the potential of newly-emerging elements.

Specifically, we think that our brains are wonderful, and so they are. Yet we can identify areas of extreme feebleness. We are extremely poor at maths and feel that those who gain first-class honours degrees in that subject must be very bright indeed. But why then do those 'geniuses' use calculators? Because a cheap pocket calculator with a tiny microchip can carry out the mechanics of maths a hundred times quicker than they can. Of course the calculator lacks imagination but the point stands nonetheless: here is a comparatively simple trick of maths that even the greatest mathematicians simply cannot do. We assume because in general we are smarter than most other animals, that we must be brighter than them in all respects. Yet this too is nonsense. Memory is generally conceded to be a component of intelligence. But animals that hide food for the winter sometimes, like nuthatches, have memories of topography that are quite out of our league. In short, it is very easy to envisage a dozen ways in which we could in theory improve the components of our present-day intelligence by leaps and bounds. There is no *a priori* reason why a human being should not combine the qualities of, say, Einstein, Shakespeare, Mozart, Darwin, J. M. W. Turner, a nuthatch, and a pocket calculator. Indeed there is no *a priori* reason why such a paragon should not be considered ordinary.

But the qualities of known geniuses could well prove mundane compared to what *might* be possible. For example many creatures, including homing pigeons, have been shown to possess some magnetic sense, by which they can orientate themselves relative to the Earth's field. Could not future lineages – in theory – develop such a sense to a high degree? On the other hand, no creature present or past is known to respond to, or transmit, long-wave electromagnetic radiation (that is, radio waves). Yet it seems there would be nothing in such an ability to offend any known laws of physics. In theory, then, we could envisage future creatures that carry their own two-way radios in their heads. Combine this with a more advanced magnetic sense and we can envisage creatures that might be able to pin-point their positions anywhere on the Earth's surface. It is obviously very difficult to envisage natural circumstances that would favour emergence of such creatures, but that is not my point. I am simply asking the more fundamental question, 'Of what is life really capable?'.

Of course, even if such mechanisms are possible, there is no guarantee that they will evolve. Natural selection can realise only a subset of the theoretical possibilities, and it will realise only a small proportion of that subset on this Earth before the Earth itself finally dies. But we simply do not know what could evolve before this planet dies, because we simply do not know the potential of present-day life. At least, we can make a few crude points: the known laws of physics tell us, for example, that pigs *qua* pigs will never fly. But we really do not understand enough about the properties of matter to state categorically that the abilities of present-day creatures represent the full repertoire of possibility. There could be many surprises in store of which built-in radio is simply a rather glib example.

So we can see the future evolution of living things on Earth as a kind of obstacle race. Living things as a whole might have the potential to do a whole range of things that at present are unknowable and unpredictable. The question is, which and how many of those things will in practice be realised? It would be nice if there were creatures around in the future intelligent enough to take note. Indeed it would be nice, speaking chauvinistically, if those creatures included future members of our own lineage.

However, the chances that any untapped potential will be realised, by whatever lineage, depend very much on our actions over the next few hundred years. But those actions must not be geared only to those short-term needs. The events of this planet can take far longer than that to unfold. We surely have the potential to survive as a species for at least a million years – there is no reason to doubt that. But if we want our descendants to claim that million years, and to do so in the company of other creatures, then we must plan right now with this in mind. In short, as I commented in the Prologue, we cannot claim to be taking our species and our planet seriously until we acknowledge that a million years is a proper unit of political time.

Index

Numbers in italics refer to figures